Cooperative Learning &

Geometry

High School Activities

by Becky Bride

Kagan

Kagan Publishing
981 Calle Amanecer
San Clemente, CA 92673
1(800) 933-2667
www.KaganOnline.com

ISBN: 978-1-879097-68-1

TABLE OF CONTENTS

Chapter 1: DEFINITIONS

Chapter 2: ANGLES AND LINES

Chapter 3: CONSTRUCTIONS

Chapter 4: TRIANGLES

Chapter 5: POLYGONS AND QUADRILATERALS

Cooperative Learning and High School Geometry: Becky Bride
Kagan Publishing • 1 (800) WEE-CO-OP • www.KaganOnline.com

I

TABLE OF CONTENTS CONT...

Chapter 6:
SIMILARITY

Chapter 7:
PYTHAGOREAN THEOREM AND SPECIAL RIGHT TRIANGLES

Chapter 8:
AREA

Chapter 9:
VOLUME

Chapter 10:
CIRCLES

Cooperative Learning and High School Geometry: Becky Bride
Kagan Publishing • 1 (800) WEE-CO-OP • www.KaganOnline.com

ACKNOWLEDGMENTS

Many people have helped to make this book a reality. Thank you to my family, who put up with me as I wrote in airports, on airplanes, and in the car as we traveled for our summer vacation. They were kind to share the computer with me and were very patient with me as I spent hours typing and editing the text. Without their support and encouragement, it wouldn't have happened. Thank you to my geometry classes of the 2000-2001 and 2001-2002 school years who have helped me pilot many of the activities. Using their suggestions, I reworded some of the activities so they were easier to understand.

To Spencer and Laurie Kagan, thank you, for introducing me to the structural approach to cooperative learning, which is the foundation of this book. It has given me a chance to share with other teachers how the structural approach to cooperative learning, can be used in a mathematics classroom. Thinking of different structures to use to give the book variety has been a source of professional growth for me.

Many thanks to the staff at Kagan Publishing, who took a rough draft and made it look terrific. The creative book layout was designed by Denise Alphabet. Kathy Tomlinson edited the text. The icons and technical illustrations were the brainstorm of Alex Core. Celso Rodriguez illustrated the cover. Thank you to Jennifer McDonald, Dina Kushnir, and James Michael Shunneson for reviewing the book. Their suggestions for changes, corrections, and comments were very helpful during the editing phase. A special thanks to Miguel Kagan, who was my consultant, mentor, and project manager. He always had a solution for any problem I sent his way and offered encouragement and support.

Most of all, thank you to all the teachers who will use this book so their students' experience with geometry is rich, engaging, and fun-filled.

Cooperative Learning and High School Geometry: Becky Bride
Kagan Publishing • 1 (800) WEE-CO-OP • www.KaganOnline.com

III

INTRODUCTION

Have you ever asked your students if they had any questions on homework? When you saw hands go up did you ask, "What problems do you want to see"? Did the students ever reply "All of them"? This was a common occurrence in my mathematics classroom. It made me question why I bothered to come to school each day since my teaching efforts from the day before seemed fruitless. I felt like I was teaching mathematics to concrete blocks instead of students. Since I couldn't change the students, I began to reevaluate what I did as a teacher. I began to search for a way to structure my classroom so that students would be more successful. In my search, I found Kagan Cooperative Learning. I had put students together before to work on projects and it was disaster. What I learned was that I had done group work, NOT cooperative learning. I never knew there was a difference.

Spencer Kagan has developed a way to structure student-to-student interaction so that there are no "hogs" (children that do it all) and no "logs" (children who contribute nothing). Inherent in each structure is a means to ensure individual accountability, equal participation, and positive interdependence, and have a minimum of 25 percent of the class overtly active at once. I was very intrigued. I went to every workshop I could to learn more about the structural approach to cooperative learning.

Then, five years ago, I began to use Dr. Kagan's structural approach to Cooperative Learning in my classroom. The results were incredible! The prior year I would spend on average 5 hours a week after school in help sessions for any student(s) who did not understand the material I had taught. There were on average anywhere from 7-20 students per day who came for after school help. The year I began implementing the structural approach to cooperative learning, my after school help sessions for students present in class were no longer needed. Only students who were absent from class and missed my instruction and the cooperative structures to process my curriculum came after school for help. I was amazed. That gave me time to lesson plan and grade papers. Before cooperative learning, I would spend anywhere from 20-40 minutes a class period (sometimes the entire period) to answer questions on the homework. With cooperative learning we spend 2-10 minutes to check homework and answer questions. Amazingly, the mistakes students make now on the homework are careless errors rather than conceptual mistakes. This has given me precious teaching time.

Academic achievement has also been phenomenal. In a typical geometry class, I have students in grades 9-12. Ninth graders are very sharp. The eleventh and twelfth graders struggle at best. Before using cooperative learning, the upperclassmen's six weeks grades were D's or F's. Using the Kagan Cooperative Learning, the juniors and seniors now make B's and C's. The academic achievement of the other students has also improved with many more A's and B's. Because the students are more successful, they feel much better about themselves, their attitude toward math has improved, and they take more mathematics classes! Students of average ability, whom I had three years ago in geometry class, are now in my calculus class, as seniors. Ten years ago if I'd had these students, most would have never considered taking trigonometry, let alone calculus.

Cooperative Learning and High School Geometry: Becky Bride
Kagan Publishing • 1 (800) WEE-CO-OP • www.KaganOnline.com

INTRODUCTION CONTINUED...

The students enjoy coming to class because of the interaction they have with their peers. It is amazing how much bonding takes place among team members. When I change the seating chart, most students are sad to say goodbye. We do a short activity that brings closure to the group, then they meet their new teammates and begin the bonding process again.

Besides incredible advances for my students, using Kagan Cooperative Structures has had a major impact on me. When I leave the school everyday, I now feel that the students and I have accomplished incredible feats. I feel that my teaching is now productive and the classroom is certainly a whole lot more fun. Before cooperative learning, I would count the days until summer, beginning in March. Now the school year ends and I can't believe it went so fast. I am no longer burned out by May and am excited to return in August. My transformation and that of my students is awesome!

My belief in Kagan Cooperative Learning is so great that I am now a national trainer for Kagan Professional Development. As I was doing workshops, I would hear math teachers say that cooperative learning must not be real successful in high school, because they didn't see any math curriculum for sale that was above grade 8. What better way to demonstrate to teachers that Kagan Cooperative Learning is as valuable in a high school mathematics classroom as it is in a middle or elementary classroom than to write a book that shows how versatile and encompassing cooperative learning can be? It was a labor of love. I chose to dedicate the entire book to geometry because it is such an incredible course and one that can be taught concretely. Included in the book are not only

blackline masters and transparencies that use Dr. Kagan's structures to process all major topics in a high school geometry course, but also exploratory activities so students can concretely develop the concepts.

The book is divided into 10 chapters. The first chapter deals with vocabulary development. This lays a large foundation on which to build. A chapter on angles and lines (parallel and perpendicular) follows. Chapter 3 is devoted to constructions, compass and straightedge and patty paper. These are included in chapter 3 because many of the exploratory exercises in subsequent chapters require them. Chapter 4 explores triangles and the properties that guarantee that two triangles are congruent. The chapter on polygons and quadrilaterals follows and precedes the chapter on similarity because students need to compute missing angles in polygons to determine if two polygons are similar. Chapter 7 works with the Pythagorean Theorem and the special right triangles because activities in the area, volume, and circle chapters require students to use these concepts. Chapter 8 is a chapter on area of two-dimensional and three-dimensional figures. Chapter 9 works with volume. The final chapter of the book deals with properties of arcs, chords, and angles in circles. This chapter is last because the National Council of Teachers of Mathematics has suggested that these topics be de-emphasized. The properties included in this chapter are the concepts needed to develop trigonometry concepts when the students take trigonometry.

Each chapter consists of several lessons. Each lesson consists of one or more exploratory activities with each exploration followed by one or more activ-

Cooperative Learning and High School Geometry: Becky Bride
Kagan Publishing • 1 (800) WEE-CO-OP • www.KaganOnline.com

v

ities designed to help students process the concepts just investigated. Each activity used to process concepts just learned is based on one of Dr. Kagan's many structures. The use of these structures ensures that cooperative learning is taking place rather than group work.

The lessons begin with a brief synopsis of the activities, followed by teacher notes and directions for each structure used in the activities, and end with blackline masters or transparencies for each activity. The teacher notes for any activity name the structure it was designed for, materials needed, and step-by-step directions. The chapters, lessons and activities are numbered sequentially. Each blackline or transparency has corresponding numbers in the upper right-hand corner. The first number designates the chapter, the second designates the lesson, and the last designates the activity. This system makes navigating the book very easy. Because copying costs have been such an issue since I began teaching 20 years ago, activities that could be made with very large print have been included as transparencies to save the user of this book printing costs. Any activities that couldn't be designed for use with an overhead projector, are presented as blackline masters.

The blackline masters are designed to use as a class set. All work is done on a sheet of paper supplied by a partner or team member. Answers are included on the transparencies or blacklines

when work is necessary to solve the problems. Otherwise, answers are included in the teacher's directions. Students love the instant feedback they get from having the answers to check their work.

This book was written for teachers. I wanted to share with teachers how all geometry concepts could be developed with hands-on activities and processed using a variety of Kagan structures. I used a variety of structures in this book because it is fun to use different ones, to expose teachers to structures they may have not used, and to demonstrate how the structures can be used with many different concepts. My hope is that this book opens a whole new world for you and your students. How I wish I had a resource like this when I began teaching.

VI

Cooperative Learning and High School Geometry: Becky Bride
Kagan Publishing • 1 (800) WEE-CO-OP • www.KaganOnline.com

DEFINITIONS

Most of the definitions found in a typical geometry book are located in this chapter, so that they can be found easily. Definitions involving circles and solids will be found in the chapters devoted to those subjects.

LESSON 1
UNDEFINED TERMS AND ONE-DIMENSIONAL FIGURES

The first activity of this lesson and each lesson to follow involves student-generated definitions. This deepens the students' understanding of definitions and gives them ownership. It also integrates language arts into the mathematics classroom as students try to be as concise and grammatically correct as possible.

The first stage of generating a class definition is to begin with each student writing his/her own definition based on diagrams of examples and counterexamples of the term being defined. This gives each student time to compare and contrast, analyze, and develop his/her own definition, guaranteeing each student the opportunity to think through the definition. This can be assigned as homework to save class time since the next two stages must be done in class. If you feel your students may just copy the definition out of the book then don't assign this part for homework.

The second stage involves each team taking their individual definitions and developing a team definition for each word assigned. The RoundTable structure is used to equalize the recording of the definitions. The development of the definition involves the Team Discuss structure.

The third stage involves developing one class definition from the team definitions that everyone can agree on (including the teacher). When the class and teacher have agreed that the definition is acceptable, the students write the definition in their notes.

This method takes more time to develop definitions compared to the teacher defining them for the students. The benefits of student-generated definitions far exceed those of teacher-or textbook-generated ones. Developing their own definitions requires students to think on a Blooms Taxonomy level of 4, 5, or 6. The discourse that takes place is amazing. Students begin to fine tune their ability to accurately communicate their thoughts.

When the teacher draws a diagram of what was said and the students realize that was not what they meant, real growth begins with articulating thoughts. Students understand why every concept or word of a definition is necessary.

A prerequisite to defining any word is discussing the three parts necessary for a good definition. This will assist the students with creating quality definitions and ultimately save time. The three parts are as follows:

1. Stating the term
2. Stating the nearest classification
3. Stating those items that make it unique.

As an example, examine the words collinear points and coplanar points.

Collinear points are
Coplanar points are

At this point the first part of defining a word is satisfied. The terms have been stated. When the second part is written the definitions look like this:

Collinear points are a set of points
Coplanar points are a set of points

The definitions are exactly the same after part 2 is complete, and students can see the need for the third part. With the completion of part three the definitions become:

Collinear points are a set of points that lie on one line.
Coplanar points are a set of points that lie on one plane.

As the class takes the team definitions to form a class definition, the students will have to come to consensus on all three parts. The first 2 parts are usually very quick to reach consensus. The third part takes some time.

Cooperative Learning and High School Geometry: Becky Bride
Kagan Publishing • 1 (800) WEE-CO-OP • www.KaganOnline.com

ACTIVITY 1

DEVELOPING DEFINITIONS FOR ONE-DIMENSIONAL FIGURES

1. Have students generate their own definitions first or give adequate think time for each student to formulate a definition in their mind.

2. As a team, the students will discuss how to define the term.

3. Once the team reaches consensus, then student 1 will record the team definition on a sheet of paper.

4. Repeat steps 1-3 with a different student recording each time on the same sheet of paper.

Notes:
To develop a class definition, spin the team spinner to choose a team and the student spinner to choose a student of the chosen team to read the team's definition. Record the team's definition on the board. Ask the class if they agree with part 1 and then part 2 of the definition, reworking what they want to change. Then begin working with part three, drawing a picture of what was communicated to help students see where refinement is needed. Sometimes asking students if part of the definition could be reworded using fewer words will get the students thinking again. Once everyone has agreed, including the teacher, then it is recorded as the definition the class will use. You may find that lower level classes prefer a somewhat longer definition if it has more meaning for them. Honors classes will try to be as concise as possible.

▶ **Structure**
· Team Discuss with RoundTable recording

▶ **Materials**
· 1 Blackline 1.1.1 per student
· 1 sheet of paper and pencil per team

Not only is knowing a definition important, but knowing the notation, drawing a diagram, and labeling it correctly is also important. The next activity works on all three.

Tip:
During step 2, prior to discussion, RoundRobin could be used for students to share the definitions they wrote. To do this, each student reads his/her definition to the team.

ACTIVITY 2

DRAW WHAT I SAY

1. Student 1 fans the cards face down.

2. Student 2 picks a card and reads it to Student 3, allowing 5 seconds of think time.

3. Student 3 draws a diagram of what was said, correctly labeling it.

4. Student 4 checks Student 3's work and praises, or coaches, then praises.

5. Students pass cards to the next person in a clockwise direction and steps 1-4 begin again, rotating roles one student in the clockwise direction. This process is repeated for a specific time limit or until cards are exhausted.

▶ **Structure**
· Fan-N-Pick

▶ **Materials**
· 1 set of Fan-N-Pick cards per team (Blackline 1.1.2)

Cooperative Learning and High School Geometry: Becky Bride
Kagan Publishing • 1 (800) WEE-CO-OP • www.KaganOnline.com

3

ACTIVITY
3

UNIONS AND INTERSECTIONS OF ONE-DIMENSIONAL FIGURES

▶ **Structure**
· Boss/Secretary

▶ **Materials**
· 1 Blackline 1.1.3 per pair of students
· 1 sheet of paper and pencil per pair of students

1. Student A supplies one sheet of paper, folded in half lengthwise with his/her name in one column and a partner's name in the other column.

2. Student B is the first boss and Student A is the first secretary.

3. As the boss, Student B tells Student A how to do the problem. Student A, the secretary, records what Student B says in Student B's column of the paper.

4. If the boss makes a mistake, then the secretary coaches and praises once the boss does it correctly. Otherwise, the secretary praises the boss.

5. Reverse roles for each problem and repeat steps 3 and 4.

Answers: *1.* $\overline{BC}$ *2.* $\overline{BD}$ *3.* $\overrightarrow{BE}$ *4.* $\overline{AE}$ *5.* $\varnothing$ *6.* $\overleftrightarrow{CD}$
7-10 answers will vary

ACTIVITY
4

PROCESSING MIDPOINT

▶ **Structure**
·Pairs Check

▶ **Materials**
· 1 Blackline 1.1.4 per pair of students
· 1 sheet of paper and pencil per pair of students

1. Student B supplies one sheet of paper, folded in half lengthwise with each member of the pair writing their name at the top of one column.

2. Student B does problem 1, recording his/her work on his/her side of the paper while Student A watches and coaches if necessary.

3. Student A checks Student B's work, then coaches and/or praises. Roles reverse for the next problem.

4. After every 2 problems, the pair checks their answers with the other pair in their team, coaching and/or praising each others' work.

5. Repeat steps 2-4, reversing roles until all the problems are done.

Cooperative Learning and High School Geometry: Becky Bride
Kagan Publishing · 1 (800) WEE-CO-OP · www.KaganOnline.com

ACTIVITY 1
DEVELOPING DEFINITIONS FOR ONE-DIMENSIONAL FIGURES

Structure: Team Discuss With RoundTable Recording

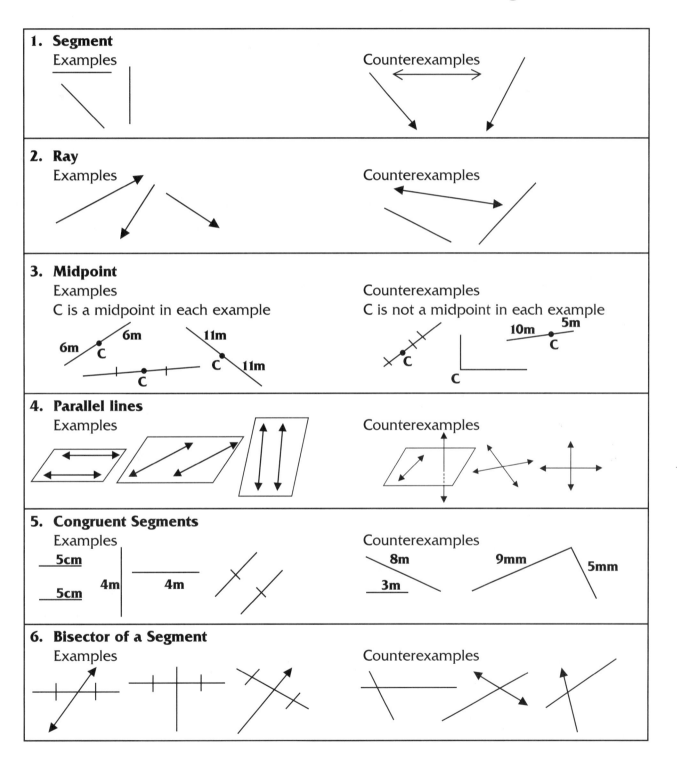

1. Segment
Examples   Counterexamples

2. Ray
Examples   Counterexamples

3. Midpoint
Examples   Counterexamples
C is a midpoint in each example   C is not a midpoint in each example

4. Parallel lines
Examples   Counterexamples

5. Congruent Segments
Examples   Counterexamples

6. Bisector of a Segment
Examples   Counterexamples

Cooperative Learning and High School Geometry: Becky Bride
Kagan Publishing • 1 (800) WEE-CO-OP • www.KaganOnline.com

5

2 DRAW WHAT I SAY

DEFINITIONS

Structure: Fan-N-Pick

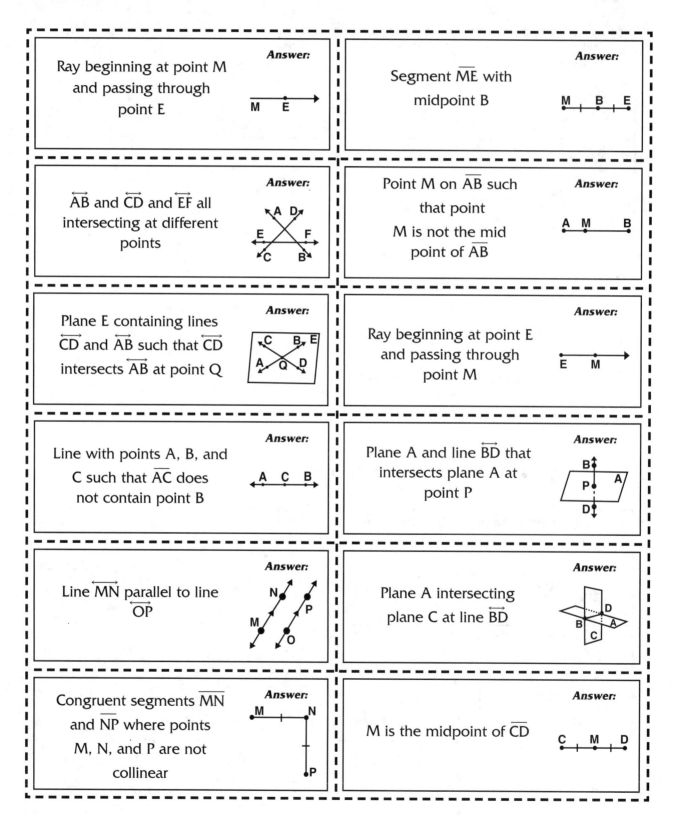

Ray beginning at point M and passing through point E **Answer:** M• E→	Segment ME with midpoint B **Answer:** M—B—E
AB and CD and EF all intersecting at different points **Answer:**	Point M on AB such that point M is not the mid point of AB **Answer:** A—M——B
Plane E containing lines CD and AB such that CD intersects AB at point Q **Answer:**	Ray beginning at point E and passing through point M **Answer:** E•——M→
Line with points A, B, and C such that AC does not contain point B **Answer:** A—C—B	Plane A and line BD that intersects plane A at point P **Answer:**
Line MN parallel to line OP **Answer:**	Plane A intersecting plane C at line BD **Answer:**
Congruent segments MN and NP where points M, N, and P are not collinear **Answer:**	M is the midpoint of CD **Answer:** C—M—D

Cooperative Learning and High School Geometry: Becky Bride
Kagan Publishing • 1 (800) WEE-CO-OP • www.KaganOnline.com

ACTIVITY
3

UNIONS AND INTERSECTIONS OF ONE-DIMENSIONAL FIGURES

DEFINITIONS

Structure: Boss/Secretary

A   B   C   D   E   F

1. $\overline{AC} \cap \overline{BE}$

2. $\overrightarrow{DA} \cap \overrightarrow{BF}$

3. $\overleftrightarrow{CE} \cup \overleftrightarrow{BD}$

4. $\overline{AC} \cup \overline{CE}$

5. $\overline{EF} \cap \overline{BD}$

6. $\overrightarrow{DF} \cup \overrightarrow{EC}$

7. Write an expression whose intersection is $\overline{CD}$.

8. Write an expression whose union is $\overrightarrow{DA}$.

9. Write an expression whose union is $\overleftrightarrow{BE}$.

10. Write an expression whose intersection is $\overrightarrow{CE}$.

Cooperative Learning and High School Geometry: Becky Bride
Kagan Publishing • 1 (800) WEE-CO-OP • www.KaganOnline.com

7

ACTIVITY
4 **PROCESSING MIDPOINT**

Structure: Pairs Check

Solve each problem below writing an equation when necessary. B is the midpoint of $\overline{AC}$.

A   B   C

1. If AC = 17, find BC.

2. If AB = 4, find AC.

3. If AB = 3x - 8 and BC = x + 12, find the value of x.

4. If BC = 5x - 9 and AB = 2x + 21, find the value of x.

5. If AB = 4x + 1 and AC = 5x + 20, find the length of $\overline{BC}$.

6. If BC = 2x - 3 and AC = 2x + 10, find the length of $\overline{AB}$.

Answers:
1. 8.5
2. 8
3. 10
4. 10
5. 25
6. 13

Cooperative Learning and High School Geometry: Becky Bride
Kagan Publishing • 1 (800) WEE-CO-OP • www.KaganOnline.com

LESSON 2
ANGLES

This Lesson begins with an activity for students to generate definitions involving angles. Then activities follow to process the definitions from naming an angle many different ways, to algebra involving equations and inequalities, and practice drawing, labeling and making diagrams.

ACTIVITY 1

DEVELOPING DEFINITIONS INVOLVING ANGLES

1. Have students generate their own definitions first or give adequate think time for each student to formulate a definition in his/her mind.

2. As a team, the students will discuss how to define the term.

3. Once the team reaches consensus, then student 1 will record the team definition on a sheet of paper.

4. Repeat steps 1-3 with a different student recording each time on the same sheet of paper.

Notes:
To develop a class definition, spin the team spinner to choose a team and the student spinner to choose a student of the chosen team to read the team's definition. Record the team's definition on the board. Ask the class if they agree with part 1 and then part 2 of the definition, reworking what they want to change. Then begin working with part three, drawing a picture of what was communicated to help students see where refinement is needed. Sometimes asking students if part of the definition could be reworded using fewer words will get the students thinking again. Once everyone has agreed, including the teacher, then it is recorded as the definition the class will use.

▶ **Structure**
· Team Discuss with RoundTable Recording

▶ **Materials**
· 1 Blackline 1.2.1 per team
· 1 sheet of paper and pencil per team

Tip:
During step 2, prior to the discussion, the RoundRobin structure could be used for students to share the definitions they wrote. To do this, each student takes a turn reading his/her definition to the team.

ACTIVITY 2

NAMING ANGLES

1. Student A names the angle using three letters

2. Student B gives specific praise (i.e.: You did a nice job of remembering to put the vertex in the middle) and then names the same angle a different way.

3. Student A gives specific praise then names the angle in yet another way.

4. Repeat steps 1-3 alternating student A and student B for 60 seconds.

▶ **Structure**
· RallyRobin

▶ **Materials**
· Transparency 1.2.2

Cooperative Learning and High School Geometry: Becky Bride
Kagan Publishing · 1 (800) WEE-CO-OP · www.KaganOnline.com

9

ACTIVITY

3

MEASURING AND CLASSIFYING ANGLES

▶ **Structure**
• Pairs Check

▶ **Materials**
• 1 Blackline 1.2.3 per pair of students
• 1 protractor per pair of students

1. Student A states what type of angle (acute, right, or obtuse) the first angle appears to be, measures it, records the measurement, then records the type it is, based on the measurement.

2. Student B checks student A's work, and coaches and/or praises.

3. Student B repeats step 1 for problem 2.

4. Student A repeats step 2 for problem 2.

5. Pairs check with other pairs at their table.

6. Repeat steps 1-5, reversing roles, until all the problems are done.

Note:
The purpose of the student first stating the type of angle (acute, right, obtuse) before measuring is to focus their attention on which numbers on the protractor will be appropriate to read.

ACTIVITY

4

PROCESSING THE ANGLE DEFINITIONS

▶ **Structure**
• Find the Fiction

▶ **Materials**
• 1 sheet of paper and pencil per student

1. All students write 3 statements involving the definitions—two true and one false. Encourage students to involve more than one definition
(i.e.: 2 obtuse angles can be supplementary).

2. One student stands and reads his/her 3 statements.

3. The seated teammates discuss and come to a consensus as to which statement is false.

4. If the seated teammates are correct, the student standing praises them.

5. If the seated teammates are wrong, then the teammate standing coaches the team. The seated teammates then praise the standing teammate for challenging them.

6. Repeat steps 2-5 until each teammate has had a chance to read his/her statements.

Tip:
Allowing the current definitions and the definitions from the previous lesson to be used helps to develop the student's long term memory.

Cooperative Learning and High School Geometry: Becky Bride
Kagan Publishing • 1 (800) WEE-CO-OP • www.KaganOnline.com

ACTIVITY 5
PROCESSING COMPLEMENTARY AND SUPPLEMENTARY ANGLES

1. Student A supplies one sheet of paper, folded in half lengthwise with his/her name in one column and a partner's name in the other column.

2. Student B is the first boss and Student A is the first secretary.

3. As the boss, Student B tells Student A how to do the problem. Student A, the secretary, records what Student B says in Student B's column of the paper.

4. If the boss makes a mistake, then the secretary coaches and praises once the boss does it correctly. Otherwise, the secretary praises the boss.

5. Reverse roles for each problem and repeat steps 3 and 4.

▶ **Structure**
 · Boss/Secretary

▶ **Materials**
 · Transparency 1.2.5
 · 1 sheet of paper and pencil per pair of students

ACTIVITY 6
EQUATIONS AND INEQUALITIES WITH ANGLE DEFINITIONS

1. Each student supplies one sheet of paper.

2. Teammate 1 writes problem 1 on his/her paper, Teammate 2 writes problem 2, Teammate 3 writes problem 3, and Teammate 4 writes problem 4.

3. Each teammate writes an equation or inequality needed to find the values of x for which their angle would be the type stated. They initial their work and pass the paper to the next person in a clockwise direction.

4. On the paper just received, each teammate checks the previous teammate's work—coaches if wrong, praises once it is right, and then does one step to solve the equation or inequality. They initial

their work and pass the paper to the next person in a clockwise direction.

5. On the paper just received, each teammate checks the previous teammate's work, coaching if necessary, and finishes solving the equation or inequality. They initial their work and pass the paper to the next person in a clockwise direction one more time.

6. On the paper they receive, each student will check the previous work and coach if necessary. Then the student will write the answer, using a complete sentence.

Tips:
Model this process for students.

Each teammate could write in a different color rather than initial work.

▶ **Structure**
 · Simultaneous RoundTable

▶ **Materials**
 · Transparencies 1.2.6a and 1.2.6b
 · 1 sheet of paper and pencil per student

Example:
If $\angle A = 3x - 15$, find a value or range of values for x that would ensure that $\angle A$ is an obtuse angle.

Round 1: $90 < 3x - 15 < 180$

Round 2:
$90 + 15 < 3x - 15 + 15 < 180 + 15$
$= 105 < 3x < 195$

Round 3: $\dfrac{105}{3} < \dfrac{3x}{3} < \dfrac{195}{3}$
$= 35 < x < 65$

Round 4: *The values for x ensuring that $\angle A$ is an obtuse angle are any numbers between 35 and 65.*

Chapter 1: Definitions

Lesson Two

Cooperative Learning and High School Geometry: Becky Bride
Kagan Publishing · 1 (800) WEE-CO-OP · www.KaganOnline.com

11

ACTIVITY
7

PROCESSING BISECTOR OF AN ANGLE

▶ **Structure**
• Boss/Secretary

▶ **Materials**
• Transparency 1.2.7
• 1 sheet of paper and pencil
  per pair of students

1. Student A supplies one sheet of paper, folded in half lengthwise with his/her name in one column and a partner's name in the other column.

2. Student B is the first boss and Student A is the first secretary.

3. As the boss, Student B tells Student A how to do the problem. Student A, the secretary, records what Student B says in Student B's column of the paper.

4. If the boss makes a mistake, then the secretary coaches and praises once the boss does it correctly. Otherwise, the secretary praises the boss.

5. Reverse roles for each problem and repeat steps 3 and 4.

ACTIVITY
8

PROCESSING PERPENDICULAR BISECTOR OF A SEGMENT

▶ **Structure**
• RallyCoach

▶ **Materials**
• Transparency 1.2.8
• 1 sheet of paper and pencil
  per pair of students

1. Student A folds a sheet of paper in half lengthwise and puts his/her name at the top of one column and a partner's name at the top of the other column.

2. Student A does the first problem on his/her side of the paper.

3. Student B watches and checks Student A's work and gives praise, or coaches, then praises the work.

4. Repeat steps 2-3 reversing roles until all the problems are done.

Chapter 1: Definitions
L e s s o n T w o

ACTIVITY

9 DRAW WHAT I SAY

1. Student 1 fans the cards face down.

2. Student 2 picks a card and reads it to Student 3, allowing 5 seconds of think time.

3. Student 3 draws a diagram of what was said, correctly labeling it.

4. Student 4 checks Student 3's work and praises, or coaches, then praises.

5. Cards are passed to the next person in a clockwise direction and steps 1-4 begin again, rotating roles one student in the clockwise direction. This process is repeated for a specific time limit or until cards are exhausted.

▶ **Structure**
• Fan-N-Pick

▶ **Materials**
• 1 set of Fan-N-Pick cards per team (Blackline 1.2.9)
• 1 sheet of paper and pencil per team

ACTIVITY

10 REVIEW OF LESSONS 1 AND 2

1. Each student is given a card.

2. Students mix around the room trading cards while music plays.

3. When the music stops students stop.

4. Teacher gives the next set of directions for finding matches.

5. Students search and find their match.

Tips:
To work on curriculum during the mix stage, students can pair. If a student has a card with a figure on it, he/she will ask a partner to describe the notation for the figure (i.e. You would write AB with a

segment bar on top).
If a student has a card with the notation on it then he/she would describe how to draw and label the figure. Then the students trade cards.

Have students use gambits as they meet to exchange cards and as they leave to find someone else with whom to exchange.

During the match stage students can talk, or it can be done silently.

To help students find matches, have students that have found their match move to the outside perimeter of the room so there are fewer students to search through.

If students have difficulty, repeat the structure.

▶ **Structure**
• Mix-Music-Match

▶ **Materials**
• 1 set of Mix-Music-Match cards for the class (Blackline 1.2.10)

To collect the cards, ask that both cards be given to one member of each pair. Then as the students return to their seats they will hand the pairs of cards to the teacher. This way the matches are together, so when the next class comes in with a different number of students, the teacher will be able to ensure that matches can be made when the cards are distributed.

Chapter 1: Definitions
Lesson Two

Cooperative Learning and High School Geometry: Becky Bride
Kagan Publishing • 1 (800) WEE-CO-OP • www.KaganOnline.com

13

ACTIVITY 1
DEVELOPING DEFINITIONS INVOLVING ANGLES

Structure: Team Discuss With RoundTable Recording

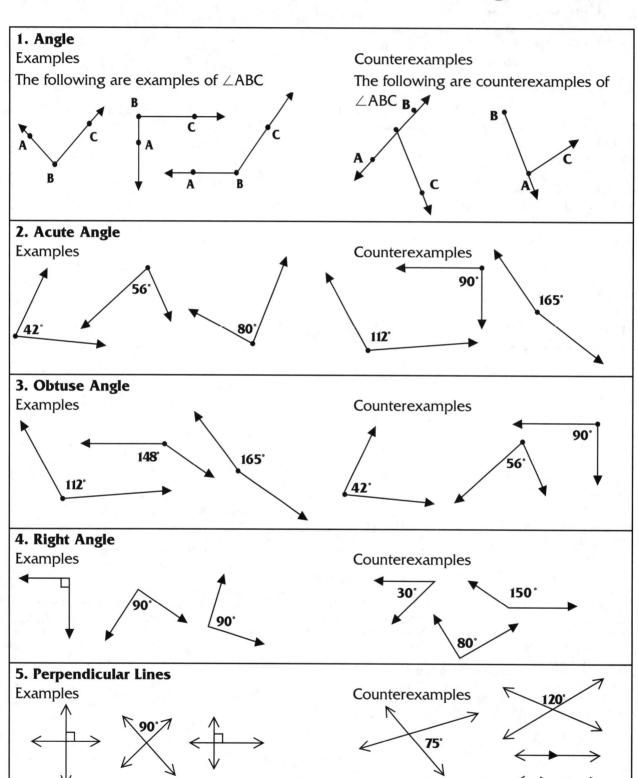

1. Angle

Examples

The following are examples of ∠ABC

Counterexamples

The following are counterexamples of ∠ABC

2. Acute Angle

Examples

Counterexamples

3. Obtuse Angle

Examples

Counterexamples

4. Right Angle

Examples

Counterexamples

5. Perpendicular Lines

Examples

Counterexamples

Cooperative Learning and High School Geometry: Becky Bride
Kagan Publishing • 1 (800) WEE-CO-OP • www.KaganOnline.com

DEVELOPING DEFINITIONS INVOLVING ANGLES

Structure: Team Discuss With RoundTable Recording

6. Complementary Angles

Examples   Counterexamples

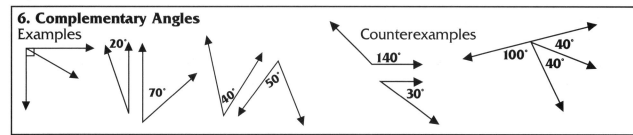

7. Supplementary Angles

Examples   Counterexamples

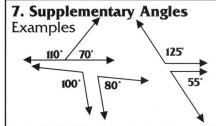 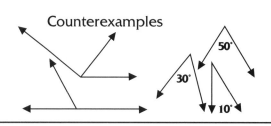

8. Vertical Angles

Examples
∠1 and ∠2 are a pair of vertical angles

Counterexamples
∠1 and ∠2 are not a pair of vertical angles

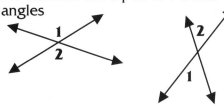 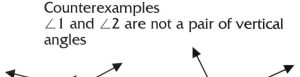

9. Adjacent angles

Examples
∠1 and ∠2 are adjacent angles

Counterexamples
∠1 and ∠2 are not adjacent angles

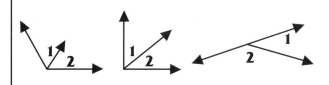 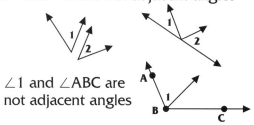

∠1 and ∠ABC are not adjacent angles

10. Linear Pair of Angles

Examples
∠1 and ∠2 are a linear pair

Counterexamples
∠1 and ∠2 are not a linear pair

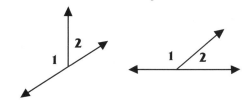 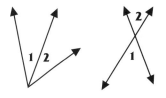

Cooperative Learning and High School Geometry: Becky Bride
Kagan Publishing • 1 (800) WEE-CO-OP • www.KaganOnline.com

15

ACTIVITY 2 NAMING ANGLES

Structure: RallyRobin

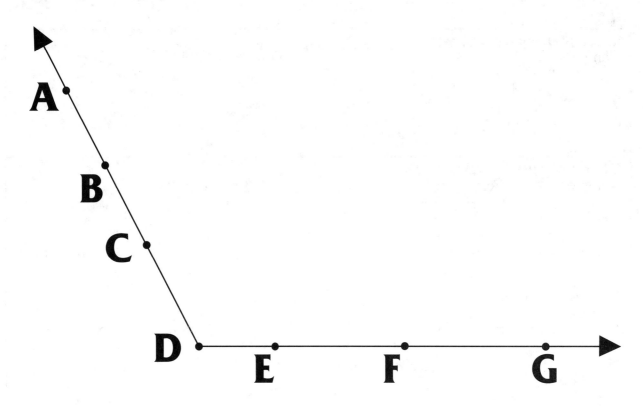

Cooperative Learning and High School Geometry: Becky Bride
Kagan Publishing • 1 (800) WEE-CO-OP • www.KaganOnline.com

ACTIVITY 3 MEASURING AND CLASSIFYING ANGLES

Structure: Pairs Check

Directions:
Measure each angle to the nearest degree.

1.

2.

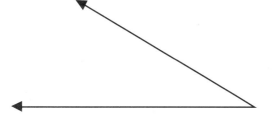

3.

4.

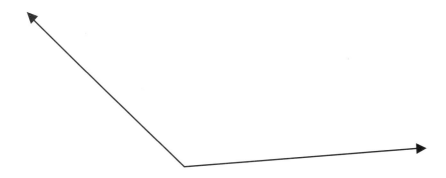

Cooperative Learning and High School Geometry: Becky Bride
Kagan Publishing • 1 (800) WEE-CO-OP • www.KaganOnline.com

17

PROCESSING COMPLEMENTARY AND SUPPLEMENTARY ANGLES

DEFINITIONS

Structure: Boss/Secretary

For each problem, write an equation and solve.

1. Two angles are complementary. If one angle measures 4x + 3 and the other angle measures 2x + 21, find the measure of each angle.

2. An angle measures 2x + 7 and its supplement measures 3x - 17. Find the measure of each angle.

3. An angle measures 4x + 3 and its supplement measures 5x + 6. Find the measure of each angle.

4. An angle measures 7x - 13. Its complement measures 4x + 15. Find the measure of each angle.

Answers:
1. x = 11; 43° and 47°
2. x = 38; 83° and 97°
3. x = 19; 79° and 101°
4. x = 8; 43° and 47°

Cooperative Learning and High School Geometry: Becky Bride
Kagan Publishing • 1 (800) WEE-CO-OP • www.KaganOnline.com

EQUATIONS AND INEQUALITIES WITH ANGLE DEFINITIONS

DEFINITIONS

Structure: Simultaneous RoundTable

1. If m∠A = 5x - 10, find the value(s) for x that would ensure that ∠A was an obtuse angle.

2. If m ∠B = 3x - 6, find the value(s) for x that would ensure that ∠B was an acute angle.

3. If m∠C = 4x + 2, find the value(s) for x that would ensure that ∠C was a right angle.

4. If m∠D = 6x + 12, find the value(s) for x that would ensure that ∠D was an obtuse angle.

Answers:
1. 20 < x < 38
2. 2 < x < 32
3. x = 22
4. 13 < x < 28

Cooperative Learning and High School Geometry: Becky Bride
Kagan Publishing • 1 (800) WEE-CO-OP • www.KaganOnline.com

19

ACTIVITY 6 EQUATIONS AND INEQUALITIES WITH ANGLE DEFINITIONS

Structure: Simultaneous RoundTable

Directions:

1. Write an equation or inequality to model the problem, initial your equation or inequality, then pass your paper 1 person in a clockwise direction.

2. Check the equation or inequality and coach if necessary. Do one step to begin solving the equation or inequality, initial your work, then pass your paper 1 person in a clockwise direction.

3. Check the work previously done and coach if necessary. Finish solving the equation or inequality, initial your work, then pass your paper 1 person in a clockwise direction.

4. Check the work previously done and coach if necessary. Write a complete sentence to answer the problem. Initial your sentence.

Cooperative Learning and High School Geometry: Becky Bride
Kagan Publishing • 1 (800) WEE-CO-OP • www.KaganOnline.com

PROCESSING
BISECTOR OF AN ANGLE

DEFINITIONS

Structure: Boss/Secretary

$\overrightarrow{EF}$ bisects ∠DEG. *The diagram is not drawn to scale.*

1. If m∠DEG = 88°, find m∠FEG.

2. If m∠FED = 27°, find m ∠ GED.

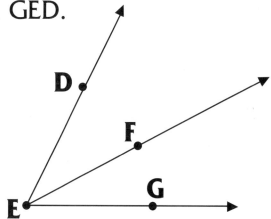

3. If m∠DEF = 3x + 1 and m∠DEG = 5x + 19, find the value of x.

4. If m∠DEF = 5x - 3 and m∠FEG = 2x + 15, find the value of x.

5. If m∠FEG = 6x - 7 and m∠FED = 2x + 41, find the m∠DEG.

6. If m∠FEG = 4x + 3 and m∠DEG = 2x + 36, find the m∠FED.

Answers:
1. 44°
2. 54°
3. x = 17
4. x = 6
5. x = 12; 130°
6. x = 5; 23°

Cooperative Learning and High School Geometry: Becky Bride
Kagan Publishing • 1 (800) WEE-CO-OP • www.KaganOnline.com

21

ACTIVITY 8
PROCESSING PERPENDICULAR BISECTOR OF A SEGMENT

DEFINITIONS

Structure: RallyCoach

$\overleftrightarrow{DE}$ is the perpendicular bisector of $\overline{AC}$.
The diagram is not drawn to scale

1. If AC = 17m, find AB.

2. Find m ∠DBC.

3. If m ∠ABE = 6x, find x.

4. If AB = 4x + 1 and AC = 3x + 42, find x.

5. If AB = 9x - 7 and BC = 2x + 21, find x.

6. Find $\frac{2}{3}$ m ∠DBC.

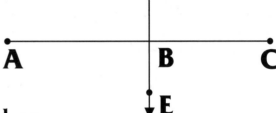

Answers:
1. 8.5m
2. 90°
3. 15°
4. x = 8
5. x = 4
6. 60°

Cooperative Learning and High School Geometry: Becky Bride
Kagan Publishing • 1 (800) WEE-CO-OP • www.KaganOnline.com

9 DRAW WHAT I SAY

Structure: Fan-N-Pick

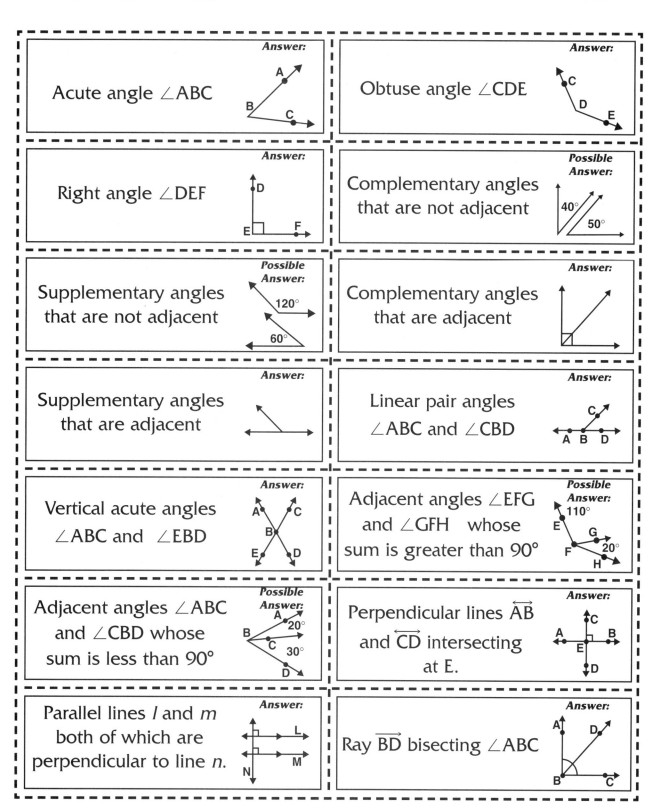

Cooperative Learning and High School Geometry: Becky Bride
Kagan Publishing • 1 (800) WEE-CO-OP • www.KaganOnline.com

23

ACTIVITY 10 REVIEW OF LESSONS 1 AND 2

Structure: Mix-Music-Match

∠ABC	(angle with B as vertex, ray to A upward, ray to C right)
∠BCA	(angle with C as vertex, ray up-left to B, ray right through A)
∠BAC	(angle with A as vertex, ray up to B, ray right to C)
$\overleftrightarrow{AB}$	(line through A and B)
perpendicular bisector of $\overline{CD}$	(segment CD with perpendicular bisector)
$\overline{MN}$	(segment from M to N)
$\overrightarrow{AB}$	(ray from A through B)
$\overrightarrow{BA}$	(ray from B through A)
plane B	(parallelogram labeled B)

Cooperative Learning and High School Geometry: Becky Bride
Kagan Publishing • 1 (800) WEE-CO-OP • www.KaganOnline.com

ACTIVITY 10

REVIEW LESSONS 1 AND 2

Structure: Mix-Music-Match

vertical angles ∠1 and ∠2	
linear pair angles ∠1 and ∠2	
adjacent angles ∠3 and ∠4	
supplementary angles	
complementary angles	
obtuse angle	
acute angle	
right angle	
an angle bisected by a ray	

Cooperative Learning and High School Geometry: Becky Bride
Kagan Publishing • 1 (800) WEE-CO-OP • www.KaganOnline.com

25

LESSON 3
POLYGONS

This lesson contains definitions for polygons. It begins with an activity in which the students generate the definitions and more activities follow to process the definitions. For the first activity, either the Blackline 1.3.1 can be used, or examples and counterexamples of the definitions can be made on geoboards, which are then displayed for all students to see. The geoboards add variety. Activity 3 is fun and challenging. Two blackline masters are included—one working with convex polygons only and the other dealing with convex and concave. The convex only blackline is included for informal or average-level geometry courses, so students can process the definitions without having to deal with the definitions of concave and convex. The second blackline has students focus on convex and concave since each polygon included on the master has both represented. This is a great communication builder. Students learn to be more specific in their directions. Activity 4 gives the students an opportunity to practice drawing and labeling polygons. It is an activity that gets the students up out of their seats while they process. In Activity 5, perimeter will be processed using the Boss/Secretary structure. The definition of regular polygon and algebra skills will be reinforced.

DEVELOPING DEFINITIONS OF POLYGONS

▶ **Structure**
· Team/Discuss

▶ **Materials**
· 1 Blackline 1.3.1 per student
· Optional geoboards
· 1 sheet of paper and pencil per student for step 1
· 1 sheet of paper and pencil per team for step 2

Tip:
During step 2, prior to the discussion, the RoundRobin structure could be used for students to share the definitions they wrote. To do this, each student takes a turn reading his/her definitions.

1. Have students generate their own definitions first or give adequate think time for each student to formulate a definition in his/her mind.

2. As a team, the students will discuss how to define the term.

3. Once the team reaches a consensus, then student 1 will record the team definition on a sheet of paper.

4. Repeat steps 1-3 with a different student recording each time on the same sheet of paper.

Notes:
To develop a class definition, spin the team spinner to choose a team and the student spinner to choose a student of the chosen team to read the team's definition. Record the team's definition on the board. Ask the class if they agree with part 1 and then part 2 of the definition, reworking what they want to change. Then begin working with part three, drawing a picture of what was communicated to help students see where refinement is needed. Sometimes asking students if part of the definition could be reworded using fewer words will get the students thinking again. Once everyone has agreed, including the teacher, then it is recorded as the definition the class will use.

ACTIVITY

2 MAKE WHAT I SAY

1. Student 1 fans the cards face down.

2. Student 2 picks a card and reads it to Student 3, allowing 5 seconds of think time.

3. Student 3 makes the figure on the geoboard using a rubber band(s).

4. Student 4 checks Student 3's figure and praises, or coaches, then praises.

5. Students pass cards to the next person in the clockwise direction and steps 1-4 begin rotating roles one student in the clockwise direction. This process is repeated for a specific time limit or until cards are exhausted.

▶ **Structure**
• Fan-N-Pick

▶ **Materials**
• 1 geoboard per team
• Rubber bands for the geoboard
• 1 set of Fan-N-Pick cards per team (Blackline 1.3.2)

ACTIVITY

3 MATCH MY POLYGONS

1. Each student has a set of polygons. Face-to-face partners will work together for this structure.

2. A barrier is set up between each face-to-face pair of partners. Backpacks, books, or manila folders fastened at the top with paper clips work well for barrier.

3. One student is the sender; the other is the receiver. The sender arranges his/her polygons to form a picture or pattern. Then the sender, using the new polygon vocabulary, describes as clearly as possible to the receiver how to arrange his/her polygons in the same pattern as the sender.

4. The receiver attempts to match the sender's pattern by listening to the description.

5. When the sender and receiver are finished, the students check to see how similar their polygon arrangement is.

6. Sender/receiver roles reverse and steps 3-5 are repeated.

Tips:
The first time this activity is done, have students cut out the polygons. That way the teacher doesn't have to do it.

Resealable snack-size plastic bags are a great way to store each set of polygons.

▶ **Structure**
• Match Mine

▶ **Materials**
• 1 set of polygons for each student
• Scissors (for the first time the blackline is used)
• Paperclips or resealable snack-size plastic bags in which to store each set of polygons
• Blackline 1.3.3a and/or 1.3.3b

Make copies of half of the sets of polygons on one color of paper and the other half on a different color of paper. Each pair of students would have one set of each color. This way if their pieces get mixed up they are easy to sort when it is time to pack up the polygons.

Cooperative Learning and High School Geometry: Becky Bride
Kagan Publishing • 1 (800) WEE-CO-OP • www.KaganOnline.com

27

ACTIVITY

4

DRAW AND LABEL POLYGONS

▶ **Structure**
· Find Someone Who...

▶ **Materials**
· 1 Blackline 1.3.4 per student
· 1 pencil per student

1. Students mix in the class, keeping a hand raised until they find a new partner that is not a teammate. They greet each other with a gambit.

2. In pairs, Student A asks a question from the worksheet; Student B explains how to draw and label the figure as Student A draws what Student B has said on his/her own worksheet.

3. Student B checks and initials the diagram.

4. Student B asks a question from his/her worksheet; Student B records what Student A says on Student B's worksheet.

5. Student A checks and initials the diagram.

6. Partners shake hands, give a goodbye gambit, part, and raise a hand again as they search for a new partner.

7. Students repeat steps 1-6 until their worksheets are complete.

8. When their worksheets are completed, students sit down; seated students can be approached by others as a resource. Students cannot pair with the same student twice.

9. In teams, students compare answers; if there is disagreement or uncertainty, they raise four hands to ask a team question.

ACTIVITY

5

PROCESSING PERIMETER

▶ **Structure**
· Boss/Secretary

▶ **Materials**
· 1 Blackline 1.3.5 per pair of students
· 1 sheet of paper and pencil per pair of students

1. Student A supplies one sheet of paper, folded in half lengthwise with his/her name in one column and a partner's name in the other column.

2. Student B is the first boss and Student A is the first secretary.

3. As the boss, Student B tells Student A how to do the problem. Student A, the secretary, records what Student B says in Student B's column of the paper.

4. If the boss makes a mistake, then the secretary coaches and praises once the boss does it correctly. Otherwise, the secretary praises the boss.

5. Reverse roles for each problem and repeat steps 3 and 4.

ACTIVITY

1 DEVELOPING DEFINITIONS OF POLYGONS

Structure: Team Discuss

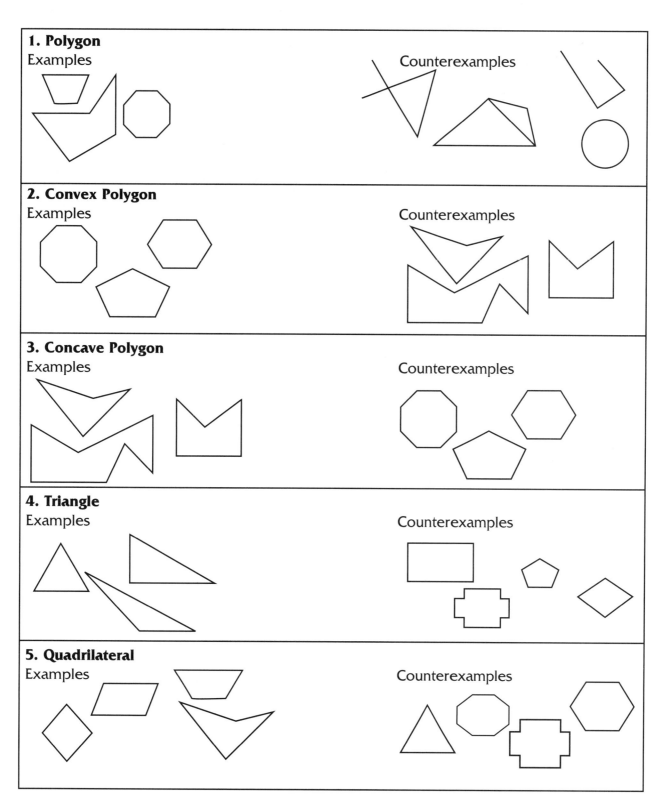

1. Polygon
Examples   Counterexamples

2. Convex Polygon
Examples   Counterexamples

3. Concave Polygon
Examples   Counterexamples

4. Triangle
Examples   Counterexamples

5. Quadrilateral
Examples   Counterexamples

Cooperative Learning and High School Geometry: Becky Bride
Kagan Publishing • 1 (800) WEE-CO-OP • www.KaganOnline.com

29

DEVELOPING DEFINITIONS OF POLYGONS

Structure: Team Discuss

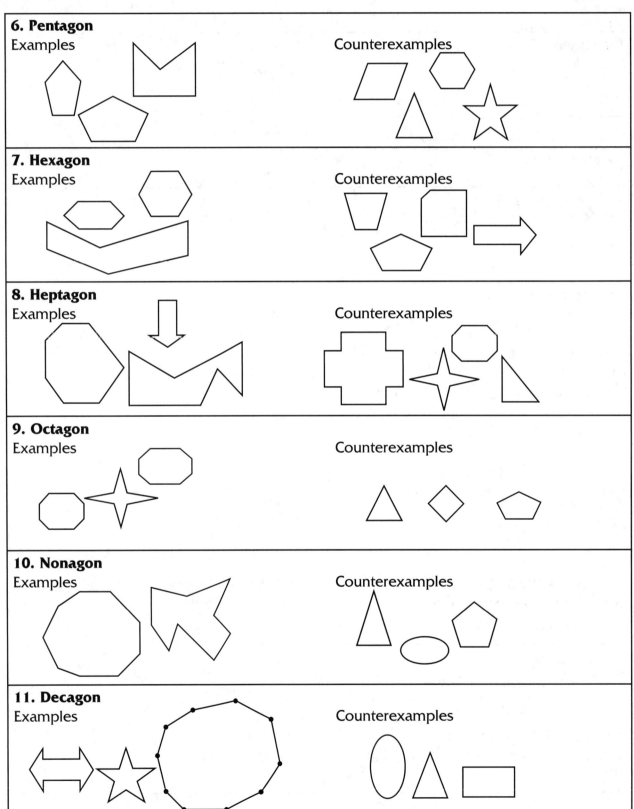

6. Pentagon
Examples   Counterexamples

7. Hexagon
Examples   Counterexamples

8. Heptagon
Examples   Counterexamples

9. Octagon
Examples   Counterexamples

10. Nonagon
Examples   Counterexamples

11. Decagon
Examples   Counterexamples

Cooperative Learning and High School Geometry: Becky Bride
Kagan Publishing • 1 (800) WEE-CO-OP • www.KaganOnline.com

ACTIVITY 1

DEVELOPING DEFINITIONS OF POLYGONS

Structure: Team Discuss

12. Undecagon

Examples 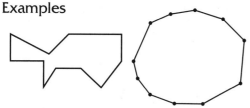   Counterexamples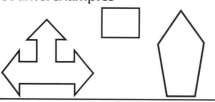

13. Dodecagon

Examples 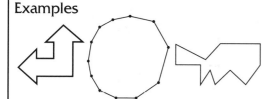   Counterexamples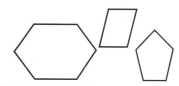

14. Regular Polygon

Examples 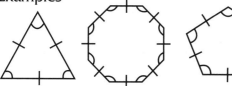   Counterexamples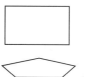

15. Perimeter of a polygon

Examples

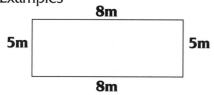

Perimeter of the polygon above is
5m + 8m + 5m + 8m = 26m

Perimeter of the polygon above is
6cm + 6cm + 5cm + 7cm + 5cm = 29cm

Counterexamples

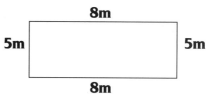

Perimeter of the polygon above is
5m + 8m = 13m

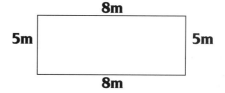

Perimeter of the polygon above is
(5m)(8m) = 40m²

Cooperative Learning and High School Geometry: Becky Bride
Kagan Publishing • 1 (800) WEE-CO-OP • www.KaganOnline.com

31

2 MAKE WHAT I SAY

Structure: Fan-N-Pick

Convex pentagon	Convex hexagon with two equal sides
Convex heptagon	Convex nonagon
Concave pentagon with three equal sides	Concave quadrilateral with one obtuse angle
Convex octagon with at least two equal sides	Concave decagon with at least one right angle
Concave heptagon with only one right angle	Concave undecagon

Cooperative Learning and High School Geometry: Becky Bride
Kagan Publishing • 1 (800) WEE-CO-OP • www.KaganOnline.com

ACTIVITY
3

MATCH MY POLYGONS

DEFINITIONS

Structure: Match Mine

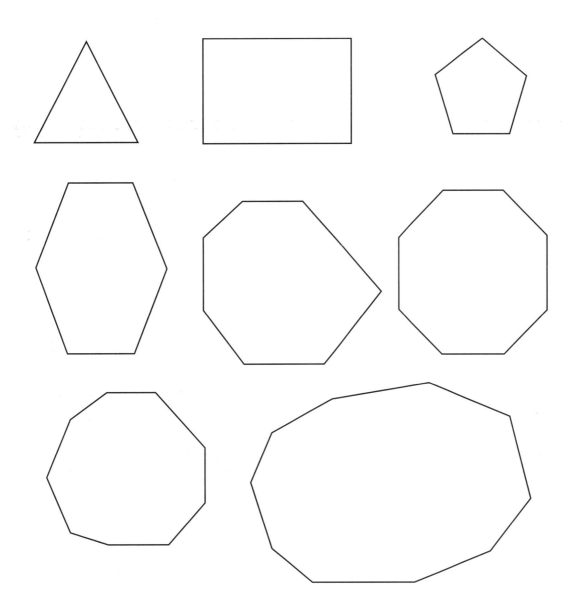

Cooperative Learning and High School Geometry: Becky Bride
Kagan Publishing • 1 (800) WEE-CO-OP • www.KaganOnline.com

33

ACTIVITY 3 MATCH MY POLYGONS

DEFINITIONS

Structure: Match Mine

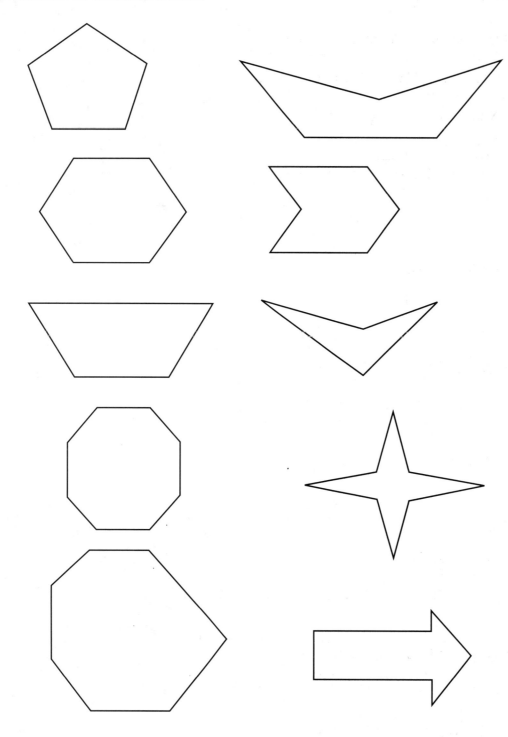

Cooperative Learning and High School Geometry: Becky Bride
Kagan Publishing • 1 (800) WEE-CO-OP • www.KaganOnline.com

ACTIVITY 4
DRAW AND LABEL POLYGONS

Structure: Find Someone Who...

Find Someone Who can draw, mark, and label:

1. A convex quadrilateral, *QUAD*, with a right angle at A.

2. Concave pentagon, *PENTA*, with sides PE = EN = NT.

3. Regular octagon, *OCTAGNIE*.

4. Regular hexagon, *HEXAGN*.

5. Triangle, *TRI*, with an obtuse angle at vertex T.

6. Regular quadrilateral, *LATE*.

7. Concave heptagon, *HEPTAGN*, with HE = TA.

8. Convex pentagon, *PTNOG,* with $\overline{TN} \,||\, \overline{GO}$.

Cooperative Learning and High School Geometry: Becky Bride
Kagan Publishing • 1 (800) WEE-CO-OP • www.KaganOnline.com

35

ACTIVITY 5

PROCESSING PERIMETER

DEFINITIONS

Structure: Boss/Secretary

Find the perimeter or an expression of the perimeter for the following figures.
(Note: figures are not necessarily drawn to scale)

1.

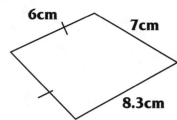

6cm 7cm 8.3cm

2.

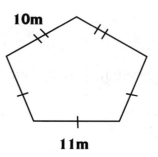

10m 11m

3. Regular hexagon

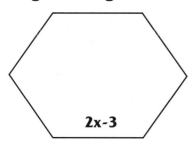

2x-3

4.

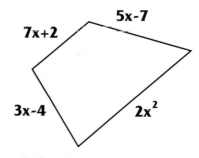

5x-7 7x+2 3x-4 $2x^2$

5.

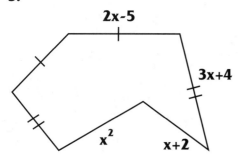

2x-5 3x+4 x^2 x+2

6. Regular pentagon

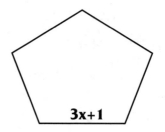

3x+1

Answers:
1. 27.3cm
2. 53m
3. 12x - 18
4. $2x^2 + 15x - 9$
5. $x^2 + 11x$
6. 15x + 5

Cooperative Learning and High School Geometry: Becky Bride
Kagan Publishing • 1 (800) WEE-CO-OP • www.KaganOnline.com

LESSON 4
TRIANGLES

This lesson contains the definitions for the different types of triangles, altitude of a triangle, and median of a triangle. It begins with the development of the definitions, then processes altitude and median, and finishes with a concept map.

1 DEVELOPING DEFINITIONS OF TRIANGLES

1. Have students generate their own definitions first or give adequate think time for each student to formulate a definition in their mind.

2. As a team, the students will discuss how to define the term.

3. Once the team reaches a consensus, then Student 1 will record the team definition on a sheet of paper.

4. Repeat steps 1-3 with a different student recording each time on the same sheet of paper.

Notes:
To develop a class definition, spin the team spinner to choose a team and the student spinner to choose a student of the chosen team to read the team's definition. Record the team's definition on the board. Ask the class if they agree with part 1 and then part 2 of the definition, reworking what they want to change. Then begin working with part three, drawing a picture of what was communicated to help students see where refinement is needed. Sometimes asking students if part of the definition could be reworded using fewer words will get the students thinking again. Once everyone has agreed, including the teacher, then it is recorded as the definition the class will use.

▶ **Structure**
• Team Discuss

▶ **Materials**
• 1 Blackline 1.4.1 per pair of students
• 1 sheet of paper and pencil per team

Tip:
During step 2, prior to the discussion, the RoundRobin structure could be used for students to share the definitions they wrote. To do this, each student takes a turn reading his/her definitions.

Cooperative Learning and High School Geometry: Becky Bride
Kagan Publishing • 1 (800) WEE-CO-OP • www.KaganOnline.com

37

Chapter 1: Definitions Lesson Four

2 PROCESSING MEDIAN OF A TRIANGLE

▶ Structure
· Simultaneous RoundTable

▶ Materials
· Transparencies 1.4.2a and 1.4.2b
· 1 sheet of paper or patty paper per student
· 1 straightedge per student
· 1 pencil and highlighter per student

1. Each student puts his/her name in the upper corner of the paper. Have Student 1 draw an acute triangle, Student 2 an obtuse triangle, Student 3 a right triangle, and Student 4 any type he/she wants to draw.

2. Each student traces over his/her triangle with a highlighter.

3. On the paper that each student has, he/she chooses a vertex and then identifies the opposite side. (Circling the vertex and writing "opp" on the side opposite the circled vertex helps students to focus on only those parts. The other two sides can be distracting.)

4. Each student needs to locate the midpoint of their chosen side either by a) measuring the side; b) eyeballing the point; or c) if using patty paper they can pinch to find the midpoint. The segment with the midpoint needs to be marked correctly to show it is a midpoint.

5. Students then connect the circled vertex to the midpoint using a straightedge to complete the median.

6. Students initial their medians and the papers are passed to the next person in a clockwise direction.

7. Students check the median already drawn on the paper they receive and coach their teammate if necessary.

8. On the paper they just received, the students repeat steps 3-6 to construct a second median in the triangle.

9. The students repeat step 7 then steps 3-6 on the paper they receive to complete the third median.

Tips:
Make sure when the students check the previous students' work they make sure the correct markings are on the triangle.

Highlighting the triangle makes it easier to see the original triangle when the students are doing the second and third medians.

Patty paper is wonderful for this activity because it is so easy to locate a midpoint of a segment by putting the segments endpoints together and pinching the midpoint.

This could lead to a discussion on how all medians meet at a point of concurrency.

Cooperative Learning and High School Geometry: Becky Bride
Kagan Publishing • 1 (800) WEE-CO-OP • www.KaganOnline.com

ACTIVITY
3

PROCESSING ALTITUDE OF A TRIANGLE

Round 1

1. Each student puts his/her name in the upper right corner of the paper. Using a straight-edge each student draws an acute triangle on the paper (make sure the triangles drawn aren't too small or too big.

2. Each student highlights his/her triangle.

3. Using the corner of another sheet of paper or patty paper (ensures a right angle) students slide the edge of their paper along 1 side of the triangle until the perpendicular side of the paper touches the opposite vertex. Students then trace along the edge of the paper from the vertex to the side of the triangle. (I tell students that the side of the triangle is the track of a sliding glass door and the paper being slid is the door.)

4. Students mark the right angle and initial the altitude, then pass the paper to the next person in a clockwise direction.

5. Students check the altitude already drawn on the paper they receive and coach their teammates if necessary.

6. Each student repeats steps 3-4 on the new paper received to draw the second altitude.

7. Students repeat step 5 for the second altitude. Then steps 3-4 to complete the third altitude.

Round 2

Repeat the above directions for a right triangle. The students will see that two of the sides of a right triangle are also the altitudes.

Round 3

Have the students draw an obtuse triangle on their paper and repeat the directions above. (This may have to be repeated several times for the students to become comfortable with it.) Modeling this round is very helpful.

Notes:
This exercise with the obtuse triangle will emphasize why the definition includes the part about being perpendicular to the line containing the opposite side. Doing this exercise when the altitude of a triangle is defined helps when students have to construct altitudes later in the course.

Structure
· Simultaneous RoundTable

Materials
· Transparencies 1.4.3a and 1.4.3b
· 1 sheet of paper or patty paper per student
· 1 straightedge per student
· 1 pencil and highlighter per student

Tips:
For lower level students or if the students are confused, using the sliding technique in a simpler diagram may be helpful. Have students draw three segments on their paper with a point at least an inch above the segment. Using the Simultaneous RoundTable structure, have students practice drawing a perpendicular to the segment passing through the point above using the sliding technique described in step 3.

If students are still having difficulty drawing altitudes of triangles after using the tip above, have the students circle a vertex and then label the opposite side with "opp." The segment labeled "opp" is the sliding door track, and the vertex circled is the one that will indicate when they should stop.

Cooperative Learning and High School Geometry: Becky Bride
Kagan Publishing • 1 (800) WEE-CO-OP • www.KaganOnline.com

39

Chapter 1: Definitions
Lesson Four

ACTIVITY

4

GUESS MY TRIANGLE

Structure
• Draw It

Materials
• 1 set of Draw It cards per team (Blackline 1.4.4)
• 1 sheet of paper and pencil per team

1. Cards are stacked, shuffled, and placed face-down in the center of the table.

2. Student 1 picks the top card and reads it silently. On a sheet of paper the student draws a picture of the triangle making sure to mark it correctly (box for right angles, appropriate marks to show congruent segments etc.)

3. Teammates guess the type of triangle. Student 1 continues drawing until a teammate guesses correctly.

4. When a teammate guesses correctly, student 1 shows the answer and congratulates the teammate who identified the triangle.

5. The process is repeated with student 2 picking a card and drawing the content for teammates to guess.

ACTIVITY

5

DRAW, LABEL, AND MARK WHAT I SAY

▶ Structure
• Boss/Secretary

▶ Materials
• 1 Blackline 1.4.5 per pair of students
• 1 sheet of paper and pencil per pair of students

1. Student A supplies one sheet paper, folded in half lengthwise with his/her name in one column and a partner's name in the other column.

2. Student B is the first boss and Student A is the first secretary.

3. As the boss, Student B tells Student A how to do the problem. Student A, the secretary, records what Student B says in Student B's column of the paper.

4. If the boss makes a mistake, then the secretary coaches and praises once the boss does it correctly. Otherwise, the secretary praises the boss.

5. Reverse roles for each problem and repeat steps 3 and 4.

Cooperative Learning and High School Geometry: Becky Bride
Kagan Publishing • 1 (800) WEE-CO-OP • www.KaganOnline.com

ACTIVITY

6 CONCEPT MAPPING

Notes:

The last activity for this lesson has students work with the definitions and make a graphic organizer. The bridges that the students will make between definitions requires them to determine whether a triangle can be both isosceles and right, or right and acute, etc. Some combinations work and others do not. This is definitely a higher level thinking activity. When students have to draw a bridge connecting two core concepts which requires them to go over another line (bridge) they need to draw a curve over that line to show that the two lines aren't together.

1. Each teammate signs his/her name in the upper right corner of the team paper with the color pen or pencil he/she is using.

2. One teammate writes "triangle" in the center of the team paper in a rectangle.

3. Teammates RoundTable (take turns, using their color pen or pencil), writing in the core concepts. Core concepts are placed in ovals connected by lines to the main idea.

4. Continuing in the RoundTable format, teammates add details and make bridges between related ideas.

Structure
• Team Word Web

Materials
• 1 sheet of paper per team
• 4 different colors of pens or pencils per team

Tips:

Teammates each have a different color to write with so that it is very apparent whether the participation was equal.

Step 4 can be done as a free-for-all with all teammates writing at the same time. If you are concerned that all won't get equal opportunity to write, then use the RoundTable format.

Below is a sample of what the web could look like at the end.

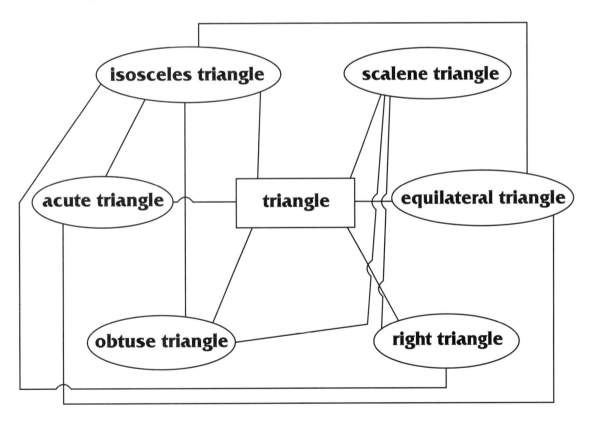

Cooperative Learning and High School Geometry: Becky Bride
Kagan Publishing • 1 (800) WEE-CO-OP • www.KaganOnline.com

DEVELOPING DEFINITIONS OF TRIANGLES

ACTIVITY **1**

Structure: Team Discuss

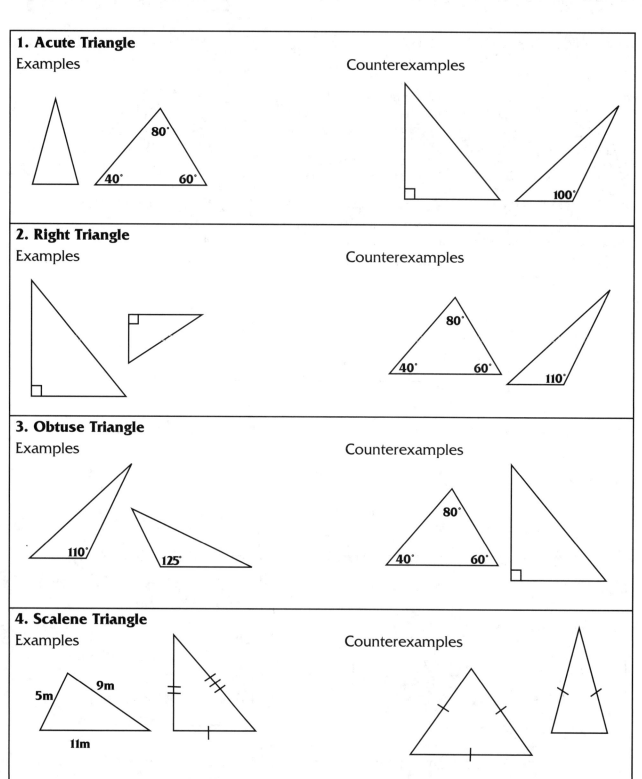

1. Acute Triangle

Examples   Counterexamples

80°
40°   60°

100°

2. Right Triangle

Examples   Counterexamples

80°
40°   60°

110°

3. Obtuse Triangle

Examples   Counterexamples

110°
125°

80°
40°   60°

4. Scalene Triangle

Examples   Counterexamples

9m
5m
11m

Cooperative Learning and High School Geometry: Becky Bride
Kagan Publishing • 1 (800) WEE-CO-OP • www.KaganOnline.com

DEVELOPING DEFINITIONS OF TRIANGLES

ACTIVITY 1

DEFINITIONS

Structure: Team Discuss

5. Isosceles Triangle

Examples

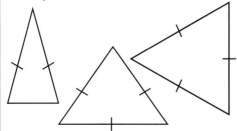

Counterexamples

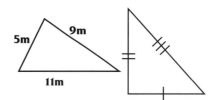

6. Equilateral Triangle

Examples

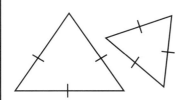

Counterexamples

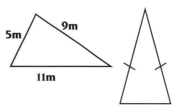

7. Median of a Triangle

Examples

$\overline{AB}$ is a median

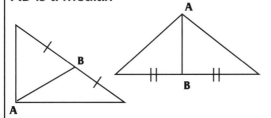

Counterexamples

$\overline{AB}$ is not a median

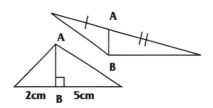

8. Altitude of a Triangle

Examples

$\overline{AB}$ is an altitude

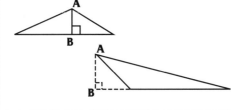

Counterexamples

$\overline{AB}$ is not an altitude

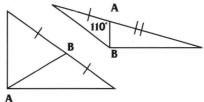

Cooperative Learning and High School Geometry: Becky Bride
Kagan Publishing • 1 (800) WEE-CO-OP • www.KaganOnline.com

43

PROCESSING MEDIAN OF A TRIANGLE

DEFINITIONS

Structure: Simultaneous RoundTable

1. Student 1: Draw an acute triangle (using a straightedge) that covers about one-third of your paper and highlight the triangle.

2. Student 2: Draw an obtuse triangle (using a straightedge) that covers about one-third of your paper and highlight the triangle.

3. Student 3: Draw a right triangle (using a straightedge) that covers about one-third of your paper and highlight the triangle.

4. Student 4: Draw any type of triangle (using a straightedge) that covers about one-third of your paper and highlight the triangle.

Cooperative Learning and High School Geometry: Becky Bride
Kagan Publishing • 1 (800) WEE-CO-OP • www.KaganOnline.com

PROCESSING MEDIAN OF A TRIANGLE

Structure: Simultaneous RoundTable

Directions:

1. Draw one median of the triangle that is on your paper. Mark the diagram appropriately, initial the median, and pass your paper 1 person in the clockwise direction.

2. Check the median your teammate drew and coach if necessary. Praise your teammate for a job well done. Draw a second median of the triangle that is on the paper you just received. Mark the diagram appropriately, initial the median, and pass your paper 1 person in the clockwise direction.

3. Check the median your teammate drew and coach if necessary. Praise your teammate for a job well done. Draw a third median of the triangle that is on the paper you just received. Mark the diagram appropriately and initial the median.

Cooperative Learning and High School Geometry: Becky Bride
Kagan Publishing • 1 (800) WEE-CO-OP • www.KaganOnline.com

45

ACTIVITY 3 PROCESSING ALTITUDE OF A TRIANGLE

Structure: Simultaneous RoundTable

Round 1:

All students: Draw an acute triangle (using a straightedge) that covers about one-third of a sheet of paper. Highlight the triangle.

Round 2:

All students: Draw a right triangle (using a straightedge) that covers about one-third of a sheet of paper. Highlight the triangle.

Round 3:

All students: Draw an obtuse triangle (using a straightedge) that covers about one-third of a sheet of paper. Highlight the triangle.

Cooperative Learning and High School Geometry: Becky Bride
Kagan Publishing • 1 (800) WEE-CO-OP • www.KaganOnline.com

Structure: Simultaneous RoundTable

Directions:

1. On the paper you currently have, draw an altitude on the triangle. Mark the diagram appropriately, initial the altitude, and pass the paper 1 person in the clockwise direction.

2. On the paper you just received, check the altitude already drawn and coach and/or praise your teammate for a job well done. Draw a second altitude on the triangle. Mark the diagram appropriately, initial the altitude, and pass the paper 1 person in the clockwise direction.

3. Check the altitude already drawn on the paper you receive and coach if necessary. Praise your teammate for a job well done. Draw a third altitude on the triangle of the paper you received. Mark the diagram appropriately, and initial the altitude.

Cooperative Learning and High School Geometry: Becky Bride
Kagan Publishing • 1 (800) WEE-CO-OP • www.KaganOnline.com

47

ACTIVITY 4

GUESS MY TRIANGLE

DEFINITIONS

Structure: Draw It

Scalene obtuse triangle

Possible Answer:

10
6
5

Scalene acute triangle

Possible Answer:

5   6
7

Scalene right triangle

Possible Answer:

3   5
4

Isosceles right triangle

Possible Answer:

Isosceles acute triangle

Possible Answer:

Isosceles obtuse triangle

Possible Answer:

9   5
5

Equilateral triangle

Possible Answer:

Regular triangle

Possible Answer:

Cooperative Learning and High School Geometry: Becky Bride
Kagan Publishing • 1 (800) WEE-CO-OP • www.KaganOnline.com

ACTIVITY 5
DRAW, LABEL, AND MARK WHAT I SAY

Structure: Boss/Secretary

Sketch, label, and mark the figure described below.

1. Isosceles triangle, *MNP*, with vertex angle M.

2. Right triangle, *DOG*, with right angle G.

3. Acute triangle, *ABC*, with median AM.

4. Obtuse triangle, *CAT*, with obtuse angle C and altitude AD.

5. Equilateral triangle, *EQL*.

6. Isosceles triangle, *ISC*, with vertex angle S and median SL.

7. Right triangle, *RGT*, with right angle T and altitude TD.

8. Scalene triangle, *SCL*.

Cooperative Learning and High School Geometry: Becky Bride
Kagan Publishing • 1 (800) WEE-CO-OP • www.KaganOnline.com

49

LESSON 5
QUADRILATERALS

This lesson includes the definitions of parallelogram, trapezoid, kite, rectangle, rhombus, and square. It begins with development of the definitions and concludes with processing the definitions and several reviews of all the terms from this chapter. Several definitions for a square can be generated by changing its nearest classification. It is worth exploring when defining a square.

1 DEVELOPING DEFINITIONS FOR QUADRILATERALS

▶ **Structure**
· Team Discuss

▶ **Materials**
· 1 Blackline 1.5.1 per student
· 1 sheet of paper and pencil per student for step 1
· 1 sheet of paper and pencil per team for step 2

1. Have students generate their own definitions first or give adequate think time for each student to formulate a definition in their mind.

2. As a team, the students will discuss how to define the term.

3. Once the team reaches a consensus, then Student 1 will record the team definition on a sheet of paper.

4. Repeat steps 1-3 with a different student recording each time on the same sheet of paper.

Notes:
To develop a class definition, spin the team spinner to choose a team and the student spinner to choose a student of the chosen team to read the team's definition. Record the team's definition on the board. Ask the class if they agree with part 1 and then part 2 of the definition, reworking what they want to change. Then begin working with part three, drawing a picture of what was communicated to help students see where refinement is needed. Sometimes asking students if part of the definition could be reworded using fewer words will get the students thinking again. Once everyone has agreed, including the teacher, then it is recorded as the definition the class will use.

Tip:
During step 2, prior to the discussion, the RoundRobin structure could be used for students to share the definitions they wrote. To do this, each student takes a turn reading his/her definitions.

ACTIVITY

2 PROCESSING QUADRILATERALS WITH ALGEBRA

1. Student A folds a sheet of paper in half lengthwise and puts his/her name at the top of one column and a partner's name at the top of the other column.

2. Student A does problem 1 on his/her side of the paper.

3. Student B checks Student A's work and gives praise, or coaches, then praises the work.

4. Student B repeats step 2 for the next problem.

5. Student A repeats step 3 for the next problem.

6. Pairs check with the other pair at their table and coach each other if necessary.

7. Repeat steps 1-6 until all the problems are done.

▶ **Structure**
• Pairs Check

▶ **Materials**
• Blackline 1.5.2 per pair of students
• 1 sheet of paper and pencil per pair of students

ACTIVITY

3 GUESS MY QUADRILATERAL

Notes:
Activity 3 focuses the students' thinking on correctly marking a quadrilateral. As the teammates guess, they could mention a quadrilateral that is correct but not specific enough (i.e. parallelogram when the figure drawn is a rectangle). Encourage the students to validate those answers but to have their teammates get more specific. This may help the students begin to see the relationships between many of the quadrilaterals.

1. Cards are stacked, shuffled, and placed face-down in the center of the table.

2. Student 1 picks the top card and reads it silently. On a sheet of paper, the student draws a picture of the quadrilateral making sure to mark it correctly (box for right angles, appropriate marks to show congruent segments, arrows for parallel sides etc.)

3. Teammates guess the type of quadrilateral. Student 1 continues drawing until a teammate guesses correctly.

4. When a teammate guesses correctly, Student 1 shows the answer and congratulates the teammate who identified the quadrilateral.

▶ **Structure**
• Draw It

▶ **Materials**
• 1 set of Draw It Cards per team (Blackline 1.5.3)
• 1 sheet of paper and pencil per team

5. The process is repeated rotating roles to the next person in a clockwise direction.

Cooperative Learning and High School Geometry: Becky Bride
Kagan Publishing • 1 (800) WEE-CO-OP • www.KaganOnline.com

51

ACTIVITY

4 ALWAYS, SOMETIMES, NEVER AND QUADRILATERALS

▶**Structure**
· Inside-Outside Circle

▶**Materials**
· 1 Blackline 1.5.4 per student
· 1 pen or pencil per student

Notes:
This activity requires higher level thinking. Always, sometimes, never questions are difficult for the average student but well worth the exercise. It makes them think and broadens their understanding. Announce the answer to each question after each pair has agreed on an answer. It is very likely that the correct answer will prompt some class discussion. As the students work through the worksheet they will get better at thinking through the questions. This activity is a great prerequisite for Activity 5. Students will gain a richer understanding of the team word webs if Activity 4 is done before Activity 5. It helps students with the bridges.

1. Ask the As to stand and form a large circle with everyone facing the inside of the circle.

2. Ask the Bs to get up and go stand in front of their partner (students should be face to face now with the Bs facing out and As facing in.

3. Inside circle students ask question 1 from their worksheet; outside circle students answer, explaining their thinking. If the inside student disagrees, the pair discusses until they reach a consensus. The teacher gives the answer when all pairs have reached a consensus.

4. Partners switch roles: Outside circle students ask, listen, then discuss until they agree. The teacher gives the answer when all pairs have reached a consensus.

5. Students thank each other for working together.

6. Inside circle students rotate clockwise to a new partner per teacher's instructions. (Outside students could do the rotating or both inside and outside students can rotate in opposite directions).

7. Repeat steps 3-6 until all questions are answered.

Answers to Blackline 1.5.4
1. A	*2. N*	*3. N*	*4. S*
5. N	*6. S*	*7. A*	*8. N*
9. N	*10. N*	*11. N*	*12. S*
13. S	*14. A*	*15. N*	*16. N*
17. N	*18. A*	*19. A*	*20. N*

ACTIVITY

5 CONCEPT MAPPING QUADRILATERALS

▶ **Structure**
· Team Word Mapping

▶ **Materials**
· 1 piece of paper for the team
· 4 different colored pens or pencils per team

1. Each teammate signs his/her name in the upper right corner of the team paper with the color pen or pencil he/she is using.

2. One teammate writes quadrilateral in the center of the team paper in a rectangle.

3. Teammates RoundTable (take turns, using their color pen or pencil) and write the core concepts in ovals connected by lines to the main idea.

4. Continuing to work in the RoundTable format, teammates add details and make bridges between related ideas.

Tips:
Teammates each have a different color to write with so that it is very apparent whether the participation was equal.

Step 4 can be done as a free-for-all with all teammates writing at the same time. If you are concerned that all won't get equal opportunity to write, then use the RoundTable format.

Chapter 1: Definitions
Lesson Five

6 REVIEW 1: DRAW, MARK, AND LABEL

1. Student 1 fans the cards face down.

2. Student 2 picks a card and reads it to Student 3, allowing 5 seconds of think time.

3. Student 3 draws a diagram of what was said, correctly labeling and marking it.

4. Student 4 checks Student 3's work and praises, or coaches, then praises.

5. Cards are passed to the next person in a clockwise direction and steps 1-4 begin again with roles rotating one student in the clockwise direction. This process is repeated for a specific time limit or until cards are exhausted.

▶ **Structure**
  • Fan-N-Pick

▶ **Materials**
  • 1 set of Fan-N-Pick Cards per team (Blackline 1.5.6)
  • 1 sheet of paper and pencil per team

7 REVIEW 2 (ALL DEFINITIONS)

1. Students mix in the class, keeping a hand raised until they find a new partner who is not a teammate. They greet each other with a gambit.

2. In pairs, Student A asks a question from the worksheet; Student B explains the answer making false statements true as Student A writes what Student B has said on his/her own worksheet.

3. Student B checks and initials the problem.

4. Student B asks a question from the worksheet; partner B records what partner A says on his/her own worksheet.

5. Student A checks and initials the problem.

6. Partners shake hands, give a goodbye gambit, part, and raise a hand again as they search for a new partner.

7. Students repeat steps 1-6 until their worksheets are complete.

8. When their worksheets are completed, students sit down; seated students can be approached by others as a resource. Students cannot pair with the same student twice.

9. In teams, students compare answers; if there is disagreement or uncertainty and a consensus cannot be reached, then they raise four hands to ask a team question.

▶ **Structure**
  • Find Someone Who...

▶ **Materials**
  • 1 Blackline 1.5.7 per student
  • 1 pen or pencil per student

Variation: You may use Inside-Outside Circle for this activity.

Answers:

1. F	13. F
2. T	14. F
3. F	15. F
4. F	16. F
5. F	17. F
6. F	18. T
7. T	19. F
8. F	20. F
9. F	21. T
10. F	22. F
11. F	23. T
12. T	24. F

Cooperative Learning and High School Geometry: Becky Bride
Kagan Publishing • 1 (800) WEE-CO-OP • www.KaganOnline.com

53

DEVELOPING DEFINITIONS FOR QUADRILATERALS

Structure: Team Discuss

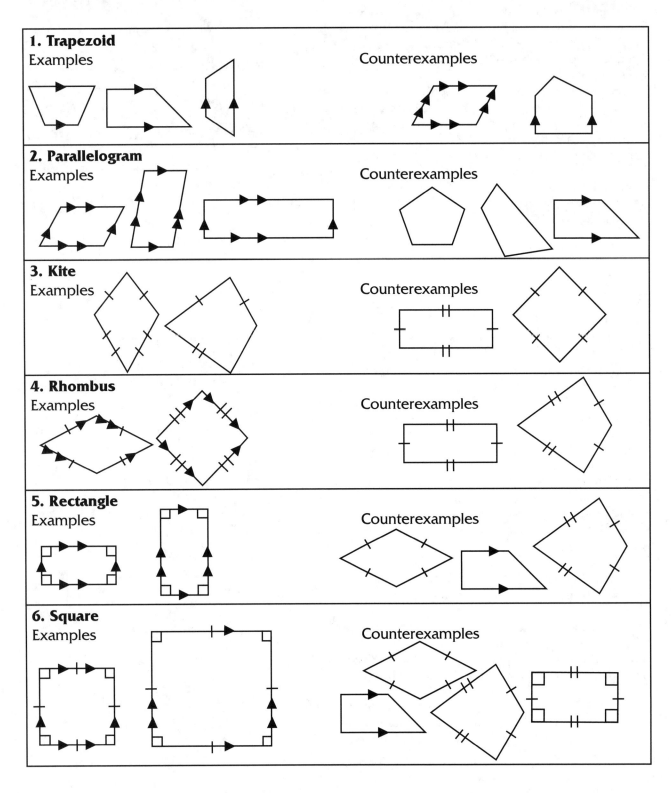

1. Trapezoid
Examples   Counterexamples

2. Parallelogram
Examples   Counterexamples

3. Kite
Examples   Counterexamples

4. Rhombus
Examples   Counterexamples

5. Rectangle
Examples   Counterexamples

6. Square
Examples   Counterexamples

Cooperative Learning and High School Geometry: Becky Bride
Kagan Publishing • 1 (800) WEE-CO-OP • www.KaganOnline.com

PROCESSING QUADRILATERALS WITH ALGEBRA

Structure: Pairs Check

For each problem solve for x.

ABCD is a kite.

1. AB = 4x + 5 and CB = 15 - x.

2. AD = 9x + 12 and DC = 6x + 42

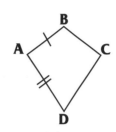

RECT is a rectangle.

3. m∠E = 6x - 18

4. m∠T = 7x + 13

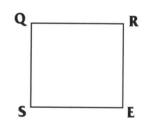

SQRE is a square.

5. SQ = 5x - 16 and RE = x + 24

6. SQ = 9x + 14 and QR = 2x + 63

RHOM is a rhombus.

7. RH = 7x + 18 and OM = 90 - 2x

8. RM = 12x - 5 and OM = 7x + 25

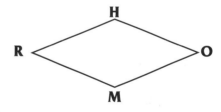

Answers:
1. 2
2. 10
3. 18
4. 11
5. 10
6. 7
7. 8
8. 6

Cooperative Learning and High School Geometry: Becky Bride
Kagan Publishing • 1 (800) WEE-CO-OP • www.KaganOnline.com

ACTIVITY

3

GUESS MY QUADRILATERAL

Structure: Draw It

Rectangle	**Rhombus**
Square	**Trapezoid**
Parallelogram	**Kite**

Cooperative Learning and High School Geometry: Becky Bride
Kagan Publishing • 1 (800) WEE-CO-OP • www.KaganOnline.com

ALWAYS, SOMETIMES, NEVER AND QUADRILATERALS

ACTIVITY 4

Structure: Inside-Outside Circle

Answer each of the following with either always, sometimes, or never.

1. A parallelogram is _____ a quadrilateral.

2. A trapezoid is _____ a kite.

3. A kite is _____ a rectangle.

4. A quadrilateral is _____ a square.

5. A square is _____ a trapezoid.

6. A rhombus is _____ a square.

7. A square is _____ a rhombus.

8. A trapezoid is _____ a rectangle.

9. A rectangle _____ has only one right angle.

10. A kite _____ has four equal sides.

11. A parallelogram is _____ a trapezoid.

12. A quadrilateral is _____ a rectangle.

13. A rectangle is _____ a square.

14. A square is _____ a rectangle.

15. A trapezoid _____ has two pairs of opposite sides parallel.

16. A kite is _____ a trapezoid.

17. A parallelogram is _____ a kite.

18. A trapezoid is _____ a quadrilateral.

19. A square is _____ a quadrilateral.

20. A trapezoid _____ has five sides.

Cooperative Learning and High School Geometry: Becky Bride
Kagan Publishing • 1 (800) WEE-CO-OP • www.KaganOnline.com

57

ACTIVITY 6 REVIEW 1: DRAW, MARK, AND LABEL

Structure: Fan-N-Pick

A scalene right triangle TSR with right angle at S	A pair of perpendicular lines with a pair of vertical angles named $\angle 1$ and $\angle 2$
Angle bisector $\overrightarrow{AB}$ of angle DAC	A regular quadrilateral SQRE
An acute scalene triangle LMN with altitude $\overline{LS}$ and median $\overline{NO}$	An obtuse triangle OBT with obtuse angle at B and altitude $\overline{TS}$
A midpoint on segment $\overline{AB}$	Parallelogram GRAM with one diagonal
An isosceles right triangle BIG with right angle at I and median $\overline{IM}$	Trapezoid TRAP with obtuse angles at $\angle P$ and $\angle A$

Cooperative Learning and High School Geometry: Becky Bride
Kagan Publishing • 1 (800) WEE-CO-OP • www.KaganOnline.com

ACTIVITY

6 REVIEW 1: DRAW, MARK, AND LABEL

Structure: Fan-N-Pick

An isosceles right triangle ABC with the right angle at B	A pair of parallel lines m and n that are perpendicular to line l
An isosceles obtuse triangle CDF with the obtuse angle at F	A pair of complementary angles that are adjacent
A pair of supplementary angles with one angle 35°	An equilateral triangle XYZ with altitude $\overline{XB}$
An isosceles triangle TUV with an angle bisector $\overrightarrow{UW}$	Kite KITE with $\overline{KE}$ and $\overline{TE}$ longer than $\overline{KI}$ and $\overline{IT}$
A regular hexagon GEOMTR with 2 diagonals drawn	Rectangle RECT with RT > RE

ACTIVITY

7 REVIEW 2 ALL DEFINITIONS

Structure: Find Someone Who...

Answer the following questions True or False. False questions need to be made true.

1. An equiangular polygon is always equilateral.

2. Concave polygons have *dents*.

3. Supplementary angles are two angles that add to be 90°.

4. An angle bisector is a segment that cuts a triangle into two equal parts.

5. Perpendicular lines intersect and form a 180° angle.

6. If all the sides of a polygon are equal, then it is a regular polygon.

7. An isosceles triangle can have three equal sides.

8. An isosceles triangle is always an equilateral triangle.

9. An obtuse triangle may contain only one acute angle.

10. All acute triangles have at least a 90° angle.

11. A scalene triangle has all equal sides.

12. Complementary angles are two angles that add up to 90°.

13. A counterexample is an example that proves a statement true.

14. A dodecagon is a polygon with ten sides.

15. The altitude of a triangle is a segment that starts at a vertex and is parallel to the opposite side or the opposite side extended.

16. A linear pair of angles are angles that are opposite of each other and formed by two intersecting lines.

17. Parallel lines intersect at 90° angles.

18. A median of a triangle is a segment with one endpoint on the vertex of a triangle and the other endpoint on the midpoint of the opposite side.

19. Perpendicular lines never intersect.

20. A trapezoid is a pentagon with one pair of parallel sides.

21. A square is a rhombus.

22. All rectangles are squares.

23. A square is a rectangle.

24. A trapezoid is a parallelogram.

Cooperative Learning and High School Geometery: Becky Bride
Kagan Publishing • 1 (800) WEE-CO-OP • www.KaganOnline.com

ANGLES AND LINES

This chapter explores properties of linear pair angles and vertical angles. It also explores angles involved with parallel lines. Slopes of lines are investigated along with the relationship of the slopes of parallel and perpendicular lines. Students are requested to write the equations of lines, so this chapter supports skills learned in Algebra 1.

LESSON 1: VERTICAL AND LINEAR PAIR ANGLES

ACTIVITY 1: Exploring Vertical Angles
ACTIVITY 2: Exploring Linear Pair Angles
ACTIVITY 3: Angles and Algebra

LESSON 2: PARALLEL LINES AND SPECIAL ANGLES

ACTIVITY 1: Recognizing Corresponding, Alternate Interior, Alternate Exterior, and Same-Side Interior Angles
ACTIVITY 2: Exploring Corresponding, Alternate Interior, Alternate Exterior, and Same-Side Interior Angles
ACTIVITY 3: Processing Angles and Parallel Lines
ACTIVITY 4: Parallel Lines, Angles, and Algebra
ACTIVITY 5: Show Me Why!
ACTIVITY 6: Parallel Lines, Angles, and Algebra, Advanced
ACTIVITY 7: Describe It!
ACTIVITY 8: Converse: Working in Reverse
ACTIVITY 9: Sequence It (Working With the Converse)

LESSON 3: PREREQUISITE SKILLS FOR PARALLEL AND PERPENDICULAR LINES

ACTIVITY 1: Graphing Calculator Lab
ACTIVITY 2: Recognizing Lines With Positive, Negative, Zero, or Undefined Slopes
ACTIVITY 3: Draw What I Say
ACTIVITY 4: Tell Me the Slope and the Y-intercept
ACTIVITY 5: Graph Me
ACTIVITY 6: Calculate the Slope
ACTIVITY 7: Write My Equation

LESSON 4: PARALLEL AND PERPENDICULAR LINES

ACTIVITY 1: Who Needs Slope?
ACTIVITY 2: Exploring Parallel Lines and Slopes
ACTIVITY 3: Exploring Perpendicular Lines and Slopes
ACTIVITY 4: Processing Parallel and Perpendicular Slopes
ACTIVITY 5: Am I a Parallelogram, Rectangle, Trapezoid, or Just a Quadrilateral?
ACTIVITY 6: Write the Equation of My Parallel or Perpendicular Line
ACTIVITY 7: Write My Equation, Advanced

LESSON 1
VERTICAL AND LINEAR PAIR ANGLES

This lesson explores the properties of vertical angles and linear pair angles. The exploratory exercises in it allow concrete exploration of these properties. Proving these relationships following the concrete development will be far more effective than if no exploration was done at all. Also it shows students that mathematicians don't start with proof but begin with explorations to find patterns. Once they think a pattern is present, proof is their verification that the pattern works all the time in whatever mathematical system they are exploring. The lesson concludes with an activity to process these concepts.

ACTIVITY
1 EXPLORING VERTICAL ANGLES

▶ **Materials**
• 1 Blackline 2.1.1 per student
• 1 sheet of paper and pencil per student
• 1 straightedge per student
• 1 protractor per student or 1 sheet of patty paper per student

Have the students complete the exploration as explained in Blackline 2.1.1.

ACTIVITY
2 EXPLORING LINEAR PAIR ANGLES

▶ **Materials**
• 1 Blackline 2.1.2 per student
• 1 sheet of paper and pencil per student
• 1 straightedge per student
• 1 protractor per student

Have the students complete the exploration as explained in Blackline 2.1.2.

Cooperative Learning and High School Geometry: Becky Bride
Kagan Publishing • 1 (800) WEE-CO-OP • www.KaganOnline.com

3 ANGLES AND ALGEBRA

Notes:

This activity has two blacklines included. The first allows the processing of vertical and linear pair angles with a simple diagram. The next blackline includes complementary angles for review and has a more complex diagram. Struggling or low-level students will need 2.1.3a before 2.1.3b. Average to advanced students can handle 2.1.3b without doing 2.1.3a.

1. Student A supplies one sheet of paper, folded in half lengthwise with his/her name in one column and a partner's name In the other column.

2. Student B is the first boss and Student A is the first secretary.

3. As the boss, Student B tells Student A how to do the problem. Student A, the secretary, records what Student B says in Student B's column of the paper.

4. If the boss makes a mistake, then the secretary coaches and praises once the boss does it correctly. Otherwise, the secretary praises the boss.

5. Reverse roles for each problem and repeat steps 3 and 4.

▶ **Structure**
· Boss/Secretary

▶ **Materials**
· 1 Blackline 2.1.3a and/or 2.1.3b per pair of students
· 1 sheet of paper and pencil per pair of students

Chapter 2: Angles & Lines

Lesson One

Cooperative Learning and High School Geometry: Becky Bride
Kagan Publishing • 1 (800) WEE-CO-OP • www.KaganOnline.com

63

Blackline 2.1.1

EXPLORING VERTICAL ANGLES

1. On your sheet of paper, using a straightedge, draw two intersecting lines that are not perpendicular. It should be similar to the diagram below. Do not trace the diagram.

2. Number your angles as indicated below.

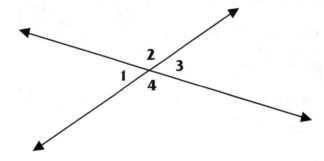

3. Either measure ∠2 and ∠4 with a protractor or trace ∠2 onto a sheet of patty paper.

4. If you measured the angles what is their relationship? If you used patty paper, place ∠2 on top of ∠4 lining up rays and vertices. What appears to be true?

5. Do the same thing for ∠1 and ∠3. What is their relationship?

6. Summarize your findings in a complete sentence.

Cooperative Learning and High School Geometry: Becky Bride
Kagan Publishing • 1 (800) WEE-CO-OP • www.KaganOnline.com

2 # EXPLORING LINEAR PAIR ANGLES

1. Using a straightedge, draw two intersecting lines that are not perpendicular. It should be similar to the diagram below. Do not trace the diagram.

2. Label your angles like the diagram below.

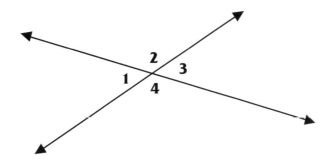

3. Measure ∠1 and ∠2 and place their measurements on the respective angles in the diagram.

4. Based on your knowledge of vertical angles, fill in the measures of ∠3 and ∠4 on the respective angles in the diagram.

5. Find the following sums:

   m∠1 + m∠2 =
   m∠2 + m∠3 =
   m∠3 + m∠4 =
   m∠1 + m∠4 =

6. What appears to be true?

7. Write a complete sentence summarizing your exploration.

Cooperative Learning and High School Geometry: Becky Bride
Kagan Publishing • 1 (800) WEE-CO-OP • www.KaganOnline.com

65

Blackline 2.1.3a

ANGLES AND ALGEBRA

Structure: Boss/Secretary

For each problem a) state what type of angles the given angles are, b) state the relationship of the angles, c) write an equation, d) solve for x, and e) find the measure of the angle requested. Note: The diagram is not necessarily drawn to scale.

1. If the m∠1 = 4x + 3 and m∠3 = 2x + 11, then find the m∠3.

2. If the m∠1 = 2x - 7 and m∠2 = 3x + 17, then find the m∠2.

3. If the m∠2 = x + 9 and the m∠3 = 2x + 3, then find the m∠4.

4. If m∠2 = 6x - 1 and m∠4 = 4x + 17, then find the m∠3.

5. If m∠1 = 4x + 1 and m∠4 = 5x + 8, then find the m∠2.

6. If m∠1 = 9x - 7 and m∠3 = 6x + 23, then find the m∠4.

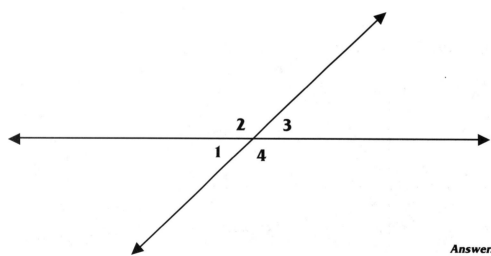

Answers for d and e:
1. x=4; 19°
2. x=34; 119°
3. x=56; 65°
4. x=9; 127°
5. x=19; 103°
6. x=10; 97°

Cooperative Learning and High School Geometry: Becky Bride
Kagan Publishing • 1 (800) WEE-CO-OP • www.KaganOnline.com

3 ANGLES AND ALGEBRA

Structure: Boss/Secretary

For each problem a) state what type of angles the given angles are, b) state the relationship of the angles, c) write an equation, d) solve for x, and e) find the measure of the angle requested. Note: The diagram is not necessarily drawn to scale.

1. If the m∠1 = 2x + 3 and m∠2 = 3x + 2, then find the m∠3.

2. If the m∠ABE = 2x + 5 and m∠EBC = x + 4, then find m∠2.

3. If the m∠ABD = 4x + 5 and m∠DBC = 2x + 1, then find m∠EBC.

4. If m∠4 = 4x - 1 and m∠3 = 5x - 8, then find m∠2.

5. If m∠1 = 4x - 13 and m∠3 = 2x + 19, then find the m∠4.

6. If m∠1 = 6x + 1 and m∠2 = 3x + 8, then find the m∠DBH.

7. If m∠EBG = 7x + 11 and m∠EBH = 2x + 7, then find the m∠1.

8. If m∠4 = 5x - 9 and m∠2 = 2x + 3, then find the m∠3.

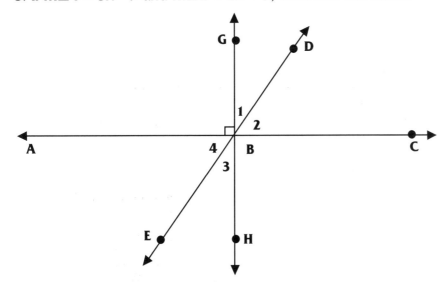

Answers:
1. x=17; 37°
2. x=57; 119°
3. x=29; 121°
4. x=11; 43°
5. x=16; 39°
6. x=9; 125°
7. x=18; 43°
8. x=4; 79°

Cooperative Learning and High School Geometry: Becky Bride
Kagan Publishing • 1 (800) WEE-CO-OP • www.KaganOnline.com

67

LESSON 2
PARALLEL LINES AND SPECIAL ANGLES

This lesson begins with an activity for students to process the recognition of corresponding angles, alternate interior angles, alternate exterior angles, and same-side interior angles. Recognition is a necessity if the students are to work successfully with the postulates and theorems that follow. The next activity explores the relationships of these angles. Following the exploratory exercise, proofs involving these angles will be more meaningful. Activity 3 processes the relationships with arithmetic and requires the students to name the postulate or theorem that justifies each. Activity 4 has students work through numerous relationships to determine the ultimate relationship between two given angles. Activity 6 takes Activity 5 one step further and asks the students to solve an equation involving the two angles once the students have identified the relationship. Paragraph proofs are required in Activity 7. Finally Activities 8 and 9 work with the converse of the postulates and theorems explored in Activity 1.

ACTIVITY 1
RECOGNIZING CORRESPONDING, ALTERNATE INTERIOR, ALTERNATE EXTERIOR, AND SAME-SIDE INTERIOR ANGLES

▶ **Structure**
· RallyTable

▶ **Materials**
· Transparency 2.2.1

Round 1
1. Student A supplies a sheet of paper and folds it in half.

2. Student B writes one pair of corresponding angles on his/her the side of paper.

3. Student A writes a different pair of corresponding angles on his/her side of the paper

4. Repeat steps 2 and 3 until time is up or the students have found all the pairs of corresponding angles.

Round 2
Repeat the above activity but have students name pairs of alternate interior angles.

Round 3
Repeat the above activity but have students name pairs of alternate exterior angles.

Round 4
Repeat the above activity but have students name pairs of same-side interior angles.

ACTIVITY

2 EXPLORING CORRESPONDING, ALTERNATE INTERIOR, ALTERNATE EXTERIOR, AND SAME-SIDE INTERIOR ANGLES

Have students complete the exploratory activity, Blackline 2.2.2. When the patty paper part of the activity is described, the students could use a protractor instead.

▶ **Materials**
• 1 Blackline 2.2.2 per student
• 1 sheet of paper per student
• 1 or 2 sheets of patty paper per student
• 1 straightedge per student
• 1 protractor per student

ACTIVITY

3 PROCESSING ANGLES AND PARALLEL LINES

Notes:
For Activity 3 it is important for students to justify the relationship between the angles. This is a preparatory exercise for the activities to follow.

1. Student B supplies one sheet of paper folded in half lengthwise and each member of the pair writes his/her name at the top of one column.

2. Student B does problem one recording his/her work on his/her side of the paper while Student A watches, checks the work, and coaches if necessary.

3. Repeat step 2 reversing roles until all the problems are done.

▶ **Structure**
•RallyCoach

▶ **Materials**
• 1 Blackline 2.2.3 per pair of students
• 1 sheet of paper and pencil per pair of students

Cooperative Learning and High School Geometry: Becky Bride
Kagan Publishing • 1 (800) WEE-CO-OP • www.KaganOnline.com

69

Chapter 2: Angles & Lines

L e s s o n   T w o

ACTIVITY

4 PARALLEL LINES, ANGLES, AND ALGEBRA

▶ Structure
· Simultaneous RoundTable

▶ Materials
· 1 Blackline 2.2.4
· Transparency 2.2.4
· 1 sheet of paper and pencil per student

1. Each student supplies one sheet of paper.

2. Teammate 1 writes problem 1 on his/her paper, Teammate 2 writes problem 2, Teammate 3 writes problem 3, and Teammate 4 writes problem 4.

3. Each teammate does the first part of their problem (step

a) on their paper. They initial their work and pass the paper to the next person in the clockwise direction.

4. On the paper just received each teammate checks the previous teammate's work—coaches if wrong, praises once it is right, and then does step b. They initial their work and pass the paper to the next person in the clockwise direction.

5. On the paper just received each teammate checks the previous teammate's work—coaches if wrong, praises once it is right, and then does step c. They initial their work and pass the paper to the next person in the clockwise direction.

6. On the paper just received, each teammate checks the previous teammate's work—coaches if wrong, praises once it is right, – and then does step d. They initial their work and pass the paper to the next person in the clockwise direction.

7. On the paper they receive, each student will check the previous work and coach if necessary. Then each student will sign the paper to indicate his/her approval of all work done.

Cooperative Learning and High School Geometry: Becky Bride
Kagan Publishing • 1 (800) WEE-CO-OP • www.KaganOnline.com

ACTIVITY

5

SHOW ME WHY

Notes:

Activity 5 is designed to develop skills needed to do proofs with parallel lines. One goal is for students to find several ways to link two angles together. This deepens their understanding and demonstrates that there is more than one way to solve the problems. For each pair of angles that the students state are supplementary or equal, they must state the postulate or theorem that justifies it. To form bridges between the relationships, I hope students will use the transitive or substitution property. Here is an example to illustrate my point.

Show why ∠1 and ∠14 are supplementary

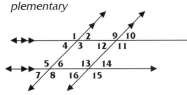

∠1 ≅ ∠9 because if lines are parallel then corresponding angles are congruent.

∠9 ≅ ∠13 because if lines are parallel then corresponding angles are congruent.

∠1 ≅ ∠13 by the transitive property of congruence.

∠13 and ∠14 are supplementary because linear pair angles are supplementary.

∠1 and ∠14 are supplementary because ∠1 was substituted for ∠13 in the step above.

There are six different rounds for the students to do, which really amounts to six different problems. The students will take turns working on one problem until it is completed and then tackle the next one.

1. Student A begins with ∠1 and finds an angle congruent or supplementary, whichever is appropriate, and records the angles' with their relationship and justification.

2. Student B checks Student A's work, coaching if necessary, and finds an angle congruent or supplementary, whichever is appropriate, to the angle Student A left off with and records the angles with their relationship and justification.

▶ **Structure**
  • RallyTable

▶ **Materials**
  • 1 Blackline 2.2.5 per pair of students
  • 1 sheet of paper and pencil per pair of students

3. Student A bridges the last two steps with the transitive property or substitution property.

4. Repeat steps 1-3, alternating students, continuing to link angles to angles, including bridges along the way, until they reach what was to be shown.

These steps are completed for each round listed on Blackline 2.2.5.

Cooperative Learning and High School Geometry: Becky Bride
Kagan Publishing • 1 (800) WEE-CO-OP • www.KaganOnline.com

ACTIVITY

6 PARALLEL LINES, ANGLES, AND ALGEBRA, ADVANCED

▶ **Structure**
  • Simultaneous RoundTable

▶ **Materials**
  • 1 Blackline 2.2.6 per team
  • Transparency 2.2.6
  • 1 sheet of paper and pencil per student

1. Each student supplies one sheet of paper.

2. Teammate 1 writes problem 1 on his/her paper, Teammate 2 writes problem 2, Teammate 3 writes problem 3, and Teammate 4 writes problem 4.

3. Each teammate does part a for the problem on his/her paper. They initial their work and pass the paper to the next person in the clockwise direction.

4. On the paper just received, each teammate checks the previous teammate's work— coaches if wrong, praises once it is right —and then does part b on the paper he/she receives. They initial their work and pass the paper to the next person in the clockwise direction.

5. On the paper just received each teammate checks the previous teammate's work— coaches if wrong, praises once it is right—and then does part c on the paper he/she receives. They initial their work and pass the paper to the next person in the clockwise direction.

6. On the paper they receive, each student will check the previous work and coach if necessary. Then each student will sign the paper showing their approval of all work done.

Tips:
Model this process for students. Each teammate could write in a different color rather than initial work.

ACTIVITY

7 DESCRIBE IT!

▶ **Structure**
  • Boss/Secretary

▶ **Materials**
  • 1 Blackline 2.2.7 per pair of students
  • 1 sheet of paper and pencil per pair of students

Notes:
Activity 7 is basically proofs in paragraph form. The Boss/Secretary structure is used so one student is responsible for the entire thinking process in one problem. This structure enables the partner to follow the thinking process so coaching can occur as needed.

1. Student A supplies one sheet of paper, folded in half lengthwise with his/her name in one column and a partner's name in the other column.

2. Student B is the first boss and Student A is the first secretary.

3. As the boss, Student B tells Student A how to do the problem. Student A, the secretary, records what Student B says in Student B's column of the paper.

4. If the boss makes a mistake, then the secretary coaches and praises once the boss does it correctly. Otherwise, the secretary praises the boss.

5. Reverse roles for each problem and repeat steps 3 and 4.

Cooperative Learning and High School Geometry: Becky Bride
Kagan Publishing • 1 (800) WEE-CO-OP • www.KaganOnline.com

ACTIVITY

8 CONVERSE: WORKING IN REVERSE

1. Student 1 supplies one sheet of paper, folded in fourths with each teammate's name at the top of one quadrant (one name per quadrant).

2. Student 1 fans the cards face down.

3. Student 2 picks a card and reads it to Student 3.

4. Student 3 answers while Student 4 records Student 3's answer on Student 3's quadrant of the paper.

5. Student 1 coaches if necessary, augments if necessary and praises.

6. Repeat steps 2-5 rotating all roles to the next person in the clockwise direction.

▶ **Structure**
• Fan-N-Pick

▶ **Materials**
• 1 sheet of paper per team
• Transparency 2.2.8
• 1 set of Fan-N-Pick cards per team (Blackline 2.2.8)

ACTIVITY

9 SEQUENCE IT: (WORKING WITH THE CONVERSE)

1. The team divides the cards as evenly as possible, keeping all cards face down.

2. Taking turns, each student reads his/her card(s) without showing their teammates the card(s).

3. The team must now order the cards in the correct sequence. Teammates can only touch the cards they initially received.

4. The team checks their answer with the answer key. Note: Answer key is Blackline 2.2.9a or 2.2.9b made into a transparency.

5. If a team is wrong they discuss it until everyone understands how to do it correctly.

6. Teams put all the pieces back in the envelope and exchange envelopes for the second problem (cards cut from Blackline 2.2.9b).

7. Repeat steps 1-6, except on step 6, when the pieces are in the envelope, the team is finished.

Tips:
Make one copy of the blind sequence cards (Blacklines 2.2.9a and 2.2.9b) before they are cut and make a transparency for each set. This will be the answer transparency.

Number the outside of the envelopes to distinguish problem 2.6.9a from 2.6.9b

▶ **Structure**
• Blind Sequencing

▶ **Materials**
• 1 set of Blind Sequence cards (Blackline 2.2.9a) per team (later Blackline 2.2.9b)
• 1 Blackline 2.2.9c per team

Make copies of the two sets of cards, Blackline 2.6.9a and 2.6.9b, on different colors of paper. That way if the cards from the two problems get mixed up it will be easy to separate them.

To make it a little more challenging, students can place their cards face down as they order them, then turn them over when they think they have done it correctly.

During step 3, RoundRobin structure can be used to structure the interaction.

Cooperative Learning and High School Geometry: Becky Bride
Kagan Publishing • 1 (800) WEE-CO-OP • www.KaganOnline.com

Chapter 2: Angles & Lines

Lesson Two

73

ACTIVITY 1 RECOGNIZING CORRESPONDING, ALTERNATE INTERIOR, ALTERNATE EXTERIOR, AND SAME-SIDE INTERIOR ANGLES

Structure: RallyTable

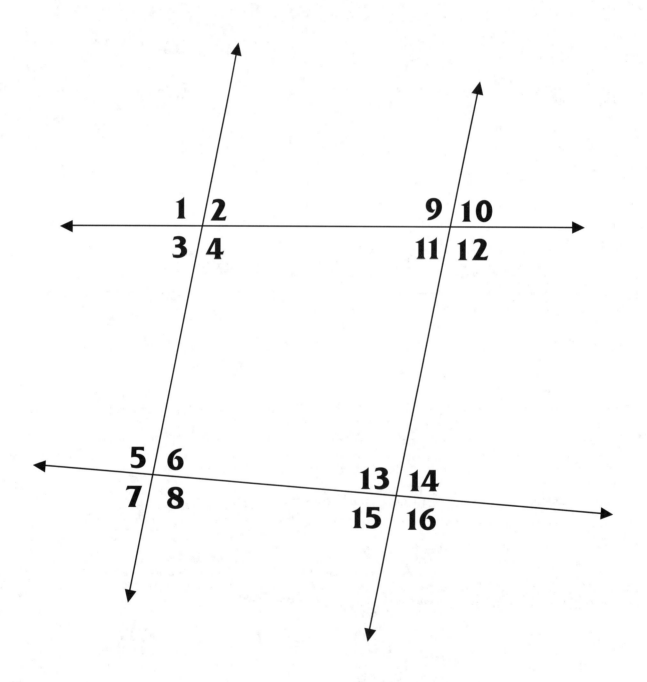

Cooperative Learning and High School Geometry: Becky Bride
Kagan Publishing • 1 (800) WEE-CO-OP • www.KaganOnline.com

2 EXPLORING CORRESPONDING, ALTERNATE INTERIOR, ALTERNATE EXTERIOR, AND SAME SIDE INTERIOR ANGLES

1. Using a straightedge, draw two lines on your paper—one on each side of the straight-edge. This ensures they are parallel. Label one line *m* and the other line *n*.

2. Draw a line intersecting the parallel lines so that it is not perpendicular to them. Label this line *t*.

3. Number your angles as shown.

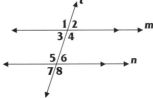

4. Using a straightedge, trace ∠1 onto a sheet of patty paper.

5. Place ∠1 on top of ∠5. What appears to be true?

6. Repeat steps 4 and 5 for angles ∠3 and ∠7, angles ∠2 and ∠6, and angles ∠4 and ∠8.

7. In a complete sentence, describe the relationship of corresponding angles when lines are parallel.

8. Using the piece of patty paper with ∠3 on it, lay ∠3 on top of ∠6. What appears to be true?

9. Using the piece of patty paper with ∠4 on it, lay it on top of ∠5. In a complete sentence, describe the relationship of alternate interior angles when lines are parallel.

10. Using the piece of patty paper with ∠1 on it, lay ∠1 on top of ∠8. What appears to be true?

11. Using the piece of patty paper with ∠2 on it, lay ∠2 on top of ∠7. In a complete sentence, describe what appears to be true about alternate exterior angles when lines are parallel.

12. Using a protractor measure ∠3. Using your knowledge of alternate interior angles find the m∠6. Using your knowledge of linear pair angles compute the measures of ∠4 and ∠5. Write these measurements on the respective angles on your diagram.

13. Compute the following sums.
    m∠3 + m∠5 = ?
    m∠4 + m∠6 = ?

14. In a complete sentence, describe the relationship of same-side interior angles when lines are parallel.

Cooperative Learning and High School Geometry: Becky Bride
Kagan Publishing • 1 (800) WEE-CO-OP • www.KaganOnline.com

75

PROCESSING ANGLES AND PARALLEL LINES

Structure: RallyCoach

Directions: m∠1 = 111°

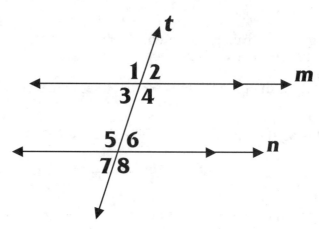

1. What type of angles are ∠1 and ∠5 and what is their relationship? Find the measure of ∠5.

2. What type of angles are ∠3 and ∠5 and what is their relationship? Find the measure of ∠3.

3. What type of angles are ∠3 and ∠6 and what is their relationship? Find the measure of ∠6.

4. What type of angles are ∠2 and ∠6 and what is their relationship? Find the measure of ∠2.

5. What type of angles are ∠2 and ∠7 and what is their relationship? Find the measure of ∠7.

6. What type of angles are ∠1 and ∠8 and what is their relationship? Find the measure of ∠8.

7. What type of angles are ∠4 and ∠5 and what is their relationship? Find the measure of ∠4.

8. What type of angles are ∠3 and ∠6 and what is their relationship? If the m∠3 = 126° then find the m∠6.

Answers:
1. 111°
2. 69°
3. 69°
4. 69°
5. 69°
6. 111°
7. 111°
8. 126°

Cooperative Learning and High School Geometry: Becky Bride
Kagan Publishing • 1 (800) WEE-CO-OP • www.KaganOnline.com

PARALLEL LINES, ANGLES, AND ALGEBRA

ACTIVITY 4

Structure: Simultaneous RoundTable

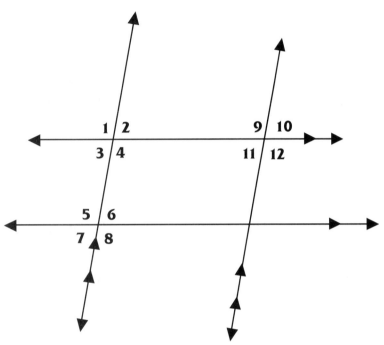

For each problem:
- **a. State the type of angles that are given.**
- **b. State the postulate or theorem that describes their relationship.**
- **c. Write an equation and solve for x.**
- **d. Find the measure of the angle requested.**

Note: Diagram is not necessarily drawn to scale.

1. If the m∠4 = 3x + 4 and m∠11 = x + 20, find the m∠2.

2. If the m∠7 = 6x - 5 and m∠2 = 2x + 43, find the m∠6.

3. If the m∠ 9 = 5x + 17 and m∠1 = 7x - 29, find the m∠8.

4. If the m∠2 = 9x - 11 and m∠11 = 7x + 3, find the m∠4.

Cooperative Learning and High School Geometry: Becky Bride
Kagan Publishing • 1 (800) WEE-CO-OP • www.KaganOnline.com

ACTIVITY
4 PARALLEL LINES, ANGLES, AND ALGEBRA

Structure: Simultaneous RoundTable

Directions:

1. Student 1 copy problem 1, Student 2 copy problem 2, Student 3 copy problem 3, and Student 4 copy problem 4 onto your paper.

2. On the paper you have, complete part a, initial your work, and pass the paper to the next person in the clockwise direction.

3. Check the previous work done on the paper you just received and coach and/or praise your teammate's work. Complete part b, initial your work, and pass the paper to the next person in the clockwise direction.

4. Check the previous work done on the paper you just received and coach and/or praise your teammate's work. Complete part c, initial your work, and pass the paper to the next person in the clockwise direction.

5. Check the previous work done on the paper you just received and coach and/or praise your teammate's work. Complete part d, initial your work, and pass the paper to the next person in the clockwise direction.

6. Check the work on the paper you just received and coach and/or praise your teammates' work. Sign the paper indicating your approval of all the work done.

Answers to Blackline 2.2.4:
1. same-side interior angles; lines parallel $\mapsto$ same side int. angles are supplementary; x = 39; m∠2 = 59°
2. alternate exterior angles; lines parallel $\mapsto$ alternate exterior angles equal; x = 12; m∠6 = 67°
3. corresponding angles; lines parallel $\mapsto$ corresponding angles equal; x = 23; m∠8 = 132°
4. alternate interior angles; lines parallel $\mapsto$ alternate interior angles equal; x = 7; m∠4 = 128°

Cooperative Learning and High School Geometry: Becky Bride
Kagan Publishing • 1 (800) WEE-CO-OP • www.KaganOnline.com

ACTIVITY

5 SHOW ME WHY!

Structure: RallyTable

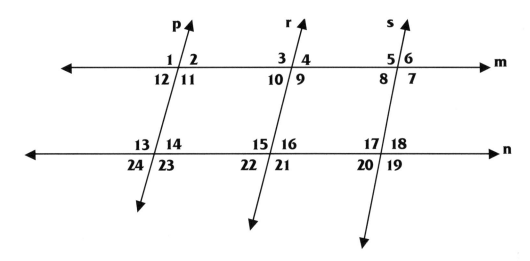

Given: $p \| r$; $r \| s$; $m \| n$. The diagram is not necessarily drawn to scale.

Round 1:
Show that m∠1 = m∠19.

Round 2:
Find the shortest way to show m ∠24 = m∠8.

Round 3:
Find the longest way to show m ∠11 = m∠19.

Round 4:
Show that ∠12 and ∠19 are supplementary.

Round 5:
Find the shortest way to show that ∠24 and ∠7 are supplementary.

Round 6:
Find the longest way to show that ∠1 and ∠18 are supplementary.

Cooperative Learning and High School Geometry: Becky Bride
Kagan Publishing • 1 (800) WEE-CO-OP • www.KaganOnline.com

79

PARALLEL LINES, ANGLES, AND ALGEBRA, ADVANCED

ACTIVITY **6**

Structure: Simultaneous RoundTable

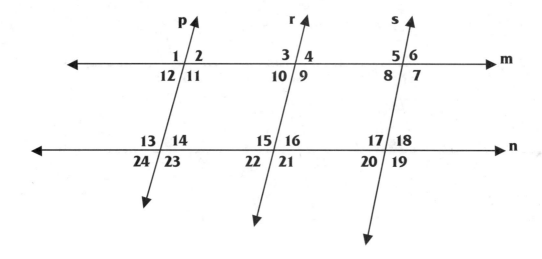

Given: *p∥r; r∥s; m∥n.* **The diagram is not necessarily drawn to scale.**

1. If m∠1 = 9x - 7 and m∠17 = 6x + 23, find the m∠20.

2. If m∠2 = 8x - 3 and m∠19 = 4x + 39, find the m∠18.

3. If m∠24 = 5x + 2 and m∠6 = 3x + 40, find the m∠4.

4. If m∠18 = 7x - 5 and m∠11 = 2x - 4, find the m∠9.

Cooperative Learning and High School Geometry: Becky Bride
Kagan Publishing • 1 (800) WEE-CO-OP • www.KaganOnline.com

ACTIVITY 6 PARALLEL LINES, ANGLES, AND ALGEBRA, ADVANCED

Structure: Simultaneous RoundTable

Directions:

1. Student 1 copy problem 1, Student 2 copy problem 2, Student 3 copy problem 3, and Student 4 copy problem 4 onto your paper.

2. On the paper you have, state whether the two given angles are equal or supplementary and explain how you determined the relationship including justifications. Initial your work, and pass the paper to the next person in the clockwise direction.

3. Check the previous work done on the paper you just received and coach and/or praise your teammate's work. Write an equation, solve for x, initial your work, and pass the paper to the next person in the clockwise direction.

4. Check the previous work done on the paper you just received and coach and/or praise your teammate's work. Find the value of the requested angle, initial your work, and pass the paper to the next person in the clockwise direction.

5. Check the work on the paper you just received and coach and/or praise your teammates' work. Sign the paper indicating your approval of all the work done.

Cooperative Learning and High School Geometry: Becky Bride
Kagan Publishing • 1 (800) WEE-CO-OP • www.KaganOnline.com

81

ACTIVITY

7 DESCRIBE IT!

Structure: Boss/Secretary

Directions:
Write a paragraph describing why the given angles have the relationship stated, including bridges and justifications.

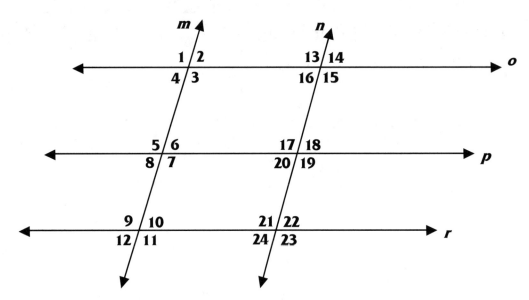

Given: $m \| n$; $o \| p$; $p \| r$. The diagram is not necessarily drawn to scale.

1. $\angle 3 \cong \angle 23$

2. $\angle 1$ and $\angle 24$ are supplementary

3. $\angle 14$ and $\angle 11$ are supplementary

4. $\angle 11 \cong \angle 13$

Cooperative Learning and High School Geometry: Becky Bride
Kagan Publishing • 1 (800) WEE-CO-OP • www.KaganOnline.com

CONVERSE: WORKING IN REVERSE

Structure: Fan-N-Pick

For each problem state which pair of lines are parallel because of the given information and state the postulate or theorem that justifies it. The diagram is not necessarily drawn to scale.

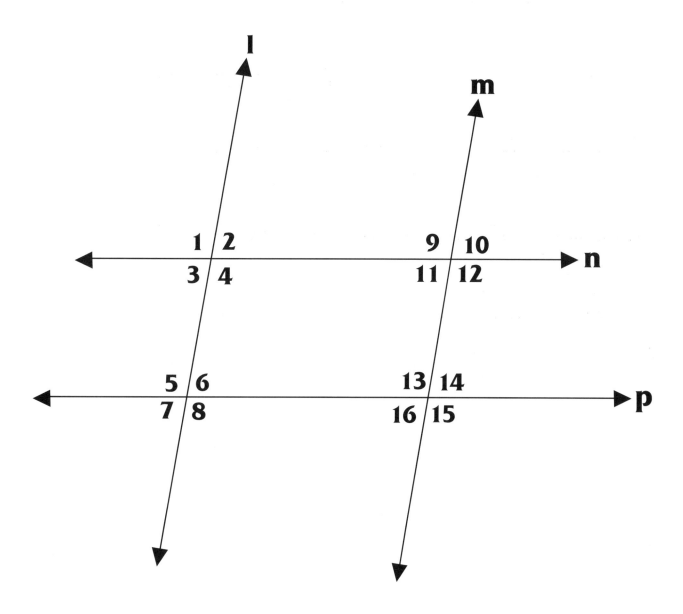

Cooperative Learning and High School Geometry: Becky Bride
Kagan Publishing • 1 (800) WEE-CO-OP • www.KaganOnline.com

83

8 CONVERSE: WORKING IN REVERSE

Structure: Fan-N-Pick

∠2 ≅ ∠6

Answer: n‖p; corresponding angles congruent ⟶ lines parallel

∠1 ≅ ∠12

Answer: l‖m; alternate exterior angles congruent ⟶ lines parallel

∠6 ≅ ∠16

Answer: l‖m; alternate interior angles congruent ⟶ lines parallel

∠5 and ∠3 are supplementary

Answer: n‖p; same-side interior angles supplementary ⟶ lines parallel

∠7 ≅ ∠14

Answer: l‖m; alternate exterior angles congruent ⟶ lines parallel

∠9 ≅ ∠13

Answer: n‖p; corresponding angles congruent ⟶ lines parallel

∠6 and ∠13 are supplementary

Answer: l‖m; same-side interior angles supplementary ⟶ lines parallel

∠1 ≅ ∠12

Answer: l‖m; alternate exterior angles congruent ⟶ lines parallel

Cooperative Learning and High School Geometry: Becky Bride
Kagan Publishing • 1 (800) WEE-CO-OP • www.KaganOnline.com

ACTIVITY 9
SEQUENCE IT!
(WORKING WITH THE CONVERSE)

Structure: Blind Sequencing

Given: m || n; ∠1 ≅ ∠13

Show: k || l

---

m || n because it was given

∠13 ≅ ∠5 because corresponding angles are equal if lines are parallel

---

∠1 ≅ ∠13 because it was given

∠1 ≅ ∠5 because of the transitive property of congruence

∠3 ≅ ∠5 because vertical angles are congruent

∠1 ≅ ∠3 because of the transitive property of congruence

---

k || l because if corresponding angles are ≅ then the lines are parallel

---

Cooperative Learning and High School Geometry: Becky Bride
Kagan Publishing • 1 (800) WEE-CO-OP • www.KaganOnline.com

85

SEQUENCE IT!
(WORKING WITH THE CONVERSE)

Structure: Blind Sequencing

> **Given:** $k \parallel l$; $m \parallel n$; $\angle 4 \cong \angle 20$

> **Show:** $n \parallel p$

> $m \parallel n$ **because it is given**

> $\angle 4 \cong \angle 2$ **because corresponding angles are equal if lines are parallel**

> $k \parallel l$ **because it is given**

> $\angle 2 \cong \angle 10$ **because corresponding angles are equal if lines are parallel**

> $\angle 4 \cong \angle 10$ **because of the transitive property of congruence**

> $\angle 10 \cong \angle 14$ **because alternate interior angles are equal if lines are parallel**

> $\angle 4 \cong \angle 14$ **because of the transitive property of congruence**

> $\angle 4 \cong \angle 20$ **because it is given**

> $\angle 14 \cong \angle 20$ **because of the transitive property of congruence**

> $n \parallel p$ **because if alternate interior angles are $\cong$ then the lines are parallel**

Cooperative Learning and High School Geometry: Becky Bride
Kagan Publishing • 1 (800) WEE-CO-OP • www.KaganOnline.com

ACTIVITY 9
SEQUENCE IT!
(WORKING WITH THE CONVERSE)

Structure: Blind Sequencing

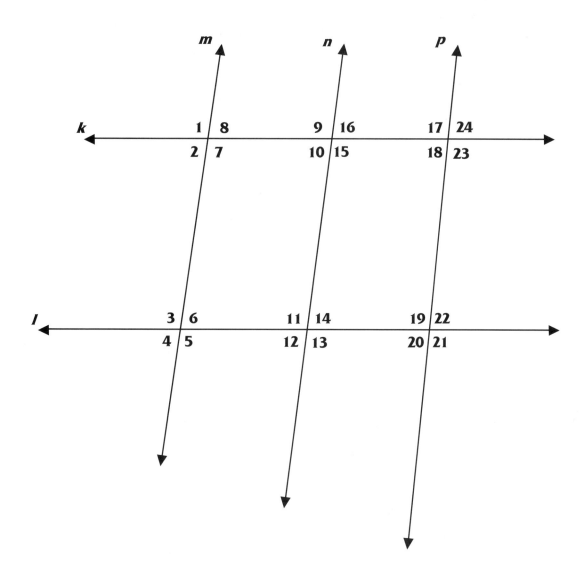

Cooperative Learning and High School Geometry: Becky Bride
Kagan Publishing • 1 (800) WEE-CO-OP • www.KaganOnline.com

87

LESSON 3
PREREQUISITE SKILLS FOR PARALLEL AND PERPENDICULAR LINES

If your students already know how to find the slope of a line and write equations of lines, go directly to Lesson 4. The purpose of this lesson is to review the Algebra skills necessary for finding slope and writing the equations of lines. Lesson 4 assumes these skills are well in place. This lesson begins with an exploratory graphing calculator lab, processes the concepts learned from the lab, processes calculating slope given two ordered pairs, and finally processes the writing of equations given the necessary information. Software that allows students to graph equations is preferable to the graphing calculator only because the computer screen is so much larger than the calculator screen that students can see relationships easier.

ACTIVITY 1
GRAPHING CALCULATOR LAB

▶ **Materials**
• 1 graphing calculator per student or pair of students (or computer software capable of graphing).
• 1 Blackline 2.3.1 per student

Have students complete Blackline 2.3.1

Notes:
After this lab, the students should know which number in the formula y = mx + b is the slope and which one is the y-intercept. The students have a much firmer grasp of these concepts.

ACTIVITY 2
RECOGNIZING LINES WITH POSITIVE, NEGATIVE, ZERO, OR UNDEFINED SLOPES

▶ **Structure**
• RallyRobin

▶ **Materials**
• Transparency 2.3.2

Notes:
Activity 2 is included so students can identify, when viewing the graph of a line, whether the slope of a line is positive, negative, zero, or undefined. This skill is necessary so when they write equations of lines and graph them, the students can spot check the slope in the equation to the orientation of the line and see if it makes sense. This skill will be helpful in later courses when students have to analyze graphs of data or slopes of tangent lines.

1. Student A tells Student B whether the slope of problem 1 is positive, negative, zero, or undefined and explains why.

2. Student B tells Student A whether the slope of problem 2 is positive, negative, zero, or undefined.

3. Repeat steps 1 and 2 until all problems are done.

Cooperative Learning and High School Geometry: Becky Bride
Kagan Publishing • 1 (800) WEE-CO-OP • www.KaganOnline.com

ACTIVITY
3

DRAW WHAT I SAY

Notes:
The next activity has students work with slope and ordered pairs on a graph in a fun way. Each student will draw a figure with six segments on a coordinate plane with each axis ranging from ±12. Student A will be the first describer while Student B draws on a blank set of axes what Student A has described. When Student A describes, he/she identifies only one ordered pair. From there, the entire picture must be described through slopes that begin at labeled points.

For example: Plot (-1, 3), label it A and from that point using a slope of 2/3, plot 3 more points and label the last one B. From point B, using a slope of -1/2, plot two more points labeling the last one C. From point B using a slope of 5 plot one point and label it D.

Using terms such as NE, SW, NW, NE, N, S, E, or W could be helpful. For example from point A, using the slope ³/₄, go in the NE direction plotting two points and labeling the last one B. Or a SW direction could be requested for slope

³/₄, which would require the student to interpret a slope of ³/₄ as -3/-4. This adds interest and helps the students to view the same slope in different ways.

1. Each student has a sheet of graph paper. Face to face partners works well for this structure.

2. A barrier is set up between each pair of face to face partners. Backpacks, books, or manila folders fastened at the top with paper clips work well for barriers.

3. One student is the sender and his/her partner is the receiver. The sender draws a figure with six segments on a coordinate plane with both x and y-axes ranging from ±12.

4. The sender tells the receiver to plot one of the points on

his/her figure. From that point, the sender gives directions using slope, so the receiver can draw segments to match the sender's figure.

5. The receiver attempts to graph the sender's figure by listening to the directions.

6. When the sender is finished, the students check to see how similar their figures are.

7. Sender/receiver roles reverse and steps 3-6 are repeated.

▶ **Structure**
• Match Mine

▶ **Materials**
• 1 sheet of double-sided graph paper per student
• 1 straightedge per student
• 1 barrier per pair of students

ACTIVITY
4

TELL ME THE SLOPE AND THE Y-INTERCEPT

1. Student A states the slope and y-intercept for problem 1.

2. Student B gives specific praise (i.e.: You did a nice job of remembering that the slope is found next to x) and then states the slope and y-intercept for the next problem.

3. Student A gives specific praise.

4. Repeat steps 1-3 alternating roles for the rest of the problems

▶ **Structure**
• RallyRobin

▶ **Materials**
• Transparency 2.3.4

Cooperative Learning and High School Geometry: Becky Bride
Kagan Publishing • 1 (800) WEE-CO-OP • www.KaganOnline.com

Chapter 2: Angles & Lines

Lesson Three

89

ACTIVITY

5 GRAPH ME

▶ **Structure**
• Boss/Secretary

▶ **Materials**
• 1 sheet of double-sided graph paper, pencil, and straight-edge per pair of students
• Transparency 2.3.5

1. Student A supplies one sheet of graph paper with his/her name on one side and a partner's name on the other side.

2. Student B is the first boss and Student A is the first secretary.

3. As the boss, student B tells Student A how to do the first

problem. Student A, the secretary, records what Student B says on Student B's side of the paper.

4. If the boss makes a mistake, then the secretary coaches and praises once the boss does it correctly. Otherwise, the secretary praises the boss.

5. Reverse roles for each problem and repeat steps 3 and 4.

ACTIVITY

6 CALCULATE THE SLOPE

▶ **Structure**
• RallyTable

▶ **Materials**
• Transparency 2.3.6
• 1 sheet of paper and pencil per pair of students

1. Student A calculates the slope for problem one.

2. Student B checks Student A's work, coaches if necessary, and initials the problem indicating his/her approval. Then Student B calculates the slope for the next problem.

3. Student A checks student B's work, coaches if necessary, and initials the problem indicating his/her approval.

4. Repeat steps 1-3 rotating roles until all the problems are finished.

ACTIVITY

7 WRITE MY EQUATION

Structure
• Pairs Check

Materials
• 1 Blackline 2.3.7
• 1 sheet of paper and pencil per pair of students

1. Student B supplies one sheet of paper folded in half lengthwise with each member of the pair writing their name at the top of one column.

2. Student B does problem 1, recording his/her work on his/her side of the paper while Student A watches and coaches if necessary.

3. Student A checks Student B's work, coaches and/or praises. Then Student A does problem 2 on his/her side of the paper.

4. Student B checks Student A's work, coaches and/or praises.

5. After every 2 problems, the pair checks their answers with the other pair in their team, coaching and/or praising each others' work.

6. Repeat steps 2-5, reversing roles until all the problems are done.

Cooperative Learning and High School Geometry: Becky Bride
Kagan Publishing • 1 (800) WEE-CO-OP • www.KaganOnline.com

ACTIVITY

1 GRAPHING CALCULATOR LAB

Objective: To determine the role of m and b in the function y = mx + b.

1. Graph the function y = x. This function will be called the parent function.
   a. Describe the graph.
   b. What is the value of m in the equation?
   c. What is the value of b in the equation?

2. Graph y = 2x. What effect did the 2 have on the graph when compared to the parent graph?

3. Graph y = 10x. What effect did the 10 have on the graph when compared to the parent graph?   3   3

4. Graph y = 5x. What effect did the 5 have on the graph when compared to the parent graph?

5. As m increased, describe what happened to the graph.

6. Clear all the graphs but the parent graph. Graph y = $\frac{1}{2}$x. What effect did the $\frac{1}{2}$ have on the graph when compared to the parent graph?

7. Graph y = $\frac{1}{4}$ x. What effect did the $\frac{1}{4}$ have on the graph when compared to the parent graph?

8. Graph y = $\frac{3}{10}$x. What effect did the $\frac{3}{10}$ have on the graph when compared to the parent graph?

9. As m decreased (0 < m < 1) describe what happened to the graph.

10. Clear all functions from the calculator except the parent graph.

11. Graph y = -x.
    a. What is the value of m in the equation?
    b. Describe the effect the negative sign had on the graph when compared to the parent graph.

12. Clear the function y = x from your calculator. The parent graph is now y = -x.

13. Graph y = -2x. What effect did the -2 have on the graph when compared to the parent graph?

14. Graph y = $\frac{-8}{3}$x. What effect did the $\frac{-8}{3}$ have on the graph when compared to the parent graph?

15. Graph y = -6x. What effect did the -6 have on the graph when compared to the parent graph?

ACTIVITY

1 GRAPHING CALCULATOR LAB

16. Describe what happened to the graphs as m < -1.

17. Clear all graphs except the parent graph. Graph $y = \frac{-1}{4}x$. What effect did the $\frac{-1}{4}$ have on the graph when compared to the parent graph?

18. Graph $y = \frac{-3}{8}x$. What effect did the $\frac{-3}{8}$ have on the graph when compared to the parent graph?

19. Graph $y = \frac{-1}{2}x$. What effect did the $\frac{-1}{2}$ have on the graph when compared to the parent graph?

20. Describe what happened to the graphs when -1 < m < 0.

21. a. Describe how the graphs of y = 5x and y = -5x are similar.
    b. Describe how the graphs of y = 5x and y = -5x are different.

22. a. Describe how the graphs of $y = \frac{3}{8}x$ and $y = \frac{-3}{8}x$ are similar.
    b. Describe how the graphs of $y = \frac{3}{8}x$ and $y = \frac{-3}{8}x$ are different.

23. Clear your calculator of all graphs. Graph y = x. This will be the parent function for the remainder of the lab.
    a. What is the value of b in the equation y = x?

24. Graph y = x + 3. What are the coordinates of the y-intercept? What effect did adding 3 have on the graph when compared to the parent function?

25. Graph y = x - 5. What are the coordinates of the y-intercept? What effect did subtracting 5 have on the graph when compared to the parent function?

26. Graph y = x + 6. What are the coordinates of the y-intercept? What effect did adding 6 have on the graph when compared to the parent function?

27. Graph y = x - 8. What are the coordinates of the y-intercept? What effect did subtracting 8 have on the graph when compared to the parent function?

28. When b > 0, describe the effect of b on the graph when compared to the parent graph.

29. When b < 0, describe the effect of b on the graph when compared to the parent graph.

30. Write a paragraph summarizing what you learned from this lab.

Cooperative Learning and High School Geometry: Becky Bride
Kagan Publishing • 1 (800) WEE-CO-OP • www.KaganOnline.com

ACTIVITY 2 RECOGNIZING LINES WITH POSITIVE, NEGATIVE, ZERO, OR UNDEFINED SLOPES

Structure: RallyRobin

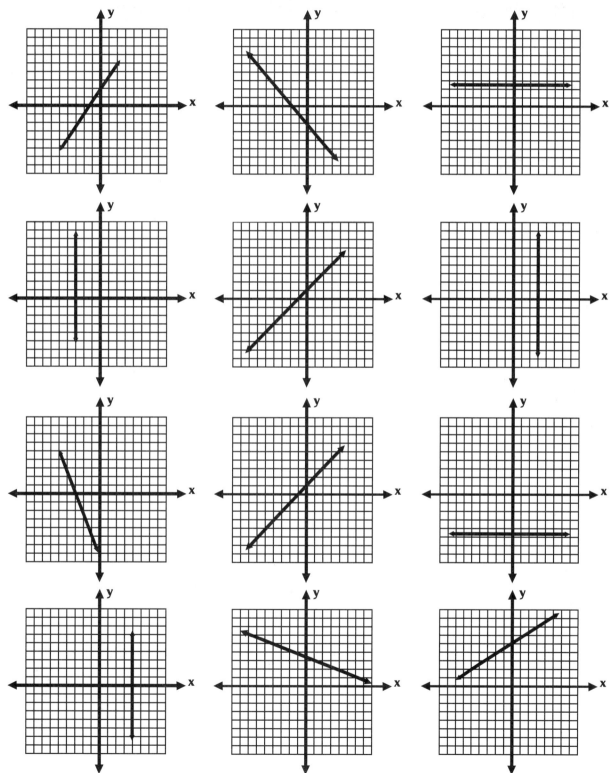

Cooperative Learning and High School Geometry: Becky Bride
Kagan Publishing • 1 (800) WEE-CO-OP • www.KaganOnline.com

93

ACTIVITY 4
TELL ME THE SLOPE AND THE Y-INTERCEPT

Structure: RallyRobin

State the a) slope, and b) y-intercept.

1. $4x - 3 = y$

2. $y = 3x + 1$

3. $y = \dfrac{-2}{3}x - 4$

4. $y = 2 - \dfrac{5}{4}x$

5. $2x + 3y = 6$

6. $4x - 2y = 8$

7. $5x - 3y = 30$

8. $x + 2y = 8$

Answers:
1. a. 4 b. (0, -3)
2. a. 3 b. (0, 1)
3. a. $\dfrac{-2}{3}$ b. (0, -4)
4. a. $\dfrac{-5}{4}$ b. (0, 2)
5. a. $\dfrac{-2}{3}$ b. (0, 2)
6. a. 2 b. (0, -4)
7. a. $\dfrac{5}{3}$ b. (0, -10)
8. a. $\dfrac{-1}{2}$ b. (0, 4)

Cooperative Learning and High School Geometry: Becky Bride
Kagan Publishing • 1 (800) WEE-CO-OP • www.KaganOnline.com

ACTIVITY

5 GRAPH ME

Structure: Boss/Secretary

For each of the following problems, graph the line.

1. 2x + 5y = 10

2. 3x - 2y = (-8)

3. 6y - 5x = 12

4. 4y + 3x = 16

Cooperative Learning and High School Geometry: Becky Bride
Kagan Publishing • 1 (800) WEE-CO-OP • www.KaganOnline.com

95

ACTIVITY
6 **CALCULATE THE SLOPE**

Structure: RallyTable

Calculate the slope of the line passing through each pair of points.

1. (4, 3) (-8, 3)

2. (1, 7) (8, 2)

3. (9, 3) (9, 4)

4. (2, 10) (1, 3)

Answers:
1. 0
2. $\frac{-5}{7}$
3. undefined
4. 7

Cooperative Learning and High School Geometry: Becky Bride
Kagan Publishing • 1 (800) WEE-CO-OP • www.KaganOnline.com

ACTIVITY
7

WRITE MY EQUATION

Structure: Pairs Check

Write the equation of the line in slope-intercept form, given the following information.

1. Passes through (4, -1) and has a slope of 3.

2. Passes through (5, 2) and has slope of -2.

3. Passes through (-6, 1) and (-5, 3).

4. Passes through (2, 7) and (4, 11).

5. Passes through (-3, -4) and (1, 8).

6. Passes through (2, 5) and (3, -2).

7. Passes through (1, 5) and (1, - 3).

8. Passes through (5, 7) and (-3, 7).

Answers:
1. y = 3x - 13
2. y = -2x + 12
3. y = 2x + 13
4. y = 2x + 3
5. y = 3x + 5
6. y = -7x + 19
7. x = 1
8. y = 7

Cooperative Learning and High School Geometry: Becky Bride
Kagan Publishing • 1 (800) WEE-CO-OP • www.KaganOnline.com

97

LESSON 4
PARALLEL AND PERPENDICULAR LINES

The first activity is included as a warm up for those who skipped lesson 3 and as a continuation for those who did lesson 3. It basically asks the students to generate real world examples of situations that involve the use of slope. The next two activities are exploratory ones that lead the students to discover the relationship between the slopes of parallel and perpendicular lines. Activity 4 is a simple processing of the concepts explored. The last three activities have students apply the relationships of parallel and perpendicular lines.

ACTIVITY

1 WHO NEEDS SLOPE?

▶ **Structure**
• Give One, Get One

▶ **Materials**
• 1 Blackline 2.4.1 and pencil per student

1. Students receive a premade Give One, Get One form, or fold a blank piece of paper lengthwise to create one.

2. With pencils down, in teams, students brainstorm applications of slope.

3. When they agree they have come up with a good application, they take their pencils and in their own words write it in the Give One column on their papers.

4. When their Give One column is full, (six items) they stand.

5. When all students are standing, each student puts a hand up, and pairs with someone who is not a teammate.

6. Students in pairs share an application, and get an application, writing on their own worksheet the application they have received in the Get One column.

7. Pairs part, put a hand up until they find a new partner, then again give one and get one.

8. When their form is full, students stand by the perimeter of the room, offering to give an application to anyone whose form is not yet full.

9. When all students have finished their forms, they return to their teams and share applications they have received.

Tips:
In step 2, the brainstorm session could be structured using RoundRobin.

In steps 6 and 7, the use of social gambits is greatly encouraged.

Cooperative Learning and High School Geometry: Becky Bride
Kagan Publishing • 1 (800) WEE-CO-OP • www.KaganOnline.com

ACTIVITY

2

EXPLORING PARALLEL LINES AND SLOPES

Students complete Blackline 2.4.2. At the end of the activity, students are expected to draw on their understanding of slope and explain that if one line has a slope of 2/3, then the vertical and horizontal change of a parallel line must be the same, or the two lines

would eventually intersect. Have students read their answers to problem 14 using a RoundRobin format so they can hear how others verbalize their findings. This may eventually help lead to better articulation for all students.

▶ **Materials**
• 1 Blackline 2.4.2 and pencil per student
• 1 straightedge per student
• 1 sheet of graph paper per student

ACTIVITY

3

EXPLORING PERPENDICULAR LINES AND SLOPES

Have students complete Blackline 2.4.3. In problem 6, students are expected to see how the vertical and horizontal lines algebraically behave

exactly the same way as the oblique lines. The final answers don't show this relationship because of 0 and division by zero is undefined.

▶ **Materials**
• 1 Blackline 2.4.3 and pencil per student
• 1 straightedge per student
• 1 sheet of graph paper per student.

ACTIVITY

4

PROCESSING PARALLEL AND PERPENDICULAR SLOPES

1. Have each student write down a number on an index card that represents a slope.

2. Ask the As to stand and form a large circle with everyone facing toward the center.

3. Ask the Bs to get up and go stand in front of their partner (students should be face to face now with the Bs facing out and As facing in).

4. The inside circle students show their cards to their outside partner and ask their partners for the parallel slope. The inside students coach and/or praise their partners.

5. The outside partners show their cards to the inside partners and ask their partners for the perpendicular slope. The outside students coach and/or praise their partners.

6. Students trade cards and thank each other for working together.

▶ **Structure**
• Inside-Outside Circle

▶ **Materials**
• 1 index card per student

7. Inside circle students rotate clockwise to a new partner. (Outside students could do the rotating or both inside and outside students can rotate in opposite directions).

8. Repeat steps 3-6 each time until the teacher is comfortable that the students understand.

Cooperative Learning and High School Geometry: Becky Bride
Kagan Publishing • 1 (800) WEE-CO-OP • www.KaganOnline.com

99

Chapter 2: Angles & Lines   Lesson Four

ACTIVITY 5

AM I A PARALLELOGRAM, RECTANGLE, TRAPEZOID, OR JUST A QUADRILATERAL?

▶ **Structure**
· Simultaneous RoundTable

▶ **Materials**
· 1 sheet of paper and pencil per student
· Transparencies 2.4.5a and 2.4.5b

1. Each student supplies one sheet of paper.

2. Teammate 1 writes problem 1 on his/her paper, Teammate 2 writes problem 2, Teammate 3 writes problem 3, and Teammate 4 writes problem 4.

3. Each teammate calculates the slope for segment $\overline{AB}$. They initial their work and pass the paper to the next person in a clockwise direction.

4. On the paper just received, each teammate checks the previous teammate's work, coaches if wrong, praises once it is right, and then calculates the slope of segment $\overline{BC}$. They initial their work and pass the paper to the next person in a clockwise direction.

5. On the paper just received, each teammate checks the previous teammate's work, coaches if wrong, praises once it is right, and then calculates the slope of segment $\overline{CD}$. They initial their work and pass the paper to the next person in a clockwise direction.

6. On the paper just received, each teammate checks the previous teammate's work, coaches if wrong, praises once it is right, and then calculates the slope of segment $\overline{DA}$. They initial their work and pass the paper to the next person in a clockwise direction.

7. On the paper they receive, the student will check the previous work and coach if necessary. Based on the slopes calculated, the student will state what type of quadrilateral figure ABCD is, choosing the most specific type possible. Then the student will write a complete sentence explaining why he/she choose that type of quadrilateral. They initial their work and pass the paper to the next person in a clockwise direction.

8. Each student checks the last step on the paper he/she just received, coach if he/she disagrees, and when a consensus is reached, will sign indicating their approval.

ACTIVITY 6

WRITE THE EQUATION OF MY PARALLEL OR PERPENDICULAR LINE

▶ **Structure**
· Boss/Secretary

▶ **Materials**
· 1 Blackline 2.4.6 per pair of students
· 1 sheet of paper and pencil per pair of student

1. Student A supplies 1 sheet paper folded in half lengthwise with his/her name in one column and a partner's name in the other column.

2. Student B is the first boss and student A is the first secretary.

3. As the boss, Student B tells Student A how to do the problem. Student A, the secretary, records what Student B says in Student B's column of the paper.

4. If the boss makes a mistake, then the secretary coaches and praises once the boss does it correctly. Otherwise, the secretary praises the boss.

5. Reverse roles for each problem and repeat steps 3 and 4.

Cooperative Learning and High School Geometry: Becky Bride
Kagan Publishing • 1 (800) WEE-CO-OP • www.KaganOnline.com

7 WRITE MY EQUATION, ADVANCED

1. Student B supplies one sheet of paper folded in half lengthwise with each member of the pair writing their name at the top of one column.

2. Student B does problem 1, recording his/her work on his/her side of the paper while Student A watches, checks the work, and coaches if necessary.

3. Repeat step 2 reversing roles until all the problems are done.

▶ **Structure**
• RallyCoach

▶ **Materials**
• 1 Blackline 2.4.7 per pair of students
• 1 sheet of paper and pencil per pair of students

Cooperative Learning and High School Geometry: Becky Bride
Kagan Publishing • 1 (800) WEE-CO-OP • www.KaganOnline.com

101

ACTIVITY

1

WHO NEEDS SLOPE?

Structure: Give One, Get One

GIVE ONE	GET ONE

Cooperative Learning and High School Geometry: Becky Bride
Kagan Publishing • 1 (800) WEE-CO-OP • www.KaganOnline.com

EXPLORING PARALLEL LINES AND SLOPES

1. Plot points $A(-10, 4)$, $B(-5, 6)$, $C(-12, 1)$, and $D(-2, 5)$ on a coordinate plane.

2. Draw a line through points A and B, and a line through points C and D.

3. Lines $\overleftrightarrow{AB}$ and $\overleftrightarrow{CD}$ are parallel.
    a. The slope of line $\overleftrightarrow{AB}$ is _____.
    b. The slope of line $\overleftrightarrow{CD}$ is _____.
    c. What is special about these two slopes?

4. Plot points $E(2, 3)$, $F(3, -1)$, $G(5, 1)$, and $H(6, -3)$ on the same coordinate plane.

5. Draw a line through points E and F, and a line through points G and H.

6. Lines $\overleftrightarrow{EF}$ and $\overleftrightarrow{GH}$ are parallel.
    a. The slope of line $\overleftrightarrow{EF}$ is _____.
    b. The slope of line $\overleftrightarrow{GH}$ is _____.
    c. What is special about these two slopes?

7. Plot points $I(10, 2)$, $J(10, 8)$, $K(13, 3)$, and $L(13, 6)$ on the same coordinate plane.

8. Draw a line through points I and J, and a line through K and L.

9. Lines $\overleftrightarrow{IJ}$ and $\overleftrightarrow{KL}$ are parallel.
    a. The slope of line $\overleftrightarrow{IJ}$ is _____.
    b. The slope of line $\overleftrightarrow{KL}$ is _____.
    c. What is special about these two slopes?

10. Plot points $M(-9, -3)$, $N(-7, -3)$, $O(-6, -6)$, and $P(1, -6)$ on the same coordinate plane.

11. Draw a line through points M and N, and a line through O and P.

12. Lines $\overleftrightarrow{MN}$ and $\overleftrightarrow{OP}$ are parallel.
    a. The slope of line $\overleftrightarrow{MN}$ is _____.
    b. The slope of line $\overleftrightarrow{OP}$ is _____.
    c. What is special about these two slopes?

13. Summarize your findings in a complete sentence.

14. Explain why these findings make sense.

Cooperative Learning and High School Geometry: Becky Bride
Kagan Publishing • 1 (800) WEE-CO-OP • www.KaganOnline.com

ACTIVITY 3 EXPLORING PERPENDICULAR LINES AND SLOPES

1. Plot points *A*(-10, 4), *B*(-6, -2), *C*(-5, 5), and *D*(-11, 1) on the same coordinate plane.

2. Draw a line through points A and B, and a line through points C and D.

3. Lines $\overleftrightarrow{AB}$ and $\overleftrightarrow{CD}$ are perpendicular.
    a. The slope of line $\overleftrightarrow{AB}$ is _____.
    b. The slope of line $\overleftrightarrow{CD}$ is _____.
    c. Describe the relationship between the slope of line $\overleftrightarrow{AB}$ and $\overleftrightarrow{CD}$.

4. Plot points *E*(1, 3), *F*(5, 2), *G*(3, 5), and *H*(2, 1) on the same coordinate plane.

5. Draw a line through points E and F, and a line through points G and H.

6. Lines $\overleftrightarrow{EF}$ and $\overleftrightarrow{GH}$ are perpendicular.
    a. The slope of line $\overleftrightarrow{EF}$ is _____.
    b. The slope of line $\overleftrightarrow{GH}$ is _____.
    c. Describe the relationship between the slope of line $\overleftrightarrow{EF}$ and $\overleftrightarrow{GH}$.

7. Plot points *I*(5, -1), *J*(5, -7), *K*(-2, -2), and *L*(5, -2) on the same coordinate plane.

8. Draw a line through points I and J, and a line through points K and L.

9. Summarize the relationship of slopes of perpendicular lines that are not vertical or horizontal lines.

10. Lines $\overleftrightarrow{IJ}$ and $\overleftrightarrow{KL}$ are perpendicular.
    a. The slope of line $\overleftrightarrow{IJ}$ is _____.
    b. The slope of line $\overleftrightarrow{KL}$ is _____.
    c. Describe the relationship between the slope of line $\overleftrightarrow{IJ}$ and $\overleftrightarrow{KL}$.

11. Describe the relationship of the slopes of perpendicular lines one of which is horizontal or vertical.

12. Explain how problems 10 and 11 are related. Use examples if necessary.

Cooperative Learning and High School Geometry: Becky Bride
Kagan Publishing • 1 (800) WEE-CO-OP • www.KaganOnline.com

ACTIVITY 5
AM I A PARALLELOGRAM, RECTANGLE, TRAPEZOID, OR JUST A QUADRILATERAL?

Structure: Simultaneous RoundTable

1. A(2, -3) B(8, 5) C(16, -1) D(10, -9)

2. A(-3, 4) B(6, 8) C(9, -2) D(0, -6)

3. A(-2, 5) B(4, 9) C(7, 0) D(-5, -8)

4. A(2, 7) B(7, 5) C(-5, -1) D(-4, 4)

Answers:
1. rectangle
2. parallelogram
3. trapezoid
4. trapezoid

Cooperative Learning and High School Geometry: Becky Bride
Kagan Publishing • 1 (800) WEE-CO-OP • www.KaganOnline.com

105

ACTIVITY 5

AM I A PARALLELOGRAM, RECTANGLE, TRAPEZOID, OR JUST A QUADRILATERAL?

Structure: Simultaneous RoundTable

1. Calculate the slope of segment $\overline{AB}$. Initial your work and pass your paper 1 person in a clockwise direction.

2. On the paper you just received, check the previous work. Coach if necessary then praise your teammate for work well done. Calculate the slope of segment $\overline{BC}$. Initial your work and pass your paper 1 person in a clockwise direction.

3. On the paper you just received, check the previous work. Coach if necessary then praise your teammate for work well done. Calculate the slope of segment $\overline{CD}$. Initial your work and pass your paper 1 person in a clockwise direction.

4. On the paper you just received, check the previous work. Coach if necessary then praise your teammate for work well done. Calculate the slope of segment $\overline{DA}$. Initial your work and pass your paper 1 person in a clockwise direction.

5. On the paper you just received, check the previous work. Coach if necessary and praise your teammate for work well done. Based on the slopes calculated, state what type of figure ABCD is, choosing the most specific type possible. Explain why you chose that figure. Pass the paper 1 person in a clockwise direction.

6. On the paper just received, check step 5. If you disagree, then discuss it with the teammate who wrote the answer to step 5. Once you and your teammate agree with the figure, sign the paper indicating your approval.

Cooperative Learning and High School Geometry: Becky Bride
Kagan Publishing • 1 (800) WEE-CO-OP • www.KaganOnline.com

ACTIVITY 6 WRITE THE EQUATION OF MY PARALLEL OR PERPENDICULAR LINE

Structure: Boss/Secretary

1. Write the equation of the line passing through (1, 3) and parallel to the line whose equation is y = 2x - 3.

2. Write the equation of the line passing through (-2, 4) and parallel to the line whose equation is y = $\frac{1x}{2}$ - 3

3. Write the equation of the line passing through (5, -3) and perpendicular to the line whose equation is y + 10x = 3.

4. Write the equation of the line passing through (-6, -3) and perpendicular to the line whose equation is 6x - y = 3.

Answers:
1. y = 2x + 1
2. y = $\frac{1x}{2}$ + 5
3. y = $\frac{1x}{10}$ - 3.5
4. y = $\frac{-1x}{6}$ - 4

Cooperative Learning and High School Geometry: Becky Bride
Kagan Publishing • 1 (800) WEE-CO-OP • www.KaganOnline.com

107

Blackline 2.4.7

WRITE MY EQUATION, ADVANCED

Structure: RallyCoach

Write the equation of the line, in standard form, described below.

1. Triangle TRI has vertices: T(-3, -2), R(2, 3), and I(5, 0). Write the equation of the line that contains the median of the triangle that passes through vertex R.

2. Triangle NGL has the vertices: N(0, 3), G(5, 0), and L(-4, -5). Write the equation of the line that contains the altitude of the triangle that passes through vertex N.

3. Triangle TAL has vertices: T(-7, -1), A(5, 6), and L(2, -3). Write the equation of the line that contains the altitude of the triangle that passes through vertex T.

4. Write the equation of the perpendicular bisector of segment $\overline{GM}$ whose endpoints are G(-3, 2) and M(7, -4).

Answers:
1. 4x - y = 5
2. 9x + 5y = 15
3. x + 3y = (-10)
4. 5x - 3y = 13

Cooperative Learning and High School Geometry: Becky Bride
Kagan Publishing • 1 (800) WEE-CO-OP • www.KaganOnline.com

CONSTRUCTIONS

This chapter is located here because some exploratory exercises in future chapters require the students to be familiar with basic constructions. Since this chapter is a means to an end, only the most critical constructions are included. If you want to delve deeper into constructions, this chapter will give you ideas of structures that can be used to process them. The Simultaneous RoundTable structure is used frequently in this chapter, because the students find it fun. When the Boss/Secretary structure is used it is done to get students to describe in detail a sequence of events. Verbal and mathematical skills can improve if the secretary literally writes exactly what the boss says, and not what he/she thinks the boss meant.

LESSON 1
SEGMENTS AND ANGLES

This lesson begins with an activity to process the construction of segments. To make it more interesting, it involves adding and subtracting segment lengths. The next activity involves practicing duplicating angles. If your class is advanced, you can probably skip activity 2. Activity 3 works with angles and involves adding and subtracting angle measures. Finally, bisecting angles will finish this lesson.

ACTIVITY 1
ADDING AND SUBTRACTING SEGMENTS

▶ **Structure**
· Simultaneous RoundTable

▶ **Materials**
· Transparencies 3.1.1a and 3.1.1b
· 1 ruler per student
· 1 compass per student
· 1 sheet of paper per student
· 1 highlighter per student

1. Each student draws a 1.5-inch segment, labeling it *a* and a 1-inch segment, labeling it *b* on his/her paper.

ex:

| 1.5" | a |
| 1" | b |

2. Each teammate writes all four problems on his/her paper.

3. Each teammate constructs a segment whose length is equal to the expression in problem one. They highlight the segment that represents their answer. They initial their work and pass the paper to the next person in a clockwise direction.

4. On the paper just received, each teammate checks the previous teammate's work, coaches if wrong, praises once it is right, and then constructs a segment whose length is equal to the expression in problem 2. They initial their work and pass the paper to the next person in a clockwise direction.

5. On the paper just received, each teammate checks the previous teammate's work, coaches if wrong, praises once it is right, and then constructs a segment whose length is equal to the expression in problem 3. They initial their work and pass the paper to the next person in a clockwise direction.

6. On the paper just received, each teammate checks the previous teammate's work, coaches if wrong, praises once it is right, and then constructs a segment whose length is equal to the expression in problem 4. They initial their work and pass the paper to the next person in a clockwise direction.

7. On the paper they receive, the student will check the previous work and coach if necessary.

Tip:
Model this for the students.

110

Cooperative Learning and High School Geometry: Becky Bride
Kagan Publishing • 1 (800) WEE-CO-OP • www.KaganOnline.com

 ACTIVITY

2 DUPLICATING ANGLES

Objective: Practice duplicating angles using a compass and straightedge.

1. Student A, as the boss, gives Student B step by step instructions on how to duplicate ∠1.

2. Student B, as the secretary, literally does what Student A describes. If this is not what Student A intended then Student A modifies his/her directions.

3. Student B coaches and/or praises Student A.

4. Reverse roles for each new problem and repeat steps 1-3.

▶ **Structure**
• Boss/Secretary

▶ **Materials**
• 1 Blackline 3.1.2 per pair of students
• 1 compass per pair of students
• 1 straightedge per pair of students
• 1 sheet of paper per pair of students

 ACTIVITY

3 ADDING AND SUBTRACTING ANGLES

1. Each student, using a straightedge, draws one very acute angle and one barely obtuse angle.

2. Each student constructs, on his/her paper, an angle whose measure is equal to the expression in problem 1 and highlights the angle that represents his/her answer. Students initial their work and pass the paper to the next person in a clockwise direction.

3. Each student checks the previous student's work, coaches if wrong and then praise once it is right. Then each student constructs on his/her paper an angle whose measure is equal to the expression in problem 2. He/she highlights the angle that represents his/her answer. Students initial their work and pass the paper to the next person in a clockwise direction.

4. Each student checks the previous student's work, coaches if wrong and then praises once it is right. Then each student constructs on his/her paper an angle whose measure is equal to the expression in problem 3. He/she highlights the angle that represents his/her answer. Students will initial their work and pass the paper to the next person in a clockwise direction.

5. Each student checks the previous student's work, coaches if wrong and then praises once it is right. Then each student constructs on his/her paper an angle whose measure is equal to the expression in problem 4. He/she highlights the angle that represents his/her answer. Students initial their work and pass the paper to the next person in a clockwise direction.

▶ **Structure**
• Simultaneous RoundTable

▶ **Materials**
• Transparencies 3.1.3a and 3.1.3b
• 1 straightedge per student
• 1 compass per student
• 1 sheet of paper per student
• 1 highlighter

6. Each student checks the previous student's work, coaches if wrong and then praises once it is right.

Tip:
It is very important that the initial angles the students draw on their paper are very acute (less than 45°) and barely obtuse (just over 90°). That way, each construction can be done.

Model this for the students.

Cooperative Learning and High School Geometry: Becky Bride
Kagan Publishing • 1 (800) WEE-CO-OP • www.KaganOnline.com

111

Chapter 3: Constructions Lesson One

4

BISECTING ANGLES

▶ Structure

· Simultaneous RoundTable

▶ Materials

· Transparencies 3.1.4a and
  3.1.4b
· 1 straightedge per student
· 1 compass per student
· 1 sheet of paper per student

1. Student 1 draws and highlights, using a straightedge, a large acute triangle on his/her paper. Student 2 draws and highlights, using a straightedge, a large obtuse triangle on his/her paper. Student 3 draws and highlights, using a straightedge, a large right triangle on his/her paper. Finally, student 4 draws and highlights a large triangle of his/her choice on his/her paper.

2. Each student bisects one angle of his/her triangle, initials his/her work, and passes his/her paper to the next person in a clockwise direction.

3. On the paper received, each student checks the previous student's work, coaches if wrong and then praise once it is right. Then each student bisects a second angle of the triangle, initials his/her work, and passes his/her paper to the next person in a clockwise direction.

4. On the paper received, each student checks the previous student's work, coaches if wrong and then praises once it is right. Then each student bisects a third angle of the triangle, initials his/her work, and passes his/her paper to the next person in a clockwise direction.

5. Each student checks the previous student's work— coach if wrong and then praise once it it right.

Tip:
Model this for the students.

Cooperative Learning and High School Geometry: Becky Bride
Kagan Publishing • 1 (800) WEE-CO-OP • www.KaganOnline.com

ADDING AND SUBTRACTING SEGMENTS

Structure: Simultaneous RoundTable

Draw two segments at the top of your paper: one segment length 1.5 inches, labeled *a* and the other segment length 1 inch, labeled *b*.

For each problem, construct a segment whose length is equal to the expression below.

1. a + b

2. a + 2b

3. 2a - b

4. 3a - 2b

Cooperative Learning and High School Geometry: Becky Bride
Kagan Publishing • 1 (800) WEE-CO-OP • www.KaganOnline.com

113

ACTIVITY 1 ADDING AND SUBTRACTING SEGMENTS

Structure: Simultaneous RoundTable

1. Construct a segment whose length is equal to the expression in problem one. Highlight the segment that represents your answer. Initial your work and pass the paper 1 person in a clockwise direction.

2. Check the previous teammate's work. Coach if necessary, then praise. Construct a segment whose length is equal to the expression in problem 2. Highlight the segment that represents your answer. Initial your work and pass the paper 1 person in a clockwise direction.

3. Check the previous teammate's work. Coach if necessary, then praise. Construct a segment whose length is equal to the expression in problem 3. Highlight the segment that represents your answer. Initial your work and pass the paper 1 person in a clockwise direction.

4. Check the previous teammate's work. Coach if necessary, then praise. Construct a segment whose length is equal to the expression in problem 4. Highlight the segment that represents your answer. Initial your work and pass the paper 1 person in a clockwise direction and check that teammate's work.

Cooperative Learning and High School Geometry: Becky Bride
Kagan Publishing • 1 (800) WEE-CO-OP • www.KaganOnline.com

2 DUPLICATING ANGLES

Structure: Boss/Secretary

1. Duplicate the angle below.

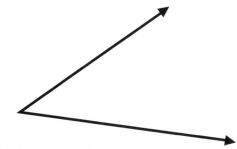

2. Duplicate the angle below.

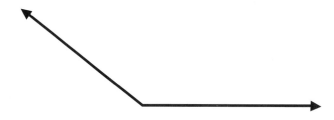

3. Duplicate the angle below.

4. Duplicate the angle below.

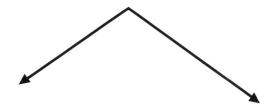

Cooperative Learning and High School Geometry: Becky Bride
Kagan Publishing • 1 (800) WEE-CO-OP • www.KaganOnline.com

115

ACTIVITY 3 ADDING AND SUBTRACTING ANGLES

Structure: Simultaneous RoundTable

Draw a very acute angle at the top of your paper and label it *a*. Draw a slightly obtuse angle at the top of your paper and label it *b*. (Similar to the ones shown).

1. a + b

2. 3a

3. b - a

4. b - 2a

Cooperative Learning and High School Geometry: Becky Bride
Kagan Publishing • 1 (800) WEE-CO-OP • www.KaganOnline.com

ADDING AND SUBTRACTING ANGLES

Structure: Simultaneous RoundTable

1. Construct an angle whose measure is equal to the expression in problem one. Highlight the angle that represents your answer. Initial your work and pass the paper 1 person in a clockwise direction.

2. Check the previous teammate's work. Coach if necessary, then praise. Construct an angle whose measure is equal to the expression in problem 2. Highlight the angle that represents your answer. Initial your work and pass the paper 1 person in a clockwise direction.

3. Check the previous teammate's work. Coach if necessary, then praise. Construct an angle whose measure is equal to the expression in problem 3. Highlight the angle that represents your answer. Initial your work and pass the paper 1 person in a clockwise direction.

4. Check the previous teammate's work. Coach if necessary, then praise. Construct an angle whose measure is equal to the expression in problem 4. Highlight the angle that represents your answer. Initial your work and pass the paper 1 person in a clockwise direction and check that teammate's work.

Cooperative Learning and High School Geometry: Becky Bride
Kagan Publishing • 1 (800) WEE-CO-OP • www.KaganOnline.com

117

ACTIVITY

4

BISECTING ANGLES

Structure: Simultaneous RoundTable

Use a straightedge to draw each requested figure.

1. Student 1: Draw a large acute triangle on your paper and highlight the triangle.

2. Student 2: Draw a large obtuse triangle on your paper and highlight the triangle.

3. Student 3: Draw a large right triangle on your paper and highlight the triangle.

4. Student 4: Draw a large triangle of your choice on your paper and highlight the triangle.

Cooperative Learning and High School Geometry: Becky Bride
Kagan Publishing • 1 (800) WEE-CO-OP • www.KaganOnline.com

ACTIVITY

4

BISECTING ANGLES

Structure: Simultaneous RoundTable

1. Bisect one of the angles of the triangle on your paper, initial your work, and pass your paper to the next person in a clockwise direction.

2. On the paper you receive, check the previous teammate's work. Coach if necessary, then praise your teammate for work well done. Bisect a second angle of the triangle on your paper, initial your work, and pass your paper to the next person in a clockwise direction.

3. On the paper you receive, check the previous teammate's work. Coach if necessary, then praise your teammate for work well done. Bisect the third angle of the triangle on your paper, initial your work, and pass your paper to the next person in a clockwise direction.

4. Check the previous teammate's work. Coach if necessary, then praise your teammate for work well done.

Cooperative Learning and High School Geometry: Becky Bride
Kagan Publishing • 1 (800) WEE-CO-OP • www.KaganOnline.com

119

LESSON 2
PERPENDICULAR LINES

This lesson processes the three types of perpendicular lines that can be constructed. To distinguish one construction from another, my students have given the constructions names. I have taken the liberty to use those names in this lesson. It begins with the "fish" (so named because the arcs appear to form a fish), which is a perpendicular bisector. There are four activities on this. The first activity constructs perpendicular bisectors of segments using a compass and straightedge. The second activity has students process the patty paper construction of a perpendicular bisector. Because so many exploratory exercises use patty paper, Activity 2 is important to do. Also point out that this is an easy way to locate the midpoint of a segment. The third and fourth activities are applications of the perpendicular bisector construction. They are written for the use of a compass and straightedge, but these activities could also be done with patty paper. Activity 5 processes constructing a line perpendicular to a given line passing through a point not on the line-named "happy cyclops" (because the point appears to be the eye and the arc the mouth of a a smiling cyclops). Activity 6 is an application of the "happy cyclops." Activity 7 processes constructing a line perpendicular to a given line at a given point on the given line. It is named the "helicopter" because the segment appears to be the top blades of a helicopter, the arcs above the segment its tail blades, and the perpendicular segment the body of the helicopter. Activity 8 involves constructions that use the "helicopter." Again both of these could also be done with patty paper.

ACTIVITY

1 PERPENDICULAR BISECTOR (THE "FISH") WITH COMPASS AND STRAIGHTEDGE

▶ **Structure**
· Simultaneous RoundTable

▶ **Materials**
· Transparencies 3.2.1-2a and 3.2.1-2b
· 1 sheet of paper per student
· 1 compass per student
· 1 straightedge per student
· 1 pencil per student
· 1 highlighter per student

1. Each student draws and highlights a large triangle on his/her paper using a straightedge. Student 1 draws an obtuse triangle, Student 2 draws an acute triangle, Student 3 draws a right triangle, and Student 4 draws a triangle of his/her choice.

2. Students construct the perpendicular bisector of one of the sides of the triangle on their paper, mark the right angle and congruent segments, initial their work, and then pass their papers to the next person in a clockwise direction.

3. On the paper they receive, students check the previous student's work, coaching if necessary and then praising the teammate for a job well done. Then students construct a perpendicular bisector of a second side, mark the right angle and congruent segments, initial the work, and pass the paper to the next person in a clockwise direction.

4. On the paper they receive, students check the previous student's work, coaching if necessary and then praising their teammate for a job well done. Then students construct a perpendicular bisector of the third side, mark the right angle and congruent segments, initial their work, and pass the paper to the next person in a clockwise direction.

5. On the paper they receive, each student checks the previous student's work, coaching if necessary and then praising his/her teammate for a job well done.

ACTIVITY

2

PERPENDICULAR BISECTOR
("THE FISH") WITH PATTY PAPER

Notes:
This activity processes the patty paper construction of a perpendicular bisector "fish." To patty paper, fold a perpendicular bisector of segment $\overline{AB}$, fold the patty paper so point A lies on top of point B and flatten the patty paper. When you unfold the patty paper, the perpendicular bisector of $\overline{AB}$ is the crease running through the segment. Make sure students mark their segments to indicate the right angle and congruent segments.

Round 1:
Follow the same directions for activity 1 but use patty paper instead.

Round 2:
Repeat the activity but only locate the midpoints of the sides of the triangle by pinching the patty paper on the segment once point A is placed over point B. Have students label the midpoint and mark the segment showing congruence.

▶ **Structure**
• Simultaneous RoundTable

▶ **Materials**
• Transparencies 3.2.1-2a and 3.2.1-2b
• 1 sheet of patty paper per student
• 1 straightedge per student
• 1 pencil per student
• 1 highlighter per student

ACTIVITY

3

APPLICATION OF THE "FISH": CIRCUMSCRIBING
A CIRCLE ABOUT A TRIANGLE

1. Each student draws and highlights a triangle on his/her paper, using a straightedge. Student 1 draws an obtuse triangle, Student 2 draws an acute triangle, Student 3 draws a right triangle, and Student 4 draws a triangle of his/her choice.

2. Each student constructs the perpendicular bisector of one of the sides of the triangle on his/her paper, initials the work, and then passes the paper to the next person in a clockwise direction.

3. On the paper they receive, students check the previous student's work, coaching if necessary and then praising the teammate for a job well done. Then students construct a perpendicular bisector of a second side, initial their work, and pass the paper to the next person in a clockwise direction.

4. On the paper they receive, each student checks the previous student's work, coaching if necessary and then praising the teammate for a job well done. The students construct a perpendicular bisector of the third side, initial their work, and pass the paper to the next person in a clockwise direction. This third bisector could be eliminated. However, it is included so the students can see how accurate the center of the circle is.

5. On the paper they receive, students check the previous student's work, coaching if necessary and then praising the teammate for a job well done. Students constructs the circumscribed circle, initial their work, and pass the paper to the next person in a clockwise direction.

▶ **Structure**
• Simultaneous RoundTable

▶ **Materials**
• Transparencies 3.2.3a and 3.2.3b
• 1 sheet of paper per student
• 1 compass per student
• 1 straightedge per student
• 1 highlighter per student
• 1 pencil per student

6. On the paper they receive, each student checks the previous student's work, coaching if necessary and then praising the teammate for a job well done.

Note:
This activity can be repeated with the patty paper construction of the "fish."

Cooperative Learning and High School Geometry: Becky Bride
Kagan Publishing • 1 (800) WEE-CO-OP • www.KaganOnline.com

121

Chapter 3: Constructions
L e s s o n   T w o

ACTIVITY

4 APPLICATION OF THE "FISH": MEDIANS OF A TRIANGLE

▶ Structure
- Simultaneous RoundTable

▶ Materials
- Transparencies 3.2.4a and 3.2.4b
- 1 sheet of paper per student
- 1 compass per student
- 1 straightedge per student
- 1 highlighter and pencil per student

Notes:
Activity 4 is a little different from Activity 3 because the goal is to locate midpoints using the perpendicular bisector construction rather than using the entire perpendicular bisector. Encouraging students to just make the midpoint rather than the entire bisector will help keep the diagrams from getting hopelessly confusing.

1. Each student draws and highlights a large triangle on the paper using a straightedge. Student 1 draws an obtuse triangle, Student 2 draws an acute triangle, Student 3 draws a right triangle, and Student 4 draws a triangle of his/her choice.

2. Students construct the midpoint of one of the sides of the triangle on their paper, mark the congruent segments, draw the median to that midpoint, initial their work, and then pass their papers to the next person in a clockwise direction.

3. On the paper they receive, students check the previous student's work, coaching if necessary and then praising the teammate for a job well done. Then students construct a midpoint of a second side, mark the congruent segments, draw the median to that midpoint, initial their work, and pass the paper to the next person in a clockwise direction.

4. On the paper they receive, students check the previous student's work, coaching if necessary and then praising the teammate for a job well done. Then students construct a midpoint of the third side, mark the congruent segments, draw the third median, initial their work, and pass the paper to the next person in a clockwise direction.

5. On the paper they receive, students check the previous student's work, coaching if necessary and then praising the teammate for a job well done.

Note:
This activity can be repeated with the patty paper construction of a midpoint.

Cooperative Learning and High School Geometry: Becky Bride
Kagan Publishing • 1 (800) WEE-CO-OP • www.KaganOnline.com

ACTIVITY

5 "HAPPY CYCLOPS"

1. Students draw four segments with a point above each segment on their paper. The segments should be spread out so that students can construct perpendiculars to the line through the point not on the line. Two segments per side works well.

2. Students perform the "happy cyclops" construction for one of the segments on their paper, mark the right angle, initial their work, and pass the paper to the next person in a clockwise direction.

3. On the paper received, students check their teammate's work, coach if necessary then praise the teammate for a job well done. Then students perform the "happy cyclops" construction on another one of the segments on the paper, mark the right angle, initial their work, and pass the paper to the next person in a clockwise direction.

4. On the paper received, students check their teammate's work, coach if necessary then praise the teammate for a job well done. Then students perform the "happy cyclops" construction on another one of the segments on the paper, mark the right angle, initial their work, and pass the paper to the next person in a clockwise direction.

5. On the paper received, students check the teammate's work, coach if necessary then praise the teammate for a job well done. Then students perform the "happy cyclops" construction on the last segment on the paper, mark the right angle, initial their work, and pass the paper to the next person in a clockwise direction.

▶ Structure
· Simultaneous RoundTable

▶ Materials
· Transparencies 3.2.5a and 3.2.5b
· 1 sheet of paper per student
· 1 compass per student
· 1 straightedge per student
· 1 highlighter per student

6. On the paper received, students check their teammate's work, coach if necessary then praise the teammate for a job well done.

Note:
This activity can be repeated using a patty paper construction. To perform a "happy cyclops" patty paper construction, begin by folding the patty paper so that point A lies on segment $\overline{AB}$. Slide point A along segment $\overline{AB}$ extending $\overline{AB}$ if necessary until the given point is in the crease of the fold. Flatten the patty paper and mark the right angle.

Cooperative Learning and High School Geometry: Becky Bride
Kagan Publishing • 1 (800) WEE-CO-OP • www.KaganOnline.com

123

Chapter 3: Constructions

Lesson Two

6 APPLICATION OF THE "HAPPY CYCLOPS": ALTITUDES OF A TRIANGLE

▶ Structure
· Simultaneous RoundTable

▶ Materials
· Transparencies 3.2.6a and 3.2.6b
· 1 sheet of paper per student
· 1 compass per student
· 1 straightedge per student
· 1 highlighter and pencil per student

Notes:
Activity 6 has students construct altitudes of triangles. This not only reinforces the definition of an altitude but also practices the "happy cyclops." It is written for three rounds.

Round 1 uses only acute triangles. This gets the students used to the construction as it relates to altitudes. Round 2 uses only right triangles. These require that students extend sides to complete the construction. This helps to prepare them for the obtuse triangle and re-emphasizes that the sides that form the right angle of a right triangle are also altitudes of the triangle. The students always seem to find this surprising. Round 3 uses only obtuse triangles.

Modeling for the students helps them to see how to extend sides. Average and below average students will find this challenging. Part of the challenge is that all three altitudes are being constructed on each triangle and the diagram becomes complicated. You may want to repeat this round until the students feel comfortable with it. Advanced students may be able to work with all three types of triangles in one round.

Round 1
1. Students draw and highlight a large acute triangle on their papers using a straightedge.

2. Students construct one altitude of the triangle on their papers, mark the right angle, initial their work, and then pass their papers to the next person in a clockwise direction.

3. On the paper they receive, students check the previous student's work, coaching if necessary and then praising the teammate for a job well done. Then students construct a second altitude, mark the right angle, initial their work, and pass the paper to the next person in a clockwise direction.

4. On the paper they receive, students check the previous student's work, coaching if necessary and then praising the teammate for a job well done. Then students constructs a third altitude, mark the right angle, initial their work, and pass the paper to the next person in a clockwise direction.

5. On the paper they receive, students check the previous student's work, coaching if necessary and then praising the teammate for a job well done.

Round 2
Repeat the above instructions except have each student begin with a right triangle.

Round 3
Repeat the above instructions except, each student begin with an obtuse triangle.

Note:
These rounds can be repeated using patty paper constructions.

Cooperative Learning and High School Geometry: Becky Bride
Kagan Publishing • 1 (800) WEE-CO-OP • www.KaganOnline.com

Chapter 3: Constructions
Lesson Two

ACTIVITY

7 "HELICOPTER"

1. Students draw four segments with a point on each segment on their paper. Segments should be spread out so students can construct perpendiculars to the line through the point on the line. Two segments per side works well.

2. Students perform the "helicopter" construction for one of the segments on their paper, mark the right angle, initial their work, and pass the paper to the next person in a clockwise direction.

3. On the paper received, students check their teammate's work, coach if necessary then praise the teammate for a job well done. Then students perform the "helicopter" construction on another one of the segments on the paper, mark the right angle, initial their work, and pass the paper to the next person in a clockwise direction.

4. On the paper received, students check their teammate's work, coach if necessary then praise the teammate for a job well done. Then students perform the "helicopter" construction on another one of the segments on the paper, mark the right angle, initial their work, and pass the paper to the next person in a clockwise direction.

5. On the paper received, students check their teammate's work, coach if necessary then praise the teammate for a job well done. Then students perform the "helicopter" construction on the last segment on the paper, mark the right angle, initial their work, and pass the paper to the next person in a clockwise direction.

▶ **Structure**
• Simultaneous RoundTable

▶ **Materials**
• Transparencies 3.2.7a and 3.2.7b
• 1 sheet of paper per student
• 1 compass per student
• 1 straightedge per student
• 1 pencil per student

6. On the paper received, students check their teammate's work, coach if necessary then praise the teammate for a job well done.

Note:
This activity can be repeated using a patty paper construction. To perform a "helicopter" patty paper construction, begin by folding the patty paper so that endpoint A lies on segment $\overline{AB}$. Slide point A along segment $\overline{AB}$ extending $\overline{AB}$ if necessary until the given point on the segment is in the crease of the fold. Flatten the patty paper and mark the right angle.

ACTIVITY

8 APPLICATIONS USING THE "HELICOPTER"

1. Student A, as the boss, gives Student B step-by-step instructions on how to do problem 1.

2. Student B, as the secretary, literally does what Student A describes. If this is not what Student A intended, then Student A modifies his/her directions.

3. Student B coaches and/or praises Student A.

4. Reverse roles for each new problem and repeat steps 1-3.

▶ **Structure**
• Boss/Secretary

▶ **Materials**
• 1 Blackline 3.2.8 per pair of students
• 1 compass per pair of students
• 1 straightedge per pair of students
• 1 pencil per pair of students

Cooperative Learning and High School Geometry: Becky Bride
Kagan Publishing • 1 (800) WEE-CO-OP • www.KaganOnline.com

125

Chapter 3: Constructions
Lesson Two

PERPENDICULAR BISECTOR (THE "FISH") WITH COMPASS AND STRAIGHTEDGE

Structure: Simultaneous RoundTable

Use a straightedge to draw all triangles.

1. Student 1: Draw and highlight an obtuse triangle on your paper.

2. Student 2: Draw and highlight an acute triangle on your paper.

3. Student 3: Draw and highlight a right triangle on your paper.

4. Student 4: Draw and highlight a triangle of your choice on your paper.

Cooperative Learning and High School Geometry: Becky Bride
Kagan Publishing • 1 (800) WEE-CO-OP • www.KaganOnline.com

PERPENDICULAR BISECTOR (THE "FISH") WITH COMPASS AND STRAIGHTEDGE

Structure: Simultaneous RoundTable

1. Construct the perpendicular bisector of one of the sides of your triangle, mark the right angle and congruent segments, initial your work, and pass your paper to the next person in a clockwise direction.

2. Check the previous teammate's work, coaching if necessary, then praise for job well done. Construct a perpendicular bisector of a second side of the triangle, mark the right angle and congruent segments, initial your work, and pass your paper to the next person in a clockwise direction.

3. Check the previous teammate's work, coaching if necessary, then praise for job well done. Construct a perpendicular bisector of a third side of the triangle, mark the right angle and congruent segments, initial your work, and pass your paper to the next person in a clockwise direction.

4. Check the previous teammate's work, coaching if necessary, then praise for job well done.

Cooperative Learning and High School Geometry: Becky Bride
Kagan Publishing • 1 (800) WEE-CO-OP • www.KaganOnline.com

127

APPLICATION OF THE "FISH": CIRCUMSCRIBING A CIRCLE ABOUT A TRIANGLE

Structure: Simultaneous RoundTable

Use a straightedge when drawing triangles.

1. Student 1: Draw and highlight an obtuse triangle on your paper.

2. Student 2: Draw and highlight an acute triangle on your paper.

3. Student 3: Draw and highlight a right triangle on your paper.

4. Student 4: Draw and highlight a triangle of your choice on your paper.

Cooperative Learning and High School Geometry: Becky Bride
Kagan Publishing • 1 (800) WEE-CO-OP • www.KaganOnline.com

ACTIVITY 3 APPLICATION OF THE "FISH": CIRCUMSCRIBING A CIRCLE ABOUT A TRIANGLE

Structure: Simultaneous RoundTable

1. Construct the perpendicular bisector of one of the sides of your triangle, initial your work, and pass your paper to the next person in a clockwise direction.

2. Check the previous teammate's work, coaching if necessary, then praise for job well done. Construct a perpendicular bisector of a second side of the triangle, initial your work, and pass your paper to the next person in a clockwise direction.

3. Check the previous teammate's work, coaching if necessary, then praise for job well done. Construct a perpendicular bisector of a third side of the triangle, initial your work, and pass your paper to the next person in a clockwise direction.

4. Check the previous teammate's work, coaching if necessary, then praise for job well done. Construct the circumscribed circle about the triangle, initial your work, and pass your paper to the next person in a clockwise direction.

5. Check the previous teammate's work, coaching if necessary, then praise for job well done.

Cooperative Learning and High School Geometry: Becky Bride
Kagan Publishing • 1 (800) WEE-CO-OP • www.KaganOnline.com

129

APPLICATION OF THE "FISH": MEDIANS OF A TRIANGLE

Structure: Simultaneous RoundTable

Use straightedges when drawing triangles.

1. Student 1: Draw and highlight an obtuse triangle on your paper.

2. Student 2: Draw and highlight an acute triangle on your paper.

3. Student 3: Draw and highlight a right triangle on your paper.

4. Student 4: Draw and highlight a triangle of your choice on your paper.

Cooperative Learning and High School Geometry: Becky Bride
Kagan Publishing • 1 (800) WEE-CO-OP • www.KaganOnline.com

APPLICATION OF THE "FISH": MEDIANS OF A TRIANGLE

Structure: Simultaneous RoundTable

1. Construct a midpoint on one of the sides of your triangle, mark the congruent segments, draw the median to that midpoint, initial your work, and pass your paper to the next person in a clockwise direction.

2. Check your teammate's work, coaching if necessary, then praise for job well done. Construct a midpoint on a second side of the triangle, mark the congruent segments, draw the median to that midpoint, initial your work, and pass your paper to the next person in a clockwise direction.

3. Check your teammate's work, coaching if necessary, then praise for job well done. Construct a midpoint on a third side of the triangle, mark the congruent segments, draw the median to that midpoint, initial your work, and pass your paper to the next person in a clockwise direction.

4. Check your teammate's work, coaching if necessary, then praise for job well done.

Cooperative Learning and High School Geometry: Becky Bride
Kagan Publishing • 1 (800) WEE-CO-OP • www.KaganOnline.com

131

5 **"HAPPY CYCLOPS"**

Structure: Simultaneous RoundTable

Use a straightedge when drawing segments.

Draw four segments with a point anywhere above each segment, spread out so that teammates can do constructions on each segment. Two segments per side of your paper works well. See the examples below.

●

_____

●

_____

Cooperative Learning and High School Geometry: Becky Bride
Kagan Publishing • 1 (800) WEE-CO-OP • www.KaganOnline.com

ACTIVITY

5

"HAPPY CYCLOPS"

Structure: Simultaneous RoundTable

1. On one of the segments on your paper, perform the "happy cyclops" construction, mark the right angle, initial your work, and pass the paper to the next person in a clockwise direction.

2. Check the previous teammate's work, coaching if necessary, then praise for job well done. On another one of the segments on the paper, perform the "happy cyclops" construction, mark the right angle, initial your work, and pass the paper to the next person in a clockwise direction.

3. Check the previous teammate's work, coaching if necessary, then praise for job well done. On another one of the segments on the paper, perform the "happy cyclops" construction, mark the right angle, initial your work, and pass the paper to the next person in a clockwise direction.

4. Check the previous teammate's work, coaching if necessary, then praise for job well done. On the last of the segments on the paper, perform the "happy cyclops" construction, mark the right angle, initial your work, and pass the paper to the next person in a clockwise direction.

5. Check the previous teammate's work, coaching if necessary, then praise for job well done.

Cooperative Learning and High School Geometry: Becky Bride
Kagan Publishing • 1 (800) WEE-CO-OP • www.KaganOnline.com

133

APPLICATION OF THE "HAPPY CYCLOPS": ALTITUDES OF A TRIANGLE

Structure: Simultaneous RoundTable

Round 1:

Using a straightedge, draw and highlight a large acute triangle on your paper.

Round 2:

Using a straightedge, draw and highlight a right triangle on your paper.

Round 3:

Using a straightedge, draw and highlight an obtuse triangle on your paper.

Cooperative Learning and High School Geometry: Becky Bride
Kagan Publishing • 1 (800) WEE-CO-OP • www.KaganOnline.com

6 APPLICATION OF THE "HAPPY CYCLOPS": ALTITUDES OF A TRIANGLE

Structure: Simultaneous RoundTable

1. Construct one altitude of the triangle on your paper, mark the right angle, initial your work, and pass your paper to the next person in a clockwise direction.

2. Check the previous teammate's work, coaching if necessary, then praise for job well done. Construct a second altitude of the triangle on your paper, mark the right angle, initial your work, and pass your paper to the next person in a clockwise direction.

3. Check the previous teammate's work, coaching if necessary, then praise for job well done. Construct a third altitude of the triangle on your paper, mark the right angle, initial your work, and pass your paper to the next person in a clockwise direction.

4. Check the previous teammate's work, coaching if necessary, then praise for job well done.

Cooperative Learning and High School Geometry: Becky Bride
Kagan Publishing • 1 (800) WEE-CO-OP • www.KaganOnline.com

135

ACTIVITY

7   **"HELICOPTER"**

Structure: Simultaneous RoundTable

Using a straightedge, draw four segments with a point (other than the endpoints) marked on the segment, spread out so teammates have room to do the constructions. Two segments per side of your paper works well. See the examples below.

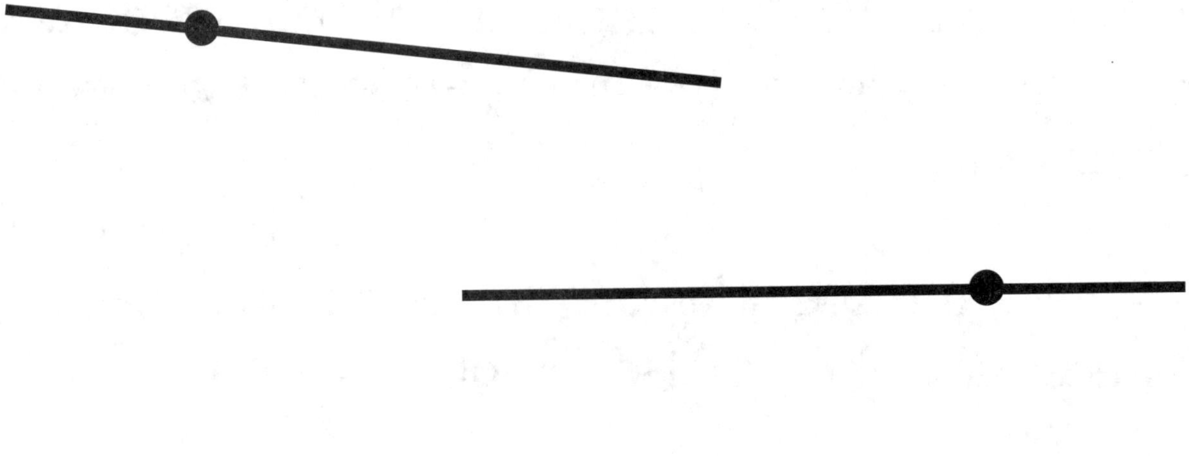

Cooperative Learning and High School Geometry: Becky Bride
Kagan Publishing • 1 (800) WEE-CO-OP • www.KaganOnline.com

ACTIVITY

7 "HELICOPTER"

Structure: Simultaneous RoundTable

1. Perform the "helicopter" construction for one of the segments on your paper, mark the right angle, initial your work, and pass the paper to the next person in a clockwise direction.

2. Check the previous teammate's work, coaching if necessary, then praise for job well done. Perform the "helicopter" construction on the second segment on the paper, mark the right angle, initial your work, and pass the paper to the next person in a clockwise direction.

3. Check the previous teammate's work, coaching if necessary, then praise for job well done. Perform the "helicopter" construction on the third segment on the paper, mark the right angle, initial your work, and pass the paper to the next person in a clockwise direction.

4. Check the previous teammate's work, coaching if necessary, then praise for job well done. Perform the "helicopter" construction on the last segment on the paper, mark the right angle, initial your work, and pass the paper to the next person in a clockwise direction.

5. Check the previous teammate's work, coaching if necessary, then praise for job well done.

Cooperative Learning and High School Geometry: Becky Bride
Kagan Publishing • 1 (800) WEE-CO-OP • www.KaganOnline.com

137

ACTIVITY 8
APPLICATIONS USING THE "HELICOPTER"

Structure: Boss/Secretary

1. Construct an isosceles right triangle △ABC, with right angle at B and BC = AB.

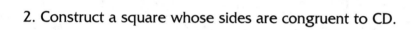

A   **B**

2. Construct a square whose sides are congruent to CD.

C   **D**

3. Construct a pentagon PENTA such that ∠P and ∠A are right angles and point N lies on the perpendicular bisector of $\overline{PA}$.

4. Construct a trapezoid TRAP with right angles at points T and R. Make RA < TP.

Cooperative Learning and High School Geometry: Becky Bride
Kagan Publishing • 1 (800) WEE-CO-OP • www.KaganOnline.com

TRIANGLES

This chapter focuses on triangles. It begins with an exploratory exercise to determine the side lengths necessary to form a triangle. It also includes an exploratory exercise to discover that the sum of the angles of a triangle is 180°. Properties of isosceles triangles are investigated. Then the chapter ends with exploratory exercises and activities for congruent triangles.

LESSON 1
SIDE LENGTHS NECESSARY TO FORM A TRIANGLE

The first activity in this lesson has students explore that the sum of the lengths of any two sides of a triangle must be greater than the third side. Using pretzels makes the activity a little more fun. The second activity processes the relationship explored in Activity 1. Having students generate three sets of lengths—two that work and one that doesn't—solidifies their understanding of this theorem.

ACTIVITY 1
EXPLORING SIDE LENGTHS OF A TRIANGLE

▶ **Materials**
  • Straws, toothpicks, or straight pretzels (4 per student)
  • 1 Blackline 4.1.1 per student
  • 1 sheet of paper and pencil per student

Students complete Blackline 4.1.1. The straws, toothpicks, or pretzels need to be equal in length. One benefit with the pretzels is cleanup is easy — the students can eat them when they are finished.

ACTIVITY 2
FIND THE FICTITIOUS TRIANGLE

▶ **Structure**
  • Find The Fiction

▶ **Materials**
  • 1 sheet of paper and pencil per student

1. All students write three sets of numbers that represent the lengths of three sides of a potential triangle—two sets that form a triangle and one set that does not form a triangle.

2. One student stands and reads his/her three sets of three segment lengths or shows the students the three sets of segment lengths he/she wrote on his/her paper.

3. Individually, each seated teammate determines which set of segment lengths can't form a triangle. Each teammate records his/her answer on his/her own paper.

4. The seated teammates show each other their answer and discuss and come to a consensus as to which set of segment lengths cannot form a triangle.

5. If the seated teammates are correct, the student standing praises them.

6. If the seated teammates are wrong then the standing teammate coaches the team. The seated teammates then praise the standing teammate for challenging them.

7. Repeat steps 2-6 until all teammates have had a chance to share their segment lengths.

1 EXPLORING SIDE LENGTHS OF A TRIANGLE

1. Take two pretzels of equal length. Bite and eat, or break and throw away, a <u>small</u> portion of 1 pretzel. <u>Break</u> the remaining part of the pretzel (the one that you removed a piece from) into two pieces. You should now have three segments of pretzel.

2. With the three segments of pretzels, form a triangle. The ends of each pretzel must touch each other (see diagram below). Describe the triangle you formed. If there is a problem forming the triangle describe the problem.

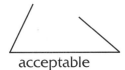
acceptable

unacceptable

3. Put the smaller two pieces together to form a larger segment and compare the length of these two pretzels together, with the unbroken pretzel. Describe the relationship.

4. Throw away or eat the two smaller pieces. This leaves you with the unbroken pretzel. Take another pretzel that is the same length as the unbroken pretzel from step 3. Break one of them into two pieces. With the three pretzels you now have (two pieces from the one you broke and the unbroken one), form a triangle making sure the ends of each pretzel touch. Describe your triangle or any problems you had forming it.

5. Place the smaller two pieces of pretzel you just worked with end to end to form a longer segment. Compare the length of the segment formed by these two pieces with the unbroken pretzel. Describe the relationship.

6. Throw away or eat one of the smaller pieces of pretzel. Take the fourth pretzel. You should now have two unbroken pretzels and a piece from the broken pretzel from step 5. With these three pretzels, form a triangle. Describe the triangle or any problems you had forming it.

7. a) Lay the broken piece of pretzel end to end with one of the unbroken pretzels and compare that length to the other pretzel you just worked with (it should also be an unbroken pretzel). Describe the relationship.

 b) Lay the other unbroken piece of pretzel end to end to form a larger segment with the broken piece and compare that length to the other unbroken pretzel. Describe the relationship.

 c) Lay the two unbroken pretzels end to end to form a larger segment and compare this length to the length of the broken pretzel. Describe the relationship.

8. Summarize you findings in one complete sentence.

Cooperative Learning and High School Geometry: Becky Bride
Kagan Publishing • 1 (800) WEE CO-OP • www.KaganOnline.com

141

LESSON 2
TRIANGLE SUM THEOREM

This lesson begins with an exploratory exercise on the sum of the angles of a triangle. Then two activities follow to process this theorem—one involving arithmetic and the other using algebra. The triangles that the students use must be cut on a cutting board to ensure straight sides.

EXPLORING THE SUM OF THE ANGLES OF A TRIANGLE

▶ Materials
- 1 Blackline 4.2.1 per pair of students
- 1 sheet of paper and pencil per pair of students

Set Up:
Cut paper triangles on a cutting board. A variety of acute, obtuse, and right triangles will be needed.

Students complete Blackline 4.2.1. Rather than tearing the triangle apart, the triangle can be folded to show the same relationship. Students fold an altitude in the triangle. Then,

fold the two angles not involved with the altitude toward each other until their vertices meet at the altitude and one side of each angle lies along the side of the triangle the two angles have in common. See figure 1. Then have the students fold the third angle so its vertex touches the other 2 vertices. Students can see that all three angles together form a straight line thus they must sum to 180.

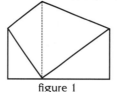

figure 1

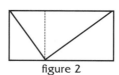

figure 2

TRIANGLE SUM THEOREM AND ARITHMETIC

▶ Structure
- Boss/Secretary

▶ Materials
- 1 sheet of paper and pencil per pair of students
- 1 Blackline 4.2.2 per pair of students

1. Student A supplies 1 sheet paper folded in half lengthwise with his/her name in one column and a partner's name in the other column.

2. Student B is the first boss and Student A is the first secretary.

3. As the boss, Student B tells Student A how to do the problem. Student A, the secretary, records what Student B says in Student B's column of the paper.

4. If the boss makes a mistake, then the secretary coaches and praises once the boss does it correctly. Otherwise, the secretary praises the boss.

5. Reverse roles for each problem and repeat steps 3 and 4.

Cooperative Learning and High School Geometry: Becky Bride
Kagan Publishing • 1 (800) WEE CO-OP • www.KaganOnline.com

ACTIVITY

3

TRIANGLE SUM THEOREM AND ALGEBRA

1. Student B supplies one sheet of paper, folded in half lengthwise and each member of the pair writes his/her name at the top of 1 column.

2. Student B does problem 1, recording his/her work on his/her side of the paper while Student A watches and coaches if necessary.

3. Student A checks Student B's work, coaches and/or praises. Then Student A does problem 2 on his/her side of the paper.

4. Student B checks Student A's work, coaches and/or praises.

5. After every 2 problems, the pair checks their answers with the other pair in their team, coaching and/or praising each others' work.

6. Repeat steps 2-5, reversing roles until all the problems are done.

▶ **Structure**
• Pairs Check

▶ **Materials**
• 1 sheet of paper and pencil per pair of students
• 1 Blackline 4.2.3 per pair of students

Cooperative Learning and High School Geometry: Becky Bride
Kagan Publishing • 1 (800) WEE CO-OP • www.KaganOnline.com

143

Blackline 4.2.1

EXPLORING THE SUM OF THE ANGLES OF A TRIANGLE

1. Number the angles of your triangle, using the numbers 1-3, and placing each number near the vertex of the triangle as shown below.

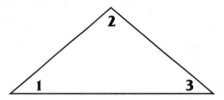

2. Tear the triangle twice, in such a way that all three angles are separated. Make sure not to tear through the vertex of an angle. See the diagram below.

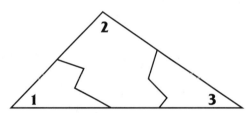

3. Rearrange the three pieces of your triangle so that the vertices of ∠1, ∠2, and ∠3 are touching and there is no space between the sides of the angles nor any overlaps. See the diagram below.

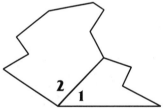

4. m∠1 + m∠2 + m∠3 = ?

5. Summarize your findings in one complete sentence.

Cooperative Learning and High School Geometry: Becky Bride
Kagan Publishing • 1 (800) WEE CO-OP • www.KaganOnline.com

TRIANGLE SUM THEOREM AND ARITHMETIC

Structure: Boss/Secretary

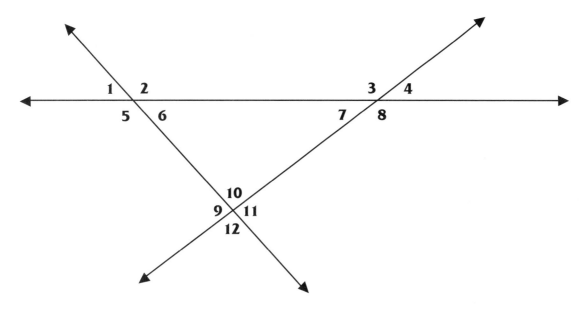

The diagram is not drawn to scale.

1. If m∠6 = 57°, m∠7 = 87°, find m∠10.

2. If m∠1 = 98°, m∠7 = 41°, find m∠10.

3. If m∠9 = 88°, m∠8 = 130°, find m∠6.

4. If m∠2 = 135°, m∠11 = 100°, find m∠7 and then find m∠3.

5. If m∠12 = 57°, m∠3 = 112°, find m∠6 and then find m∠2.

6. If m∠6 = 16° and m∠12 = 42°, find m∠8.

Answers:
1. 36°
2. 41°
3. 38°
4. 55°; 125°
5. 55°; 125°
6. 58°

Cooperative Learning and High School Geometry: Becky Bride
Kagan Publishing • 1 (800) WEE CO-OP • www.KaganOnline.com

145

TRIANGLE SUM THEOREM AND ALGEBRA

ACTIVITY 3

Structure: Pairs Check

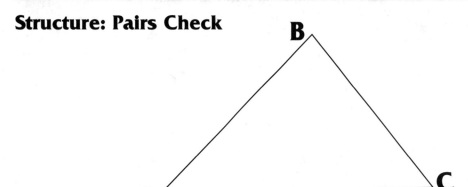

The diagram is not drawn to scale. Round answers to the nearest tenth.

1. If m∠A = x + 2, m∠B = 2x - 5, and m∠C = 3x + 9, find x.

2. If m∠A = 5x + 3, m∠B = 7 - 3x, and m∠C = 7x + 8, find x.

3. If m∠A = 2x, m∠B = 3x, and m∠C = 3x + 3, find x.

4. If m∠A = x - 7, and m∠B = 4x + 5, and m∠C = 9x - 6, find x.

5. If m∠A = 3x + 4, m∠B = 2x + 1, and m∠C = 4x + 13, find the measure of all three angles.

6. If m∠A = 7x - 6, m∠B = 2x + 13, and m∠C = 3x + 5, find the measure of all three angles.

Answers:
1. 29
2. 18
3. 22.1
4. 13.4
5. x = 18; 58°, 37°, 85°
6. x = 14; 92°, 41°, and 47°

LESSON 3
ISOSCELES TRIANGLES

This lesson includes exploratory exercises for angle relationships in isosceles triangles and its converse. Then activities follow to process both of these concepts.

1 EXPLORING BASE ANGLE RELATIONSHIPS IN ISOSCELES TRIANGLES

Have each student complete Blackline 4.3.1.

Tip:
In step 2 the compass radius can't be equal to $\overline{AB}$ because the triangle would be equilateral. The students need to investigate isosceles triangles that aren't equilateral to understand that the base angles of an isosceles triangle are equal.

> **Materials**
> • 1 sheet of patty paper per student
> • 1 Blackline 4.3.1 per student
> • 1 compass and straightedge per student

ACTIVITY

2 PROCESSING BASE ANGLES OF AN ISOSCELES TRIANGLE

Note:
In this activity, step 5 is included to give students practice writing about how a problem was solved. This integrates language arts and helps students verbalize their understanding.

1. Student 1 fans the cards face down.

2. Student 2 chooses a card and then reads the problem to Student 3.

3. Student 3 draws, labels, and marks on the team paper a triangle Student 2 just described.

4. Student 4 solves the problem on the sheet of paper describing what he/she is doing.

5. Student 1 coaches if necessary, then writes in words a description of the process Student 4 used to solve the problem.

6. The team celebrates everyone's contribution.

7. Students pass cards to the next person in a clockwise direction and repeat steps 1-6, rotating roles one student in the clockwise direction for each card remaining.

> **Structure**
> • Fan-N-Pick
>
> **Materials**
> • 1 set of Fan-N-Pick cards per team (Blackline 4.3.2)
> • 1 sheet of paper per team
> • Different color of pen or pencil for each team member

Cooperative Learning and High School Geometry: Becky Bride
Kagan Publishing • 1 (800) WEE CO-OP • www.KaganOnline.com

147

Chapter 4: Triangles
Lesson Three

ACTIVITY

3 ALGEBRA AND ANGLES IN ISOSCELES TRIANGLES

▶ **Structure**
• Boss/Secretary

▶ **Materials**
• 1 Blackline 4.3.3 per pair of students
• 1 sheet of paper and pencil per pair of students

1. Student A supplies one sheet paper, folded in half lengthwise with his/her name in one column and a partner's name in the other column.

2. Student B is the first boss and Student A is the first secretary.

3. As the boss, Student B tells Student A how to do the problem. Student A, the secretary, records what Student B says in Student B's column of the paper.

4. If the boss makes a mistake, then the secretary coaches and praises once the boss does it correctly. Otherwise, the secretary praises the boss.

5. Reverse roles for each problem and repeat steps 3 and 4.

ACTIVITY

4 EXPLORING THE CONVERSE

▶ **Materials**
• 1 Blackline 4.3.4 per student
• 1 straightedge per student
• 1 sheet of patty paper per student

Students complete Blackline 4.3.4. Instead of using patty paper, students could construct congruent angles at each endpoint of segment AB. They would then need a compass for the construction. Step 7 is included to get the students to

explain what method they used to determine which sides were congruent: measuring with a ruler, using a compass to verify, or tracing or folding patty paper. Step 8 is included to help the students organize their thoughts so their summary in step 9 will be easier to write.

ACTIVITY

5 ALGEBRA AND THE CONVERSE

▶ **Structure**
• RallyCoach

▶ **Materials**
• 1 Blackline 4.3.5 per pair of students
• 1 sheet of paper and pencil per pair of students

1. Student B supplies one sheet of paper, folded in half lengthwise and each member of the pair writes his/her name at the top of one column.

2. Student B does problem 1 recording his/her work on his/her side of the paper while Student A watches, checks the work, and coaches if necessary.

3. Repeat step 2, reversing roles until all the problems are done.

Chapter 4: Triangles
Lesson Three

148

Cooperative Learning and High School Geometry: Becky Bride
Kagan Publishing • 1 (800) WEE CO-OP • www.KaganOnline.com

ACTIVITY 1 EXPLORING BASE ANGLE RELATIONSHIPS IN ISOSCELES TRIANGLES

1. Using your straightedge, draw a segment on your paper and label one endpoint A and the other endpoint B.

2. Adjust you compass so its opening is at least over $\frac{1}{2}$ the length of segment $\overline{AB}$, or longer than the segment but not equal to the segment. With the compass point on endpoint A and draw a large arc above the segment.

3. With the same radius (leaving the compass opening the same) place the compass point on endpoint B and draw an arc that intersects the first arc. Mark the point of intersections of the two arcs C.

4. Using a straightedge, draw the segments $\overline{AC}$ and $\overline{BC}$.

5. Which sides of $\triangle ABC$ are congruent? Explain why they are congruent. Mark the congruent sides of your triangle accordingly.

6. Trace $\triangle ABC$ onto a sheet of patty paper. Some angles in $\triangle ABC$ are congruent. Use the triangle on the patty paper and the triangle on your paper to determine which angles are congruent. State which angles are congruent.

7. Describe how you would explain to a sick classmate who missed this investigation where the congruent angles are located in an isosceles triangle.

8. Summarize your findings in a complete sentence.

Cooperative Learning and High School Geometry: Becky Bride
Kagan Publishing • 1 (800) WEE CO-OP • www.KaganOnline.com

149

ACTIVITY 2 · PROCESSING BASE ANGLES OF AN ISOSCELES TRIANGLE

Structure: Fan-N-Pick

In △ABC, if AB = AC and m∠B = 42°, find the measure of the other two angles.

In △ABC, if AB = BC and m∠B = 55°, find the measure of the other two angles.

In △ABC, if ∠C is the vertex angle and m∠C = 108°, find the measure of the other two angles.

In △ABC, if ∠A is the vertex angle and m∠C = 62°, find the measure of the other two angles.

Answers:
1. m∠A = 96°; m∠C = 42°
2. m∠A = 62.5°; m∠C = 62.5°
3. m∠A = 36°; m∠B = 36°
4. m∠B = 62°; m∠A = 56°

Cooperative Learning and High School Geometry: Becky Bride
Kagan Publishing • 1 (800) WEE CO-OP • www.KaganOnline.com

ALGEBRA AND ANGLES IN ISOSCELES TRIANGLES

Structure: Boss/Secretary

△ABC is an isosceles triangle

∠B is the vertex angle

The diagram is not drawn to scale.

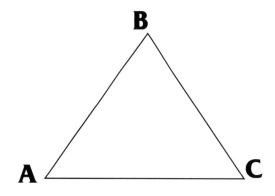

1. If m∠A = 4x + 2 and m∠C = 2x + 20, find x.

2. If m∠B = x and m∠A = 2x + 5, find x.

3. If m∠A = 21° and m∠B = 3x + 6, find x.

4. If m∠C = 5x and m∠B = 70°, find x.

5. If m∠A = 7x - 4 and m∠C = 3x +20, find m∠C.

6. If m∠A = 8x - 5 and m∠C = 3x + 25, find m∠B.

7. If AB = 5x - 3, AC = 3x + 7, and BC = 2x + 9, find x.

8. If BC = 10x - 4, AC = 2x + 18, and AB = 6x + 32, find x.

Answers:
1. 9
2. 34
3. 44
4. 11
5. 38°
6. 94°
7. 4
8. 9

Cooperative Learning and High School Geometry: Becky Bride
Kagan Publishing • 1 (800) WEE CO-OP • www.KaganOnline.com

151

ACTIVITY

4 EXPLORING THE CONVERSE

1. The goal is to make a triangle with two equal angles. On a sheet of patty paper, using a straightedge, draw a segment and label one endpoint A and the other endpoint B.

2. Draw an acute angle on your sheet of paper. Place the patty paper over the angle so the vertex of the angle lies on point A and a side of the angle lies on segment $\overline{AB}$. Trace the angle.

3. Flip the patty paper over and place the patty paper over the angle on your paper so that the vertex of the angle coincides with point B and a side of the angle lies on segment $\overline{AB}$. Trace the angle onto the patty paper using a straightedge.

4. Extend the rays of ∠A and ∠B on the patty paper until they intersect. Mark the point of intersection point C. You now have a triangle labeled ABC.

5. Which of the angles of △ABC are congruent? Explain why they are congruent.

6. Could the angle that you traced twice be a right angle or an obtuse angle? Explain.

7. Two sides of the triangle are congruent. Which sides are congruent? Describe how you determined which sides were congruent.

8. Describe how you would explain to a new student which sides of a triangle are congruent if you knew that two of the angles of the triangle were congruent.

9. Summarize your findings in a complete sentence.

Cooperative Learning and High School Geometry: Becky Bride
Kagan Publishing • 1 (800) WEE CO-OP • www.KaganOnline.com

ACTIVITY

5

ALGEBRA AND THE CONVERSE

Structure: RallyCoach

The diagram is not drawn to scale.

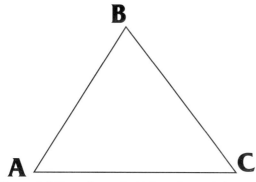

1. If $\angle A \cong \angle C$, and AB = 4x + 3, BC = 2x + 21, and AC = x + 23, find the value of x.

2. If $\angle A \cong \angle B$, and AB = 3x - 5, BC = 5x - 6, and AC = 2x + 9, find the value of x.

3. If $\angle B \cong \angle C$, and AB = x + 20, BC = 2x + 8, and AC = 5x - 4, find the value of x.

4. If $\angle A \cong \angle C$, and AB = 8x - 21, BC = x + 21, and AC = 2x + 3, find the value of x.

Answers:
1. 9
2. 5
3. 6
4. 6

Cooperative Learning and High School Geometry: Becky Bride
Kagan Publishing • 1 (800) WEE CO-OP • www.KaganOnline.com

153

TRIANGLES

LESSON 4
MIDSEGMENTS OF A TRIANGLE

This lesson begins with an exploratory exercise for students to discover the properties of midsegments of triangles. An activity follows to process these properties.

ACTIVITY

1 EXPLORING MIDSEGMENTS OF A TRIANGLE

▶ **Materials**
- 1 Blackline 4.4.1 per student
- 1 sheet of patty paper per student
- 1 straightedge per student

Have students complete Blackline 4.4.1.

ACTIVITY

2 ARITHMETIC, ALGEBRA, AND MIDSEGMENTS OF A TRIANGLE

▶ **Structure**
- Boss/Secretary

▶ **Materials**
- 1 Blackline 4.4.2 per pair of students
- 1 sheet of paper/pencil per pair of students

1. Student A supplies one sheet paper, folded in half lengthwise with his/her name in one column and a partner's name in the other column.

2. Student B is the first boss and Student A is the first secretary.

3. As the boss, Student B tells Student A how to do the problem. Student A, the secretary, records what Student B says in Student B's column of the paper.

4. If the boss makes a mistake, then the secretary coaches and praises once the boss does it correctly. Otherwise, the secretary praises the boss.

5. Reverse roles for each problem and repeat steps 3 and 4.

Cooperative Learning and High School Geometry: Becky Bride
Kagan Publishing • 1 (800) WEE CO-OP • www.KaganOnline.com

1 EXPLORING MIDSEGMENTS OF A TRIANGLE

1. Using a straightedge, draw a triangle in the space above. Label it △ABC.

2. Trace △ABC onto a sheet of patty paper, using a straightedge. Label the vertices appropriately.

3. Patty paper pinch the midpoint of side $\overline{AB}$, labeling it point M and patty paper pinch the midpoint of side $\overline{BC}$, labeling it point N.

4. Using a straightedge, draw segment $\overline{MN}$. This is a midsegment of △ABC.

5. Compare ∠BMN on the patty paper to ∠A above. Compare ∠BNM on the patty paper to ∠C above. What is the relationship of each pair of angles? What does this relationship tell you about segments $\overline{MN}$ and $\overline{AC}$? Explain.

6. Using the segment $\overline{MN}$ on your patty paper and segment $\overline{AC}$ above, determine how many segments of length equal to $\overline{MN}$ it takes to equal the length of $\overline{AC}$. Record your answer below.

7. Summarize your findings in a complete sentence.

Cooperative Learning and High School Geometry: Becky Bride
Kagan Publishing • 1 (800) WEE CO-OP • www.KaganOnline.com

155

ARITHMETIC, ALGEBRA, AND MIDSEGMENTS OF A TRIANGLE

ACTIVITY 2

Structure: Boss/Secretary

Find the value of each variable below. In each problem $\overline{MN}$ is a midsegment of the triangle. The diagrams are not drawn to scale.

1.

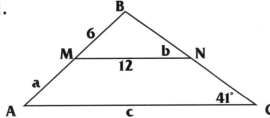

2.

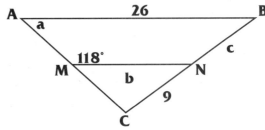

3.

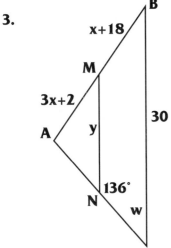

4.

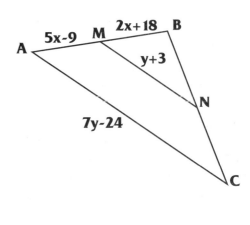

5.

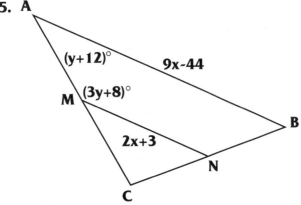

6.

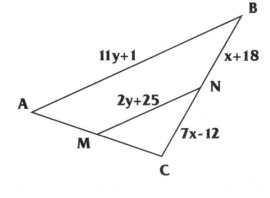

Answers:
1. 6; 41°; 24
2. 62°; 13; 9
3. 44°; 8; 15
4. 9; 6
5. 10; 40
6. 5; 7

Cooperative Learning and High School Geometry: Becky Bride
Kagan Publishing • 1 (800) WEE CO-OP • www.KaganOnline.com

LESSON 5
EXPLORING WAYS TO GUARANTEE CONGRUENT TRIANGLES

This lesson is devoted to exploring ways to guarantee congruent triangles. It is through these concrete explorations that students will understand the congruence theorems and postulates. After the concrete investigations, the proofs of the congruence theorems will make more sense. The lesson begins with exploring how many attributes are necessary to guarantee congruence. Once the students see that one or two attributes won't work, the focus turns to three attributes. The students will generate all six combinations that can be made from three segments and three sides taken three at a time. Here, students will need to focus on the order—SAS and SSA are different, yet ASS and SSA are the same. Then the six combinations will be explored to see which of them guarantees congruence. These activities take time. However, skipping them sacrifices a large portion of understanding on the students' part. On most of the exploratory activities, two segments or an angle and segment have points labeled with the same letter. Technically, this should not be done. However, it is done to help the students form the triangles.

You may want to discuss why vertices of the copied figure are labeled with the same letters but followed by a prime mark to help students do the first two exploratory activities. It is easy to see which segments correspond and which angles correspond as well as which triangle is the original and which one is the copy.

ACTIVITY 1
EXPLORING ONE ATTRIBUTE AND CONGRUENT TRIANGLES

Have students complete Blackline 4.5.1. When students do step 5 emphasize that the rays of ∠D must be extended beyond what is on the Blackline. If they don't do this, all their triangles will be congruent not due to ∠D alone but due to SAS because they left the rays the same length.

▶ **Materials**
- 1 Blackline 4.5.1 per student
- 2 sheets of patty paper per student
- 1 straightedge per student

ACTIVITY 2
EXPLORING TWO ATTRIBUTES AND CONGRUENT TRIANGLES

Have students complete Blackline 4.5.2. When students do step 6, emphasize that the rays must be extended just as in the last exploration.

▶ **Materials**
- 1 Blackline 4.5.2 per student
- 2 sheets of patty paper per student
- 1 straightedge per student

Cooperative Learning and High School Geometry: Becky Bride
Kagan Publishing • 1 (800) WEE CO-OP • www.KaganOnline.com

157

ACTIVITY

3 HOW MANY COMBOS?

▶ **Structure**
· Talking Chips

▶ **Materials**
· 1 sheet of paper per team
· 1 pencil/pen per student
· 1 pencil/pen for the team

1. Each student's pen or pencil is their talking chip. When a teammate wants to name a combination made from three sides and three angles of a triangle taken three at a time, the student will put his/her pencil in the middle of the table and name one. If the team agrees that it is a valid combination and one that has not already been named, then that student records the combo on the team paper with the team pen/pencil.

2. Only the teammates with a pen or pencil still in their hand may now offer another combination and step one is repeated.

3. Continue this process until all pens/pencils are in the middle of the table. Once all pens/pencils are in the center, each teammate picks up his/her pen/pencil and begins the process over again adding to what was already generated.

4. Give the students 4 minutes to do this activity.

Note:
This activity can be followed with the Stand-N-Share structure to share with the class all the combinations that were found.

ACTIVITY

4 IDENTIFY MY COMBO

▶ **Structure**
· Mix Pair Freeze followed by Corners

▶ **Materials**
· 1 set of Mix-Pair-Freeze cards (Blackline 4.5.4)
· Music while mixing (optional)

Note:
Activity 4 helps students to distinguish one combination from another. You may want to do this several times depending on the level of student in your class.

1. Give each student a card.

2. When the music begins the students stand up, push in their chairs, and begin to mix around the room.

3. As they mix, students will find a partner and give a greeting gambit. One student of the pair will look at his/her partner's card and tell the partner what combo is on his/her card.

4. The partner coaches and/or praises the student for the correct answer. Then roles reverse.

5. The pair will exchange cards, give a goodbye gambit, then part with their hands in the air to signal their need of a new partner.

6. Repeat steps 3-5 until the music stops. When the music stops, all students freeze. *Corners structure follows.*

7. Designate six areas of the room—1 with each combo. Posting a sheet of paper with that combo on it is helpful for this stage.

8. The students look at the card in their hand and go to the place in the room where their combo is posted.

9. Once there, the students will check each others' cards to make sure everyone has found the right place.

Cooperative Learning and High School Geometry: Becky Bride
Kagan Publishing • 1 (800) WEE CO-OP • www.KaganOnline.com

5

EXPLORING SSS

Note:
The next series of activities explore the congruence postulate and theorems. When students compare triangles within their group, they get a pretty good feel whether the combination being explored guarantees congruent triangles. Having one person from each team compare his/her team's triangles to every other team adds to the evidence that the combo guarantees congruence. If a combo being explored does not

guarantee congruence, comparing triangles with each team should ensure that all students see that the combo doesn't work.

Have students complete Blackline 4.5.5. Knowing how to construct congruent segments is a prerequisite for this activity. When the students are finished, they should see that everyone's triangle is the same.

▶ **Materials**
· 1 Blackline 4.5.5 per student
· 1 compass per student
· 1 straightedge per student
· 1 sheet of patty paper per student
· Tape per team

6

EXPLORING SAS

Have each student complete Blackline 4.5.6. When the students are finished, they should see that everyone's triangle is the same.

▶ **Materials**
· 1 Blackline 4.5.6 per student
· 1 straightedge per student
· 1 sheet of patty paper per student
· Tape per team

7

EXPLORING SSA

Have each student complete Blackline 4.5.7. When the students are finished, there should be two different triangles in the classroom. Have the students construct the tri-

angle that they do not have. This reinforces the fact that this combo does not guarantee congruence and will help when they take trigonometry and study the Law of Sines.

▶ **Materials**
· 1 Blackline 4.5.7 per student
· 1 straightedge per student
· 1 compass per student
· 1 sheet of patty paper per student
· Tape per team

8

EXPLORING ASA

Have students complete Blackline 4.5.8. The triangle they form should be congruent to all of the other triangles in the class.

▶ **Materials**
· 1 Blackline 4.5.8 per student
· 1 straightedge per student
· 1 sheet of patty paper per student
· Tape per team

Cooperative Learning and High School Geometry: Becky Bride
Kagan Publishing • 1 (800) WEE CO-OP • www.KaganOnline.com

159

Chapter 4: Triangles
Lesson Five

ACTIVITY 9

EXPLORING AAS

▶ **Materials**
- 1 Blackline 4.5.9 per student
- 1 straightedge per student
- 1 sheet of patty paper per student
- Tape

Have students complete Blackline 4.5.9. Step 4 is a little tricky and modeling it would be helpful. When they are finished everyone should have the same triangle.

ACTIVITY 10

EXPLORING AAA

▶ **Materials**
- 1 Blackline 4.5.10 per student
- 1 straightedge per student
- 1 sheet of patty paper per student
- 1 protractor per student
- Tape

Have students complete Blackline 4.5.10. There should be a lot of different triangles in the classroom.

ACTIVITY 11

EXPLORING HL (A SPECIAL CASE)

▶ **Materials**
- 1 Blackline 4.5.11 per student
- 1 straightedge per student
- 1 sheet of patty paper per student
- 1 compass per student
- 1 protractor per student
- Tape

Have students complete Blackline 4.5.11. When they are finished, everyone should have congruent triangles. Emphasize to the students that this theorem still requires three pieces of information: 1) right triangles; 2) congruent hypotenuses; and 3) one pair of congruent legs.

ACTIVITY 1 EXPLORING ONE ATTRIBUTE AND CONGRUENT TRIANGLES

A _____ B

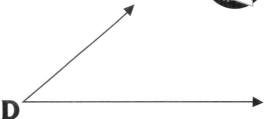

D →

1. Using a piece of patty paper and a straightedge, trace segment $\overline{AB}$ onto your patty paper labeling it A' and B' respectively. Mark $\overline{AB}$ and $\overline{A'B'}$ to show they are congruent segments.

2. Using a straightedge and using segment $\overline{A'B'}$ as 1 side, draw a $\triangle A'B'C$ on your patty paper, labeling point C.

3. Place your patty paper triangle over your partner's triangle. Are they congruent? Do the same thing with each one of your other teammates' triangles. Is your triangle congruent to any of your teammates?

4. Does having 1 side of a triangle congruent to a side of another triangle guarantee congruent triangles?

5. Using a straightedge and another sheet of patty paper, trace $\angle D$ onto the patty paper, making sure the rays of the patty paper angle are longer than the rays on the given angle. Label the angle on the patty paper D'. Mark $\angle D$ and $\angle D'$ to show their congruence.

6. Using a straightedge and using $\angle D'$ as 1 angle of your triangle, form $\triangle D'EF$, labeling vertices E and F.

7. Place your patty paper triangle over your partner's triangle. Are they congruent? Do the same thing with your other teammates' triangles. Is your triangle congruent with all of your teammates' triangles?

8. Does having one angle of a triangle congruent to an angle of another triangle guarantee congruent triangles?

9. Summarize your findings in a complete sentence.

EXPLORING TWO ATTRIBUTES AND CONGRUENT TRIANGLES

ACTIVITY 2

A   B   B   C

1. Using a straightedge, trace segment $\overline{AB}$ onto a sheet of patty paper, labeling it $\overline{A'B'}$. Mark $\overline{AB}$ and $\overline{A'B'}$ to show congruence.

2. Place B' on top of endpoint B of segment $\overline{BC}$ and using a straightedge trace $\overline{BC}$ onto the patty paper so it is a second side of what will be $\triangle A'B'C'$. Label point C on the patty paper C'. Mark $\overline{BC}$ and $\overline{B'C'}$ to show congruence.

3. Using a straightedge, join C' to A' forming $\triangle A'B'C'$.

4. Place your patty paper triangle over your partner's triangle. Are they congruent? Do the same thing with your other teammates' triangles. Is your triangle congruent with all of your teammates' triangles?

5. Do two segments in one triangle congruent to two segments in another triangle guarantee congruence?

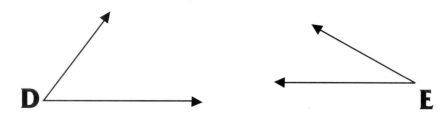

D   E

6. Using a straightedge, trace ∠D onto a sheet of patty paper, labeling it ∠D' making sure the rays of ∠D' are longer than the rays of ∠D. Even though ∠D' has longer rays, is its measure the same as ∠D? Mark ∠D and ∠D' to show congruence.

7. Place the patty paper over ∠E so that 1 ray of ∠D' lies on top of a ray of ∠E and the angles are opening toward each other. Mark point E on the patty paper as E' (this point should be on a ray of ∠D'). Using a straightedge, trace the ray of ∠E that is not lying on a ray of ∠D. Mark ∠E and ∠E' to show congruence. Your diagram should look something like the diagram below.

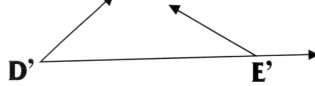

D'   E'

Cooperative Learning and High School Geometry: Becky Bride
Kagan Publishing • 1 (800) WEE CO-OP • www.KaganOnline.com

2 EXPLORING TWO ATTRIBUTES AND CONGRUENT TRIANGLES

8. If a triangle is not yet formed, extend rays of ∠D' and ∠E' until one is formed and label the point of intersection F.

9. Place your patty paper triangle over your partner's triangle. Are they congruent? Do the same thing with your other teammates' triangles. Is your triangle congruent with all of your teammates' triangles?

10. Do two angles in one triangle congruent to two angles in another triangle guarantee congruent triangles?

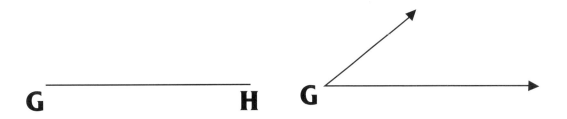

11. Using a straightedge, trace segment $\overline{GH}$ onto a sheet of patty paper labeling it $\overline{G'H'}$. Placing the patty paper over ∠G, place point G' so it lies on top of vertex G and G'H' lies along one of the rays of ∠G. Trace the ray of ∠G that is not lying on G'H' onto the patty paper extending the ray. Mark ∠G and∠G' to show congruence.

12. Somewhere on the ray of ∠G' that does not contain H', mark a point I. Using a straight-edge, join I and H' with a segment. Now you should have a triangle—△G'IH'.

13. Place your patty paper triangle over your partner's triangle. Are they congruent? Do the same thing with your other teammates' triangles. Is your triangle congruent with all of your teammates' triangles?

14. Do one angle and one segment in one triangle congruent to one angle and segment in another triangle guarantee congruent triangles?

15. Summarize your findings in a complete sentence.

Cooperative Learning and High School Geometry: Becky Bride
Kagan Publishing • 1 (800) WEE CO-OP • www.KaganOnline.com

163

ACTIVITY

4 **IDENTIFY MY COMBO**

Structures: Mix-Pair-Freeze and Corners

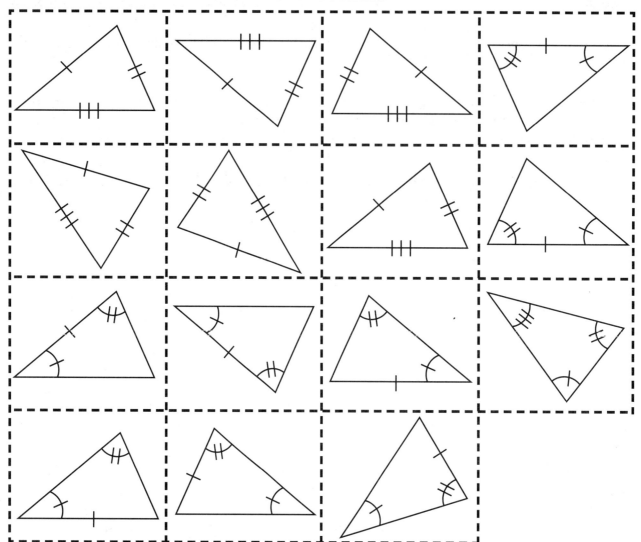

Cooperative Learning and High School Geometry: Becky Bride
Kagan Publishing • 1 (800) WEE CO-OP • www.KaganOnline.com

IDENTIFY MY COMBO

Structures: Mix-Pair-Freeze and Corners

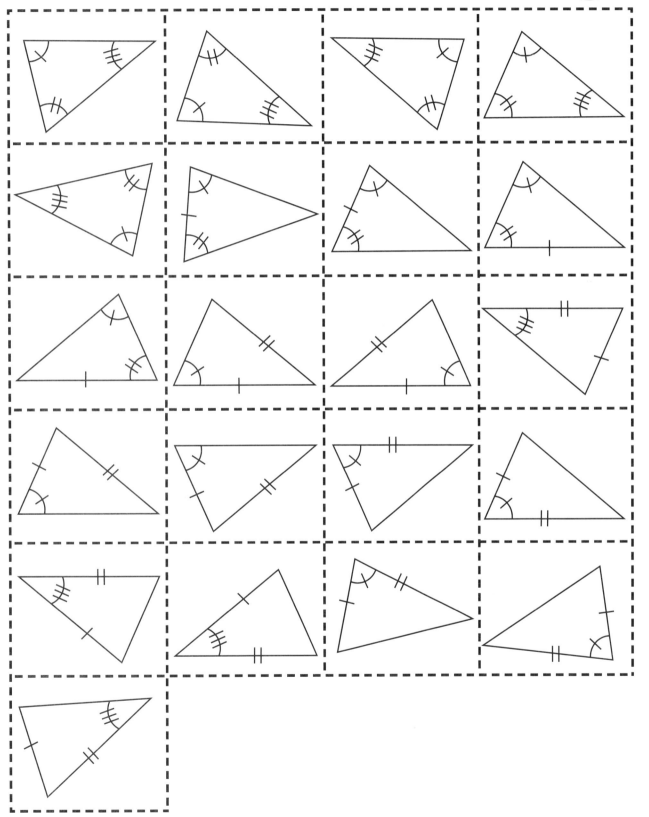

Cooperative Learning and High School Geometry: Becky Bride
Kagan Publishing • 1 (800) WEE CO-OP • www.KaganOnline.com

165

ACTIVITY 5

EXPLORING SSS

A   **B**   **B**   **C**   **C**   **A**

1. Near the bottom of a sheet of patty paper, using a straightedge, trace a segment equal in length to segment $\overline{AB}$. Label the endpoints A' and B' respectively. Mark $\overline{AB}$ and $\overline{A'B'}$ to show congruence.

2. With the compass opening equal to the length of segment $\overline{BC}$, place the compass point on B' and make a large arc above segment $\overline{A'B'}$.

3. With the compass opening equal to the length of segment $\overline{AC}$, place the compass point on A' and make an arc intersecting the first arc. Label the point of intersection of the two arcs C'. Join A' and C' with a segment and join B' and C' with a segment. Mark $\overline{BC}$ and $\overline{B'C'}$ to show congruence. Mark $\overline{AC}$ and $\overline{A'C'}$ to show congruence.

4. Double check to make sure $\overline{A'B'}$ is congruent to $\overline{AB}$, $\overline{B'C'}$ is congruent to $\overline{BC}$ and $\overline{A'C'}$ is congruent to $\overline{AC}$ by placing your patty paper over the corresponding figures on this paper.

5. Place your patty paper over each of your teammates' triangles to check for congruence. Is your triangle congruent to all of your teammates' triangles? Explain.

6. Send Student 1 with his/her patty paper triangle to each of the other teams to check to see if his/her triangle is congruent to the triangles the other teams made.

7. When Student 1 returns to the table have him/her report his/her findings. Were all the triangles in the classroom made with these three segments congruent? Does SSS guarantee congruent triangles? If not, construct another triangle that has the above segments but is not congruent to the first one you constructed.

8. Tape your patty paper triangle(s) on the back of this paper and summarize your findings in a complete sentence.

Cooperative Learning and High School Geometry: Becky Bride
Kagan Publishing • 1 (800) WEE CO-OP • www.KaganOnline.com

6 EXPLORING SAS

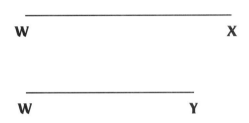

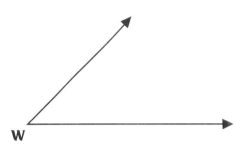

1. In the bottom left corner of a sheet of patty paper, trace ∠W labeling it ∠W'. Mark ∠W and ∠W' to show congruence.

2. Place the patty paper so 1 ray of ∠W' is on top of $\overline{WY}$ and W' is on W. Trace $\overline{WY}$ labeling point Y on the patty paper Y'. Mark $\overline{WY}$ and $\overline{W'Y'}$ to show congruence.

3. Place the patty paper so that the **other ray** of ∠W' lies on top of $\overline{WX}$ and W' is on W. Trace $\overline{WX}$ labeling point X on the patty paper X'. Mark $\overline{WX}$ and $\overline{W'X'}$ to show congruence.

4. Join Y' and X' with a segment to form △W'X'Y'.

5. Double check to make sure $\overline{W'X'}$ is congruent to $\overline{WX}$, $\overline{W'Y'}$ is congruent to $\overline{WY}$ and ∠W is congruent to ∠W' by placing your patty paper over the corresponding figures on this paper.

6. Place your patty paper over each of your teammates' triangles to check for congruence. Is your triangle congruent to all of your teammates' triangles? Explain.

7. Send Student 2 with his/her patty paper triangle to each of the other teams to check to see if his/her triangle is congruent to the triangles the other teams made.

8. When Student 2 returns to the table, have him/her report his/her findings. Were all the triangles in the classroom made with these two segments and angle congruent? Does SAS guarantee congruent triangles? If not, construct another triangle that has the above segments and angle but is not congruent to the first one you constructed.

9. Tape your patty paper triangle(s) on the back of this paper and summarize your findings in a complete sentence.

Cooperative Learning and High School Geometry: Becky Bride
Kagan Publishing • 1 (800) WEE CO-OP • www.KaganOnline.com

167

ACTIVITY

7 EXPLORING SSA

1. In the space above, using a ruler, draw a segment 9 cm long and label the endpoints G and H. Using a protractor, draw a 50° angle and label it ∠G. Finally, using a ruler draw a segment 7.5 cm long and label the endpoints H and I.

2. Near the bottom of a sheet of patty paper, trace segment $\overline{GH}$ using a straightedge. Label G and H, G' and H' respectively on the sheet of patty paper. Mark GH and G'H' to show congruence.

3. Place the patty paper over ∠G so that point G' lies on top of vertex G and $\overline{G'H'}$ lies on top of one of the rays of ∠G. Trace ∠G making the ray not on $\overline{G'H'}$ longer. Mark ∠G and ∠G' to show congruence.

4. Adjust a compass so that its opening is equivalent to the length of segment $\overline{HI}$. Place the compass point on H' and draw a large arc so that it intersects the ray of ∠G' that is opposite point H'. How many places did the arc intersect the ray? Choose a point of intersection and label it I'. Mark HI and H'I' to show congruence.

5. Join H' and I' with a segment to form △G'H'I'.

6. Double check to make sure $\overline{G'H'}$ is congruent to $\overline{GH}$, $\overline{H'I'}$ is congruent to $\overline{HI}$, and ∠G' is congruent to ∠G by placing your patty paper over the corresponding figures on this paper.

7. Place your patty paper over each of your teammates' triangles to check for congruence. Is your triangle congruent to all of your teammates' triangles? Explain.

8. Send Student 3 with his/her patty paper triangle to each of the other teams to check to see if his/her triangle is congruent to the triangles the other teams made.

9. When Student 3 returns to the table have him/her report his/her findings. Were all the triangles in the classroom made with these two segments and angle congruent? Does SSA guarantee congruent triangles? If not, construct another triangle that has the above segments and angle but is not congruent to the first one you constructed.

10. Tape your patty paper triangle(s) on the back of this paper and summarize your findings in a complete sentence below.

Cooperative Learning and High School Geometry: Becky Bride
Kagan Publishing • 1 (800) WEE CO-OP • www.KaganOnline.com

 8 EXPLORING ASA

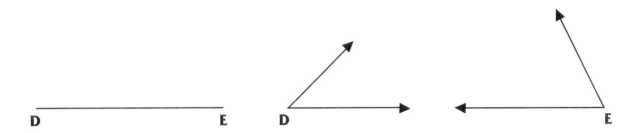

1. Using a straightedge, trace segment $\overline{DE}$ near the bottom of a sheet of patty paper, labeling points D and E, D' and E' respectively. Mark $\overline{DE}$ and $\overline{D'E'}$ to show congruence.

2. Place the sheet of patty paper over ∠D to that point D' lies on top of vertex D and segment $\overline{D'E'}$ lies on top of one of ∠ D's rays. Trace ∠D. Mark ∠D and ∠D' to show congruence.

3. Place the sheet of patty paper over ∠E so that point E' lies on top of vertex E and segment $\overline{D'E'}$ lies on top of one of ∠E's rays. Note: ∠E should be opening toward ∠D'. Trace ∠ E. Mark ∠E and ∠E' to show congruence.

4. If a triangle is not yet formed, extend the rays of ∠D' and ∠E' until they intersect. Label the point of intersection F.

5. Double check to make sure $\overline{D'E'}$ is congruent to $\overline{DE}$, ∠D' is congruent to ∠D, and ∠E' is congruent to ∠E by placing your patty paper over the corresponding figures on this paper.

6. Place your patty paper over each of your teammates' triangles to check for congruence. Is your triangle congruent to all of your teammates' triangles? Explain.

7. Send Student 4 with his/her patty paper triangle to each of the other teams to check to see if his/her triangle is congruent to the triangles the other teams made.

8. When Student 4 returns to the table have him/her report his/her findings. Were all the triangles in the classroom made with this segment and these two angles congruent? Does ASA guarantee congruent triangles? If not, construct another triangle that has the above segment and angles but is not congruent to the first one you constructed.

9. Tape your patty paper triangle(s) on the back of this paper and summarize your findings in a complete sentence below.

ACTIVITY
9 EXPLORING AAS

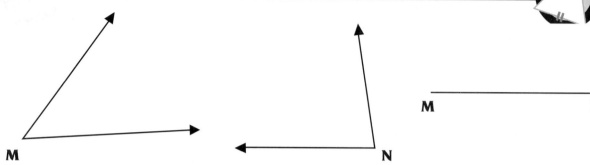

1. Using a straightedge, trace ∠M near the left corner of a sheet of patty paper, labeling its vertex M'. Mark ∠M and ∠M' to show congruence.

2. Place the patty paper over segment $\overline{MP}$ so vertex M' lies on top of point M and a ray of ∠M' lies on top of segment $\overline{MP}$. Mark the point on the ray of ∠M' that is directly over point P and label it P'. Mark $\overline{MP}$ and $\overline{M'P'}$ to show congruence.

3. On ∠N at the top of this paper use a straightedge to extend both rays.

4. Place the patty paper over ∠N so that ∠M' and ∠N open toward each other and the ray of ∠M' that does not contain P' lies on top of a ray of ∠N. This places point N on the ray of ∠M' that does not have P', Slide the patty paper, keeping the rays on top of each other until the other ray of ∠N passes through point P'. Mark N on the patty paper, labeling it N'. Trace ∠N. You should now have △M'N'P' on your patty paper. Mark ∠N and ∠N' to show congruence.

5. Double check to make sure $\overline{M'P'}$ is congruent to $\overline{MP}$, ∠N' is congruent to ∠N, and ∠M' is congruent to ∠M by placing your patty paper over the corresponding figures on this paper.

6. Place your patty paper over each of your teammates' triangles to check for congruence. Is your triangle congruent to all of your teammates' triangles? Explain.

7. Send Student 1 with his/her patty paper triangle to each of the other teams to check to see if his/her triangle is congruent to the triangles the other teams made.

8. When Student 1 returns to the table have him/her report his/her findings. Were all the triangles in the classroom made with this segment and these two angles congruent? Does AAS guarantee congruent triangles? If not, construct another triangle that has the above segment and angles but is not congruent to the first one you constructed.

9. Tape your patty paper triangle(s) on the back of this paper and summarize your findings in a complete sentence below.

Cooperative Learning and High School Geometry: Becky Bride
Kagan Publishing • 1 (800) WEE CO-OP • www.KaganOnline.com

10 EXPLORING AAA

1. In the space above, using a protractor, draw a 50° angle and label it ∠R, draw a 60° angle and label it ∠A, and draw a 70° angle, labeling it ∠T.

2. On a sheet of patty paper, using a straightedge, trace ∠ R and label it ∠R'. Mark ∠R and ∠R' to show congruence.

3. Place the patty paper over ∠A so that ∠A opens toward ∠R' and one ray of ∠R' lies on top of a ray of ∠A. Trace ∠A, labeling it ∠A' on the patty paper. Mark ∠A and ∠A' to show congruence.

4. Extend the rays of ∠R' and ∠A' until they intersect to form a triangle. Label the point of intersections T'. Mark ∠T and ∠T' to show congruence.

5. Double check to make sure ∠R' is congruent to ∠R, ∠A' is congruent to ∠A, and ∠T' is congruent to ∠T by placing your patty paper over the corresponding figures on this paper.

6. Place your patty paper over each of your teammates' triangles to check for congruence. Is your triangle congruent to all of your teammates' triangles? Explain.

7. Send Student 2 with his/her patty paper triangle to each of the other teams to check to see if his/her triangle is congruent to the triangles the other teams made.

8. When Student 2 returns to the table have him/her report his/her findings. Were all the triangles in the classroom made with these three angles congruent? Does AAA guarantee congruent triangles? If not, construct another triangle that has the above angles but is not congruent to the first one you constructed.

9. Tape your patty paper triangle(s) on the back of this paper and summarize your findings in a complete sentence below.

Cooperative Learning and High School Geometry: Becky Bride
Kagan Publishing • 1 (800) WEE CO-OP • www.KaganOnline.com

171

11 EXPLORING HL (SPECIAL CASE)

A _____ B   B _____ C

1. Near the bottom of a sheet of patty paper, trace segment $\overline{AB}$ using a straightedge and labeling the endpoints A' and B' respectively. Mark $\overline{AB}$ and $\overline{A'B'}$ to show congruence.

2. With a protractor, draw a segment perpendicular to $\overline{A'B'}$ at point A'. This makes $\angle A'$ a right angle. Extend the segment well above segment $\overline{A'B'}$. Mark $\angle A'$ to show perpendicular lines.

3. Using a compass, adjust the opening of the compass so that it is equal to the length of segment $\overline{BC}$. Place the compass point on point B' on the patty paper and swing a large arc so that the arc intersects the other ray of $\angle A'$.

4. Mark the point of intersection of the ray and the arc, C'. Using a straightedge, join point C' and B'. A triangle should be formed with vertices A', B', and C'.

5. Double check to make sure $\angle A'$ is a right angle, $\overline{A'B'}$ is congruent to $\overline{AB}$, and $\overline{B'C'}$ is congruent to $\overline{BC}$ by placing your patty paper over the corresponding figures on this paper.

6. Place your patty paper over each of your teammates' triangles to check for congruence. Is your triangle congruent to all of your teammates' triangles? Explain.

7. Send Student 3 with his/her patty paper triangle to each of the other teams to check to see if his/her triangle is congruent to the triangles the other teams made.

8. When Student 3 returns to the table have him/her report his/her findings. Were all the triangles in the classroom made with these two segments and a right angle congruent? Does HL guarantee congruent triangles? If not, construct another triangle that has the above segments and right angle but is not congruent to the first one you constructed.

9. Tape your patty paper triangle(s) on the back of this paper and summarize your findings in a complete sentence below.

Cooperative Learning and High School Geometry: Becky Bride
Kagan Publishing • 1 (800) WEE CO-OP • www.KaganOnline.com

LESSON 6
PROCESSING CONGRUENT TRIANGLES

This lesson slowly builds into proofs involving congruent triangles. It begins with identifying whether two marked triangles are congruent; progresses to marking the diagrams with given information to determine if two triangles are congruent; then there are flow chart proofs; blind sequencing with statements and reasons together, blind sequencing with statements and reasons separate; and finally proofs from scratch involving the concept, "corresponding parts of congruent triangles are congruent." The speed at which your class progresses through the next activities and the point you may choose to stop in this progression depends on the level of student you are teaching.

ACTIVITY 1

ARE WE CONGRUENT? #1

1. Student A supplies one sheet paper, folded in half lengthwise with his/her name in one column and a partner's name in the other column.

2. Student B is the first boss and Student A is the first secretary.

3. As the boss, Student B tells Student A how to do the problem. Student A, the secretary, records what Student B says in Student B's column of the paper.

4. If the boss makes a mistake, then the secretary coaches and praises once the boss does it correctly. Otherwise, the secretary praises the boss.

5. Reverse roles for each problem and repeat steps 3 and 4.

▶ **Structure**
· Boss/Secretary

▶ **Materials**
· 1 Blackline 4.6.1 per pair of students
· 1 sheet of paper and pencil per pair of students

Answers:
1. △EDF; SAS≅
2. △AER; SSS≅
3. △TAC; SAS≅
4. Can't be determined
5. Can't be determined
6. △AKR; SAS≅
7. △CDB; HL≅
8. △KEI; SAS≅

Cooperative Learning and High School Geometry: Becky Bride
Kagan Publishing • 1 (800) WEE CO-OP • www.KaganOnline.com

173

ACTIVITY

ARE WE CONGRUENT #2?

▶ Structure

• Pairs Check

▶ Materials

• 1 Blackline 4.6.2 per pair of students
• 1 sheet of paper and pencil per pair of students

Note:

The only difference between Activity 2 and Activity 1 is that the students have to take given information and mark the diagrams first, then determine if the triangles are congruent and write the postulate or theorem that justifies the congruence. For the "why" part of the problem, have students write the theorem or postulate vertically, then write a pair of segments or angles to justify each part of the theorem or postulate. Problem 1 is shown below.

$\triangle BCA \cong \triangle EDF$
$S \mapsto \overline{BC} \cong \overline{ED}$
$A \mapsto \angle C \cong \angle D$
$S \mapsto \overline{AC} \cong \overline{FD}$

1. Student B supplies one sheet of paper, folded in half lengthwise and each member of the pair writes his/her name at the top of one column.

2. Student B does problem 1, recording his/her work on his/her side of the paper while Student A watches and coaches if necessary.

3. Student A checks Student B's work, coaches and/or praises. Then Student A does problem 2 on his/her side of the paper.

4. Student B checks Student A's work, coaches and/or praises.

5. After every two problems, the pair checks their answers with the other pair in their team, coaching and/or praising each others' work.

6. Repeat steps 2-5, reversing roles until all the problems are done.

Answers:

1. S $\overline{AB} \cong \overline{ED}$ given
   A $\angle B \cong \angle D$ given
   S $\overline{BC} \cong \overline{DC}$ given
       $\triangle EDC$
2. S $\overline{MO} \cong \overline{TO}$ given
   A $\angle NOM \cong \angle POT$ vertical
       angles are equal
   S $\overline{NO} \cong \overline{PO}$ given
       $\triangle POT$
3. A $\angle W \cong \angle C$ given
   S $\overline{WA} \cong \overline{CA}$ given
   A $\angle PAW \cong \angle MAC$ vertical
       angles are congruent
       $\triangle MAC$
4. A $\angle A \cong \angle C$ given
   A $\angle ADB \cong \angle CBD$ given
   S $\overline{BD} \cong \overline{DB}$ Reflexive
       $\triangle CDB$
5. A $\angle G \cong \angle M$ given
   A $\angle GHE \cong \angle MEH$ If lines
       parallel alternate interior
       angles congruent
   S $\overline{HE} \cong \overline{EH}$ reflexive
       $\triangle HME$
6. Can't be determined

Cooperative Learning and High School Geometry: Becky Bride
Kagan Publishing • 1 (800) WEE CO-OP • www.KaganOnline.com

ACTIVITY

3

ARE WE CONGRUENT #3?

Note:
For this activity, the students must do all that was required in Activity 2 but now must justify each segment or angle they state is congruent. See the example below.

Given $\overline{AB} \cong \overline{CB}$

D is the midpoint of $\overline{AC}$
Show $\triangle ABD \cong \triangle CBD$

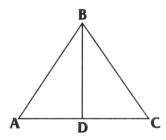

$S \mapsto \overline{AB} \cong \overline{CB}$ *Given congruent*
$S \mapsto \overline{AD} \cong \overline{CD}$ *A midpoint separates a segment into two congruent parts*
$S \mapsto \overline{BD} \cong \overline{BD}$ *It is the same segment in each triangle (Reflexive Property)*

1. Student A folds a paper in half lengthwise, putting his/her name at the top of one column and his/her partners name at the top of the other column.

2. Student A marks the diagram with the given information and marks the diagram for reflexive parts or vertical angles if appropriate.

3. Student B checks to see if he/she agrees with what has been marked on the diagram, discusses disagreements with his/her partner. The pair celebrate when they agree on the markings. Student B then determines which postulate or theorem will prove the two triangles congruent and writes that postulate or theorem vertically on the paper.

4. Student A checks the postulate or theorem that Student B chose, coaches if necessary then praises a job well done. Student A then writes one set of segments or angles with the justification that corresponds to one of the parts of the theorem or postulate chosen in step 3.

5. Student B coaches and/or praises his/her partner for the work in step 4 and then writes one set of segments or angles with the justification that corresponds to another one of the parts of the theorem or postulate chosen in step 3.

6. Student A coaches and/or praises his/her partner for the work in step 5 and then writes the last set of segments or angles with the justification that corresponds to the last part of the theorem or postulate chosen in step 3.

7. Student B coaches and/or praises his/her partner for a job well done.

8. Reverse roles and repeat steps 2-7 for each remaining problem.

▶ **Structure**
· RallyTable

▶ **Materials**
· 1 Blackline 4.6.3 per pair of students
· 1 sheet of paper and pencil per pair of students

Answers:
1. A $\angle A \cong \angle D$ *given*
   S $\overline{AC} \cong \overline{DC}$ *def. of midpoint*
   A $\angle 1 \cong \angle 2$ *given*
   $\triangle DBC$
2. Possible solution
   A $\angle 4 \cong \angle 3 \parallel$ *lines $\mapsto$ Alt. Int. $\angle s \cong$*
   A $\angle 1 \cong \angle 2 \parallel$ *lines $\mapsto$ Alt. int. $\angle s \cong$*
   S $\overline{NO} \cong \overline{TO}$ *given*
   $\triangle PTO$
3. S $\overline{AB} \cong \overline{CB}$ *given*
   A $\angle ABD \cong \angle CBD$ *def. $\angle$ bisector*
   S $\overline{BD} \cong \overline{BD}$ *reflexive*
   $\triangle CBD$
4. A $\angle A \cong \angle D$ *given*
   A $\angle B \cong \angle C$ *given*
   S $\overline{AE} \cong \overline{DE}$ *def. of midpoint*
   $\triangle DCE$
5. S $\overline{MS} \cong \overline{PS}$
   def. of segment bisector
   A $\angle 1 \cong \angle 2$ *given*
   S $\overline{AS} \cong \overline{AS}$ *reflexive*
   $\triangle PAS$
6. A $\angle ABD \cong \angle CBD$
   def. of $\angle$ bisector
   S $\overline{BD} \cong \overline{BD}$ *reflexive*
   A $\angle ADB \cong \angle CDB$
   def. of $\angle$ bisector
   $\triangle CBD$

Cooperative Learning and High School Geometry: Becky Bride
Kagan Publishing • 1 (800) WEE CO-OP • www.KaganOnline.com

175

Chapter 4: Triangles
L e s s o n   S i x

ACTIVITY

4

CHART IT!

▶ **Structure**
• Boss/Secretary

▶ **Materials**
• 1 Blackline 4.6.4 per pair of students
• 1 sheet of paper and pencil per pair of students

Note:
This activity moves the students closer to proof with a flow chart sequence.

1. Student A supplies one sheet paper, folded in half lengthwise with his/her name in one column and his/her partner's name in the other column.

2. Student B is the first boss and Student A is the first secretary.

3. As the boss, Student B tells Student A how to do the problem. Student A, the secretary, records what Student B says in Student B's column of the paper.

4. If the boss makes a mistake, then the secretary coaches and praises once the boss does it correctly. Otherwise, the secretary praises the boss.

5. Reverse roles for each problem and repeat steps 3 and 4.

Note:
This activity can be repeated using a patty paper construction. To perform a "happy cyclops" patty paper construct

ACTIVITY

5

SEQUENCE IT! #1

▶ **Structure**
• Blind Sequencing

▶ **Materials**
• 1 set of blind sequencing cards per team (Blacklines 4.6.5a, 4.6.5b, and 4.6.5c)
• 1 Blackline 4.6.5d per team
• 3 answer transparencies (blind sequence card masters Blacklines 4.6.5a, 4.6.5b, and 4.6.5c before they are cut into cards)

Note:
Make a transparency of the blind sequencing cards (Blacklines 4.6.5a, 4.6.5b, and 4.6.5c) before you cut them up. These will be the answer transparencies that students can use to check their work. Emphasize that this is one possible answer. It is sequenced so that, as the given information is put in the proof, it is immediately used in the next step to help students see the logical progression and how the given helps to develop the proof.

1. Give each team one set of blind sequence cards 4.6.5a and Blackline 4.6.5d. Have the team place the diagram face up for everyone to see.

2. Ask students to take the cards, mix them up, and place them face down on the table. Each student, taking turns, picks up one card until the cards run out. Some students may have only one card while others may have two.

3. Each student is responsible for his/her own card(s). Each student can only read and touch his/her own card(s).

4. Taking turns, each student reads his/her card(s) to the team.

5. Each student places his/her card(s) (face up or face down, your choice) in a logical sequence that justifies the triangles being congruent. Cards may be rearranged as the team discusses, but the original "owner" of each card is the only one who can move that card.

6. Teams check the answer transparency for correctness.

7. Repeat steps 1-6 for each remaining set of blind sequence cards (Blacklines 4.6.5b and 4.6.5c).

Cooperative Learning and High School Geometry: Becky Bride
Kagan Publishing • 1 (800) WEE CO-OP • www.KaganOnline.com

ACTIVITY

6

SEQUENCE IT! #2

▶ Structure
· Blind Sequencing

▶ Materials
· 1 set of blind sequencing cards per team (Blacklines 4.6.6a, 4.6.6b, and 4.6.6c)
· 1 Blackline 4.6.6d per team
· 3 answer transparencies (blind sequence card masters Blacklines 4.6.6a, 4.6.6b, and 4.6.6c before they are cut into cards)

Note:
The difference between Activity 5 and 6 is that in Activity 6, the justifications for each statement are separate from the statement. So, the students also have to get the reasons correct for each statement card.

1. Give each team one set of blind sequence cards 4.6.6a and Blackline 4.6.6d. Have the team place the diagram face up for everyone to see.

2. Ask students to take the cards, mix them up, and place them face down on the table. Each student, taking turns, picks up one card until the cards run out. Some students may have two cards while others may have three.

3. Each student is responsible for his/her own card(s). Each student can only read and touch their own card(s).

4. Taking turns, each student reads his/her card(s) to the team.

5. Each student places his/her card(s) (face up or face down, your choice) in a logical sequence that justifies the triangle's being congruent. Cards may be rearranged as the team discusses, but the original "owner" of each card is the only one who can move that card.

6. Teams check the answer transparency for correctness.

7. Repeat steps 1-6 for each remaining set of blind sequence cards (Blacklines 4.6.6b and 4.6.6c).

ACTIVITY

7

PROVE IT!

Note:
This activity takes proofs one step further by using the concept, corresponding parts of congruent triangles are congruent.

1. Student B supplies one sheet of paper, folded in half lengthwise. Each member of the pair writes his/her name at the top of one column.

2. Student B does problem one recording his/her work on his/her side of the paper while Student A watches, checks the work, and coaches if necessary.

3. Repeat step 2, reversing roles until all the problems are done.

Answers:
1. $\angle ABD \cong \angle CBD$
   def. of $\angle$ bisector
   $\overline{BD} \cong \overline{BD}$ reflexive
   $\angle ADB \cong \angle CDB$
   def. of $\angle$ bisector
   $\triangle ABD \cong \angle CBD$ ASA $\cong$
   $\angle A \cong \angle C$ CPCTC
2. $\overline{AB} \cong \overline{CB}$ given
   $\angle 1 \cong \angle 2$ def of bisector
   $\overline{BD} \cong \overline{BD}$ reflexive
   $\triangle ABD \cong \triangle CBD$ SAS $\cong$
   $\overline{AD} \cong \overline{CD}$ CPCTC
   D is midpoint of $\overline{AC}$
   def. of midpoint
3. $\overline{AB} \cong \overline{BC}$ def. of midpoint
   $\angle 1 \cong \angle 2 \parallel$ lines $\mapsto$ corr. $\angle s \cong$
   $\overline{BD} \cong \overline{AE}$ given
   $\triangle ABE \cong \triangle BCD$ SAS $\cong$
   $\angle D \cong \angle E$ CPCTC

▶ Structure
· RallyCoach

▶ Materials
· 1 Blackline 4.6.7 per pair of students
· 1 sheet of paper and pencil per pair of students

4. $\overline{AD} \cong \overline{CD}$ given
   $\overline{BD} \cong \overline{BD}$ reflexive
   $\triangle ADB$ and $\triangle CDB$ are rt. triangles def. of rt. triangle
   $\triangle ADB \cong \triangle CDB$ HL $\cong$
   $\angle ABD \cong \angle CBD$ CPCTC
   $\overline{BD}$ bisects $\angle ACB$
   def. of angle bisector

Cooperative Learning and High School Geometry: Becky Bride
Kagan Publishing • 1 (800) WEE CO-OP • www.KaganOnline.com

177

Chapter 4: Triangles Lesson Six

ACTIVITY

1

ARE WE CONGRUENT? #1

Structure: Boss/Secretary

Determine whether the following triangles are congruent. If so, complete the congruence statement and write the postulate or theorem that justifies the congruence. Otherwise, state that the "congruence cannot be determined."

1.

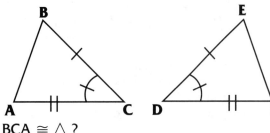

△ BCA ≅ △ ?
Justification:

2.

△ MOP ≅ △ ?
Justification:

3.

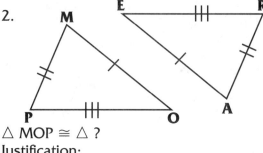

△ DOG ≅ △ ?
Justification:

4.

△ GEO ≅ △ ?
Justification:

5.

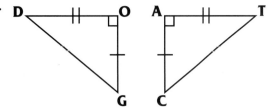

△ DON ≅ △ ?
Justification:

6.

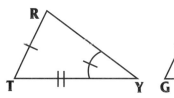

△ AKM ≅ △ ?
Justification:

7.

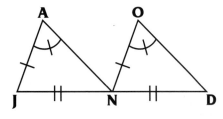

△ ABD ≅ △ ?
Justification:

8.

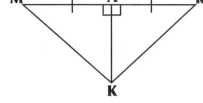

△ BIE ≅ △ ?
Justification:

Cooperative Learning and High School Geometry: Becky Bride
Kagan Publishing • 1 (800) WEE CO-OP • www.KaganOnline.com

ACTIVITY

2 ARE WE CONGRUENT? #2

Structure: Pairs Check

Draw each diagram on your own paper and mark each diagram with the given information. Determine whether the triangles are congruent. If they are congruent, write the theorem or postulate vertically, justifying each part of the theorem or postulate, and complete the triangle congruent statement.

1. Given: $\overline{AB} \cong \overline{ED}$; $\overline{BC} \cong \overline{DC}$; $\angle B \cong \angle D$

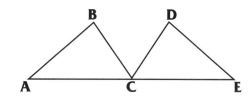

△ABC ≅ △ ?

2. Given: $\overline{MO} \cong \overline{TO}$; $\overline{NO} \cong \overline{PO}$

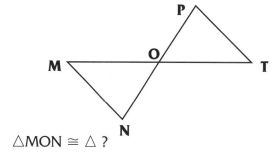

△MON ≅ △ ?

3. Given: $\angle W \cong \angle C$; $\overline{WA} \cong \overline{CA}$

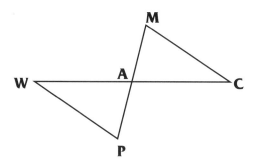

△PAW ≅ △ ?

4. Given: $\angle A \cong \angle C$; $\angle ADB \cong \angle CBD$

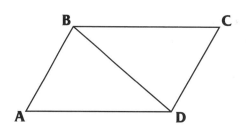

△ABD ≅ △ ?

5. Given: $\angle G \cong \angle M$

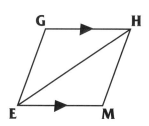

△EGH ≅ △ ?

6. Given: $\angle M \cong \angle T$; $\angle P \cong \angle N$

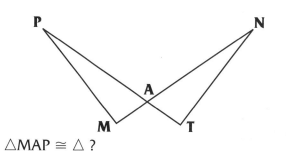

△MAP ≅ △ ?

Cooperative Learning and High School Geometry: Becky Bride
Kagan Publishing • 1 (800) WEE CO-OP • www.KaganOnline.com

179

ARE WE CONGRUENT? #3

Structure: RallyTable

For each problem: a) draw a diagram and mark the congruent parts on the diagram; b) determine if each pair of triangles are congruent; c) complete the congruence statement, then write the theorem or postulate that justifies the congruence vertically; and d) justify each part of the theorem or postulate.

1. Given: C is the midpoint of $\overline{AD}$; $\angle A \cong \angle D$; $\angle 1 \cong \angle 2$

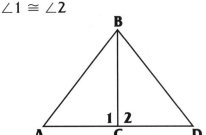

$\triangle ABC \cong \triangle$?

2. Given: $\overline{MN} \parallel \overline{PT}$; $\overline{NO} \cong \overline{TO}$

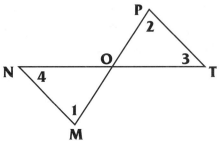

$\triangle MNO \cong \triangle$?

3. Given: $\overline{BD}$ bisects $\angle ABC$; $\overline{AB} \cong \overline{CB}$

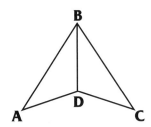

$\triangle ABD \cong \triangle$?

4. Given: E is the midpoint of $\overline{AD}$; $\angle A \cong \angle D$; $\angle B \cong \angle C$

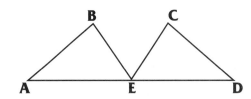

$\triangle ABE \cong \triangle$?

5. Given: $\overline{AS}$ bisects $\overline{MP}$; $\angle 1 \cong \angle 2$

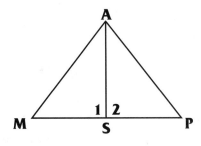

$\triangle MAS \cong \triangle$?

6. Given: $\overline{BD}$ bisects $\angle ABC$; $\overline{BD}$ bisects $\angle ADC$

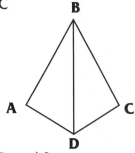

$\triangle ABD \cong \triangle$?

180

Cooperative Learning and High School Geometry: Becky Bride
Kagan Publishing • 1 (800) WEE CO-OP • www.KaganOnline.com

CHART IT!

Structure: Boss/Secretary

Fill in each of the missing parts with an appropriate statement or reason.

1. Given: ∠F ≅ ∠I; $\overline{FE} ≅ \overline{IH}$
   Prove: △EFG ≅ △HIG

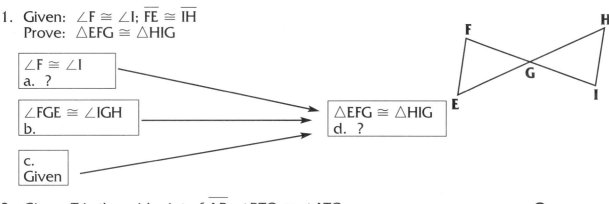

∠F ≅ ∠I
a. ?

∠FGE ≅ ∠IGH
b.

c.
Given

△EFG ≅ △HIG
d. ?

2. Given: T is the midpoint of $\overline{AB}$; ∠BTO ≅ ∠ATO
   Prove: △BOT ≅ △AOT

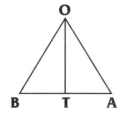

T is the midpoint of $\overline{AB}$
a. ?

$\overline{BT} ≅ \overline{AT}$
b. ?

c. ?
Given

d. ?
Reflexive (same segment)

△BOT ≅ △AOT
e. ?

3. Given: $\overline{MS}$ bisects ∠AME; $\overline{AM} ≅ \overline{EM}$
   Prove: △AMS ≅ △EMS

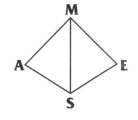

a.
Given

$\overline{MS}$ bisects ∠AME
b. ?

d. ?
An angle bisector cuts
an angle into 2 ≅ parts

△AMS ≅ △EMS
e. ?

$\overline{MS} ≅ \overline{MS}$
c. ?

4. Given: $\overline{AE} \parallel \overline{DC}$; B is the midpoint of $\overline{CE}$
   Prove: △ABE ≅ △DBC

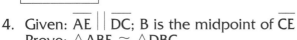

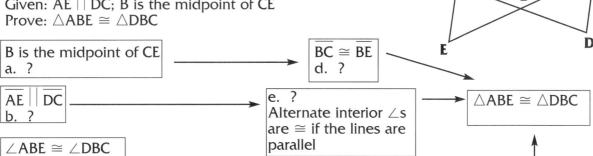

B is the midpoint of CE
a. ?

$\overline{BC} ≅ \overline{BE}$
d. ?

$\overline{AE} \parallel \overline{DC}$
b. ?

e. ?
Alternate interior ∠s
are ≅ if the lines are
parallel

△ABE ≅ △DBC

∠ABE ≅ ∠DBC
c. ?

Cooperative Learning and High School Geometry: Becky Bride
Kagan Publishing • 1 (800) WEE CO-OP • www.KaganOnline.com

181

5 SEQUENCE IT! #1

Structure: Blind Sequencing

Given: D is the midpoint of $\overline{AC}$; $\angle 1 \cong \angle 2$
Prove: $\triangle ABD \cong \triangle CBD$

D is the midpoint of $\overline{AC}$ (given)

$\overline{AD} \cong \overline{CD}$ (definition of midpoint)

$\angle 1 \cong \angle 2$ (given)

$\overline{BD} \cong \overline{BD}$ (reflexive property)

$\triangle ABD \cong \triangle CBD$ (SAS $\cong$)

Cooperative Learning and High School Geometry: Becky Bride
Kagan Publishing • 1 (800) WEE-CO OP • www.KaganOnline.com

ACTIVITY

5 SEQUENCE IT! #1

Structure: Blind Sequencing

Given: $\angle A \cong \angle C$; $\overline{BD}$ bisects $\angle ABC$
Prove: $\triangle ABD \cong \triangle CBD$

$\angle A \cong \angle C$ (given)

$\overline{BD}$ bisects $\angle ABC$ (given)

$\angle 1 \cong \angle 2$ (definition of bisector of an angle)

$\overline{BD} \cong \overline{BD}$ (reflexive property)

$\triangle ABD \cong \triangle CBD$ (AAS $\cong$)

Cooperative Learning and High School Geometry: Becky Bride
Kagan Publishing • 1 (800) WEE CO-OP • www.KaganOnline.com

183

ACTIVITY

5

SEQUENCE IT! #1

Structure: Blind Sequencing

Given: $\overline{AB} \parallel \overline{DE}$; $\overline{AB} \cong \overline{DE}$;
Prove: $\triangle ABC \cong \triangle DEC$

$\overline{AB} \parallel \overline{DE}$ (given)

$\angle B \cong \angle E$ (If parallel lines are cut by a transversal, then alternate interior angles are congruent)

$\angle A \cong \angle D$ (If parallel lines are cut by a transversal, then alternate interior angles are congruent)

$\overline{AB} \cong \overline{DE}$ (given)

$\triangle ABC \cong \triangle DEC$ (ASA $\cong$)

Cooperative Learning and High School Geometry: Becky Bride
Kagan Publishing • 1 (800) WEE CO-OP • www.KaganOnline.com

ACTIVITY

5 SEQUENCE IT! #1

Structure: Blind Sequencing

1.

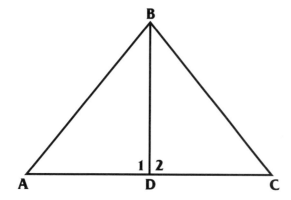

2.

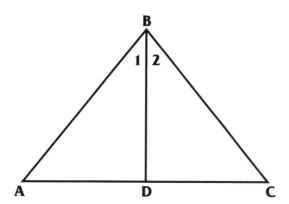

3.

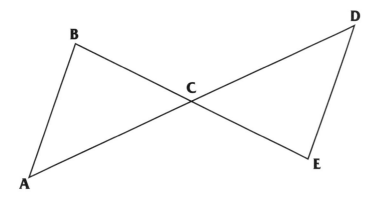

Blackline 4.6.6a

SEQUENCE IT! #2

Structure: Blind Sequencing

C is the midpoint of $\overline{BE}$	Given
$\overline{BC} \cong \overline{EC}$	Definition of midpoint
C is the midpoint of $\overline{AD}$	Given
$\overline{AC} \cong \overline{DC}$	Definition of midpoint
$\angle 1 \cong \angle 2$	Vertical angles are congruent
$\triangle ABC \cong \triangle DEC$	SAS $\cong$

Cooperative Learning and High School Geometry: Becky Bride
Kagan Publishing • 1 (800) WEE CO-OP • www.KaganOnline.com

6 SEQUENCE IT! #2

Structure: Blind Sequencing

$\angle 1$ and $\angle 2$ are right angles	Given
$\triangle ABD$ and $\triangle CDB$ are right triangles	Definition of right triangles
$\overline{BD} \cong \overline{DB}$	Reflexive property
$\overline{AD} \cong \overline{CB}$	Given
$\triangle ABD \cong \triangle CDB$	HL $\cong$

Cooperative Learning and High School Geometry: Becky Bride
Kagan Publishing • 1 (800) WEE CO-OP • www.KaganOnline.com

187

Blackline 4.6.6c

SEQUENCE IT! #2

Structure: Blind Sequencing

$\overline{BD}$ bisects $\overline{AC}$	Given
$\overline{AD} \cong \overline{CD}$	Definition of segment bisector
$\angle A \cong \angle C$	Given
$\overline{AB} \cong \overline{CB}$	If two angles of a triangle are congruent, then sides opposite those angles are congruent
$\triangle ABD \cong \triangle CBD$	SAS $\cong$

Cooperative Learning and High School Geometry: Becky Bride
Kagan Publishing • 1 (800) WEE CO-OP • www.KaganOnline.com

6 SEQUENCE IT! #2

Structure: Blind Sequencing

1. Given: C is the midpoint of $\overline{BE}$ and $\overline{AD}$
   Prove: $\triangle ABC \cong \triangle DEC$

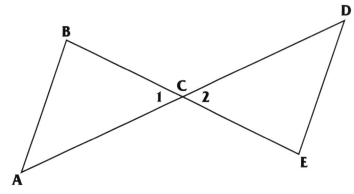

2. Given: $\angle 1$ and $\angle 2$ are right angles; $\overline{AD} \cong \overline{CB}$
   Prove: $\triangle ABD \cong \triangle CDB$

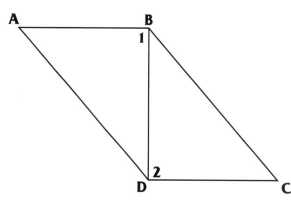

3. Given: $\angle A \cong \angle C$; $\overline{BD}$ bisects $\overline{AC}$
   Prove: $\triangle ABD \cong \triangle CBD$

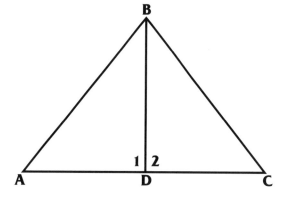

Cooperative Learning and High School Geometry: Becky Bride
Kagan Publishing • 1 (800) WEE CO-OP • www.KaganOnline.com

189

ACTIVITY

7 PROVE IT!

Structure: RallyCoach

1. Given: $\overline{BD}$ bisects $\angle ABC$;
    $\overline{DB}$ bisects $\angle ADC$
  Prove: $\angle A \cong \angle C$

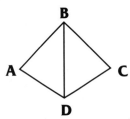

2. Given: $\overline{BD}$ bisects $\angle ABC$;
    $\overline{AB} \cong \overline{CB}$
  Prove: D is the midpoint of $\overline{AC}$

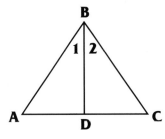

3. Given: B is the midpoint of $\overline{AC}$;
    $\overline{BD} \parallel \overline{AE}$; $\overline{BD} \cong \overline{AE}$
  Prove: $\angle D \cong \angle E$

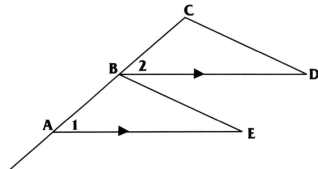

4. Given: $\angle A$ and $\angle C$ are right angles;
    $\overline{AD} \cong \overline{CD}$
  Prove: $\overline{BD}$ bisects $\angle ABC$

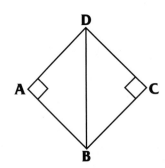

Cooperative Learning and High School Geometry: Becky Bride
Kagan Publishing • 1 (800) WEE CO-OP • www.KaganOnline.com

POLYGONS & QUADRILATERALS

This chapter begins with activities involving the sum of the interior angles and exterior angles of convex polygons and then moves into a focus on quadrilaterals. This is an excellent opportunity for the class to direct the exploratory activities. Given this opportunity, students will investigate possible relationships that textbooks don't cover. It is very powerful and students experience the development of mathematics as mathematicians have for centuries.

Lesson One processes the sum of the interior angles and exterior angles of convex polygons. Lesson Two is the first opportunity for students to lead the exploratory activities. Its focus is the properties of kites. Lesson Three explores properties of trapezoids. Lesson Four explores properties of parallelograms. Lessons Five and Six explore properties of special parallelograms. Lesson Seven contains activities to review all of the properties of quadrilaterals and their interrelationships.

LESSON 1
POLYGONS AND SUMS OF ANGLES

This lesson begins with an exploratory exercise that develops the formula to find the sum of the interior angles of a convex polygon. Three activities follow to process this. The lesson closes with an exploratory exercise to determine the sum of the exterior angles of a convex polygon, one angle per vertex, with activities following to process.

ACTIVITY
1 EXPLORING THE SUM OF THE INTERIOR ANGLES OF CONVEX POLYGONS

▶ **Materials**
• 1 Blackline 5.1.1 per student
• 1 straightedge per student
• 1 pencil per student

Have students complete Blackline 5.1.1.

ACTIVITY
2 FIND MY SUM

▶ **Structure**
• Fan-N-Pick

▶ **Materials**
• 1 set of Fan-N-Pick cards per team (Blackline 5.1.2)
• 1 sheet of paper and pencil per team

1. Student 1 fans the cards face down.

2. Student 2 picks a card and reads it to Student 3.

3. Student 3 calculates the sum of the angles of the polygon requested, explaining to the team each step he/she does. Student 3 records these calculations on the team paper and initials the work.

4. Student 4 checks the work, coaches if necessary and/or praises Student 3.

5. Cards are passed to the next person in a clockwise direction and steps 1-4 begin again, rotating roles to the next student in the clockwise direction. This process is repeated for a specific time limit or until cards are exhausted.

Cooperative Learning and High School Geometry: Becky Bride
Kagan Publishing • 1 (800) WEE CO-OP • www.KaganOnline.com

ACTIVITY

3

FIND THE MISSING MEASURE(S)

1. Student B supplies one sheet of paper, folded in half lengthwise with each member of the pair writing his/her name at the top of one column.

2. Student B does problem 1, recording his/her work on his/her side of the paper while Student A watches and coaches if necessary.

3. Student A checks Student B's work, coaches and/or praises. Then Student A does problem 2 on his/her side of the paper.

4. Student B checks Student A's work, coaches and/or praises.

5. After every two problems, the pair checks their answers with the other pair in their team, coaching and/or praising each others' work.

6. Repeat steps 2-5, reversing roles until all the problems are done.

▶ **Structure**
• Pairs Check

▶ **Materials**
• Blackline 5.1.3
• 1 sheet of paper and pencil per pair of students

ACTIVITY

4

ALGEBRA AND POLYGON ANGLE SUMS

1. Teammate 1 writes problem 1 on his/her paper, Teammate 2 writes problem 2, Teammate 3 writes problem 3, and Teammate 4 writes problem 4.

2. Each teammate writes an equation needed to find the value of x. They initial their work and pass the paper to the next person in a clockwise direction.

3. On the paper just received, each teammate checks the previous teammate's work, coaches and/or praises, and then does one step to solve the equation (combining like terms). They initial their work and pass the paper to the next person in a clockwise direction.

4. On the paper just received, each teammate checks the previous teammate's work, coaches and/or praises, and then does one step to continue to solve the equation. They initial their work and pass the paper to the next person in a clockwise direction.

5. On the paper just received, each teammate checks the previous teammate's work, coaches and/or praises, and then finishes solving the equation. They initial their work and pass the paper to the next person in a clockwise direction.

▶ **Structure**
• Simultaneous RoundTable

▶ **Materials**
• 1 Blackline 5.1.4 per pair of students
• Transparency 5.1.4
• 1 sheet of paper and pencil per student

6. On the paper just received, each student checks the previous work and coaches if necessary. Then the student signs the paper, indicating his/her approval of all the work done.

Tips:
Model this process for students. Each teammate could write in a different color rather than initial work.

Cooperative Learning and High School Geometry: Becky Bride
Kagan Publishing • 1 (800) WEE CO-OP • www.KaganOnline.com

Chapter 5: Polygons & Quadrilaterals

Lesson One

193

ACTIVITY

5 EXPLORING THE SUM OF THE EXTERIOR ANGLES OF A POLYGON

▶ **Materials**
• 1 Blackline 5.1.5 per student
• 1 straightedge per student
• 1 protractor per student
• 1 pencil per student

Have students complete Blackline 5.1.5.

ACTIVITY

6 PROCESSING EXTERIOR ANGLE SUM

▶ **Structure**
• Boss/Secretary

▶ **Materials**
• 1 Blackline 5.1.6 per pair of students
• 1 sheet of paper and pencil per pair of students

1. Student A supplies one sheet paper, folded in half lengthwise with his/her name in one column and a partner's name in the other column.

2. Student B is the first boss and Student A is the first secretary.

3. As the boss, Student B tells Student A how to do the problem. Student A, the secretary, records what Student B says in Student B's column of the paper.

4. If the boss makes a mistake, then the secretary coaches and praises once the boss does it correctly. Otherwise, the secretary praises the boss.

5. Reverse roles for each problem and repeat steps 3 and 4.

ACTIVITY

7 REGULAR POLYGONS, EXTERIOR ANGLES, AND THE NUMBER OF SIDES

▶ **Structure**
• RallyTable

▶ **Materials**
• 1 Transparency 5.1.7
• 1 sheet of paper and pencil per pair of students

1. Student A does problem 1 writing in his/her column of the paper.

2. Student B coaches and/or praises Student A for a job well done and does the next problem, writing in his/her column of the paper.

3. Student A coaches and/or praises Student B for a job well done.

4. Repeat steps 1-3, alternating students for the remainder of the questions.

Cooperative Learning and High School Geometry: Becky Bride
Kagan Publishing • 1 (800) WEE CO-OP • www.KaganOnline.com

ACTIVITY 1 EXPLORING THE SUM OF THE INTERIOR ANGLES OF CONVEX POLYGONS

Polygon	Number of sides	Number of angles	Number of triangles	Total degrees in a triangle	Total degrees in the polygon
Quadrilateral					
Pentagon					
Hexagon					
Heptagon					
Octagon					
...					
N-gon					

Complete the table above for each polygon below. Triangulate each polygon—draw diagonals from a single vertex until the polygon is separated into non-overlapping triangles. Based on the patterns observed for the first five polygons, generalize for an n-gon in the last row.

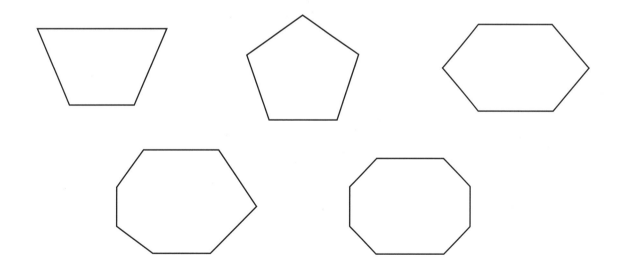

Cooperative Learning and High School Geometry: Becky Bride
Kagan Publishing • 1 (800) WEE CO-OP • www.KaganOnline.com

195

ACTIVITY 2 FIND MY SUM

Structure: Fan-N-Pick

Find the sum of the interior angles of a convex decagon. **Answer:** *1440°*	Find the sum of the interior angles of a convex nonagon. **Answer:** *1260°*
Find the sum the interior angles of a convex 16-gon. **Answer:** *2520°*	Find the sum of the interior angles of a convex dodecagon. **Answer:** *1800°*
Find the sum the interior angles of a convex 25-gon. **Answer:** *4140°*	Find the sum the interior angles of a convex 32-gon. **Answer:** *5400°*
Find the measure of one interior angle of a regular hexagon. **Answer:** *120°*	Find the measure of one interior angle of a regular pentagon. **Answer:** *108°*
Find the measure of one interior angle of a regular 20-gon. **Answer:** *162°*	Find the measure of one interior angle of a regular heptagon. **Answer:** *128.6°*

Cooperative Learning and High School Geometry: Becky Bride
Kagan Publishing • 1 (800) WEE CO-OP • www.KaganOnline.com

ACTIVITY 3

FIND THE MISSING MEASURE(S)

POLYGONS & QUADRILATERALS

Structure: Pairs Check

Find the indicated measure for each diagram. *Note: The diagrams are not drawn to scale.*

1.

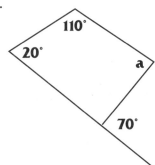

110°
20°
a
70°

2.

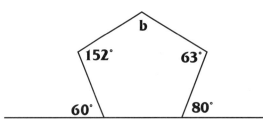

b
152°   63°
60°   80°

3.

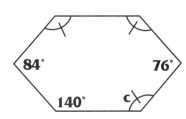

84°   76°
140°   c

4.

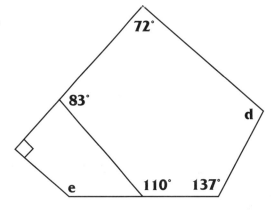

72°
83°
d
e   110°   137°

5. One interior angle of a regular decagon.

6. One interior angle of a regular octagon.

Answers:
1. 120°
2. 105°
3. 140°
4. 138°; 103°
5. 144°
6. 135°

Cooperative Learning and High School Geometry: Becky Bride
Kagan Publishing • 1 (800) WEE CO-OP • www.KaganOnline.com

ACTIVITY 4
ALGEBRA AND POLYGON ANGLE SUMS

Structure: Simultaneous RoundTable

Note: Diagrams are not drawn to scale.

1.

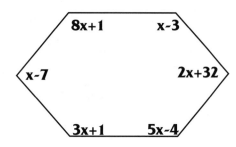

2.

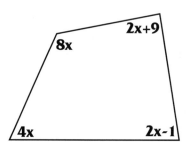

3.

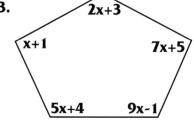

4.

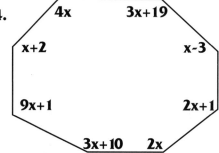

Answers:
1. 35
2. 22
3. 22
4. 42

Cooperative Learning and High School Geometry: Becky Bride
Kagan Publishing • 1 (800) WEE CO-OP • www.KaganOnline.com

ALGEBRA AND POLYGON ANGLE SUMS

Structure: Simultaneous RoundTable

1. Calculate the sum of the angles of the polygon on your paper. Initial your work and pass your paper 1 person in a clockwise direction.

2. Check the previous teammate's work, coach and/or praise a job well done. Write an equation to solve for x. Initial your work and pass your paper 1 person in a clockwise direction.

3. Check the previous teammate's work, coach and/or praise a job well done. Solve the equation. Initial your work and pass your paper 1 person in a clockwise direction.

4. Check the previous teammate's work, coach and/or praise a job well done. Sign your name showing you approve of all work done.

Cooperative Learning and High School Geometry: Becky Bride
Kagan Publishing • 1 (800) WEE-CO-OP • www.KaganOnline.com

199

ACTIVITY 5

EXPLORING THE SUM OF THE EXTERIOR ANGLES OF A POLYGON

1. On a sheet of paper, using a straightedge, Student 1, draws a convex hexagon; Student 2, draws a convex pentagon; Student 3, draws a convex quadrilateral and Student 4 draws a triangle.

2. Place the variable x in one angle of your polygon.

3. Measure the other remaining angles using a protractor.

4. Find the sum of all the interior angles of your polygon using what you learned in the last exploratory activity. Then write an equation to solve for x.

5. Solve for x. Place the answer in the appropriate angle of your figure.

6. At each angle, using a straightedge, extend one side to form one exterior angle at each vertex.

7. Calculate the measure of each exterior angle using what you know about linear pair angles.

8. What is the sum of all the exterior angles drawn on your polygon?

9. Check with your teammates and record all of their results.

10. Summarize your findings in a complete sentence.

Cooperative Learning and High School Geometry: Becky Bride
Kagan Publishing • 1 (800) WEE CO-OP • www.KaganOnline.com

ACTIVITY 6

PROCESSING EXTERIOR ANGLE SUM

Structure: Boss/Secretary

Find all missing measures. *Diagrams are not drawn to scale.*

1.

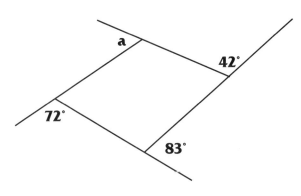

2.

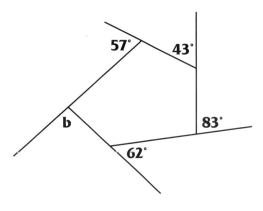

3. The pentagon is a regular pentagon.

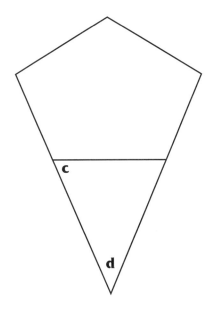

4. The hexagon is a regular hexagon

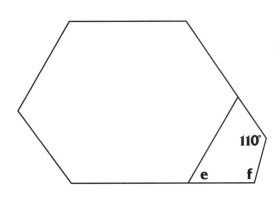

Answers:
1. 163°
2. 115°
3. c = 72°; d = 36°
4. e = 60°; f = 130°

Cooperative Learning and High School Geometry: Becky Bride
Kagan Publishing • 1 (800) WEE CO-OP • www.KaganOnline.com

201

ACTIVITY 7
REGULAR POLYGONS, EXTERIOR ANGLES, AND THE NUMBER OF SIDES

Structure: RallyTable

1. Find the number of sides of a regular polygon whose exterior angles each measure 10°.

2. Find the number of sides of a regular polygon whose exterior angles each measure 36°.

3. Find the number of sides of a regular polygon whose exterior angles each measure 72°.

4. Find the number of sides of a regular polygon whose exterior angles each measure 4°.

5. Find the number of sides of a regular polygon whose interior angles each measure 162°.

6. Find the number of sides of a regular polygon whose interior angles each measure 168°.

Answers:
1. 36 sides
2. 10 sides
3. 5 sides
4. 90 sides
5. 20 sides
6. 30 sides

Cooperative Learning and High School Geometry: Becky Bride
Kagan Publishing • 1 (800) WEE CO-OP • www.KaganOnline.com

LESSON 2
KITES

Some vocabulary development is necessary for this lesson, particularly with regard to the vertex angles of a kite and the ends of a kite. The ends of a kite are the vertices that join two consecutive congruent sides. The vertex angles of a kite are the angles whose vertices are the ends of the kite. This vocabulary will help the students verbalize their findings in the exploratory activities. The processing of each round should take no more than 45 seconds.

ACTIVITY

1 VOCABULARY

Round 1

1. Student A names the ends of the kite in problem 1.

2. Student B gives specific praise and then names the ends of the kite in the next problem.

3. Student A gives specific praise.

4. Repeat steps 1-3 alternating Student A and Student B.

Round 2
Repeat the above activity but have students name the vertex angles.

Round 3
Repeat the above activity but have students name the non-vertex angles.

▶ **Structure**
• RallyRobin

▶ **Materials**
• Transparency 5.2.1

Cooperative Learning and High School Geometry: Becky Bride
Kagan Publishing • 1 (800) WEE CO-OP • www.KaganOnline.com

203

ACTIVITY

2

EXPLORING PROPERTIES OF KITES

▶ Materials
- 2 sheets of patty paper per student
- 1 Blackline 5.2.2 per student
- Transparencies 5.2.2a, 5.2.2b, 5.2.2c
- 1 protractor per student
- 1 sheet of paper for the team to use to record possible properties

Note:
In phase 1 of this exploratory activity, teams and then the class will determine what explorations will take place. It demonstrates to students how mathematics has evolved. It is this phase that can lead to ideas that textbooks don't necessarily cover. Students will form conjectures from some of the ideas found and may discard others due to counter examples. All of this is valuable. The following properties must be investigated: discovering that non-vertex angles are congruent, that diagonals of a kite are perpendicular, and that the diagonal joining the ends of a kite is a symmetry line. Students should generate these, and more should be encouraged. The kite transparency and its two overlays were designed to maximize the number of possible relationships that students see. At this stage, encourage the students to state the relationships in general terms (non-vertex angles are equal) and then include the specific angles or segments they will work with to test the relationship ($\angle B > \angle D$).

The second phase is the actual exploration of the ideas generated, which could lead to formulation of conjectures. Since this exploratory activity is so open-ended the students will be asked to describe the process they went through to test a relationship and the results of their test, and finally to form a conjecture about whether the investigation supported the relationship studied.

The final phase includes formal proof of the conjectures. The level of the student you teach will determine how involved you want the final phase to be. Kagan structures will be used for the first two phases while the third phase, is done as a class.

Phase 1
1. Have teams discuss what they already know about kites, based on its definition. Use the Stand-N-Share structure to report the results of the team discussions, writing the results on the board. Tell students these properties need no investigation because they are true, based on the definition.

2. Place Transparency 5.2.2a on the overhead and ask each team to list possible properties that may be true about kite ABCD. Using the RoundTable structure, students take turns recording the possible properties on their team sheet of paper. Remind students to write each as a general statement about kites then include specific angles or segments that can be investigated to test the possible properties.

3. To merge the team's properties into a class list, the Stand-N-Share structure can be used. All students stand. One team is chosen, and the teammate with the paper reads one of the chosen team's properties. The students with the team paper in the other teams check off the property if it is on their sheet, otherwise they add it to their team paper. The papers rotate to the next student in a clockwise direction

and the process begins again. It is important for the teacher to list the properties on the board as a master list. This master list will be the order in which the properties will be investigated. The Stand-N-Share structure ends when all possible properties that students generated are on the board.

4. Place Transparency 5.2.2b over 5.2.2a and repeat steps 2-3.

5. Place Transparency 5.2.2c over 5.2.2a and b and repeat steps 2-3.

Phase 2
1. Each student now investigates all the possible properties listed on the board (also on their team sheets) that the class created. Blackline 5.2.2 describes what must be recorded for each possible property investigated. Have the students investigate the possible properties in the order that they are written on the board. This will make it easier for students and teams to cross reference with each other.

2. As a class, discuss which possible properties seem to be true, based on their investigations. Come to a consensus on the wording of each conjecture.

Phase 3
As a class, formally prove each conjecture that was written.

Cooperative Learning and High School Geometry: Becky Bride
Kagan Publishing • 1 (800) WEE CO-OP • www.KaganOnline.com

ARITHMETIC, ALGEBRA, AND KITES

1. Students mix in the class, keeping a hand raised until they all find new partners who are not a teammate. Partners greet each other with a gambit.

2. In pairs, Partner A asks a question from the worksheet; Partner B explains how to do the problem as Partner A writes what Partner B has said on his/her own worksheet. Partner A coaches and/or praises a job well done.

3. Partner B checks and initials the problem.

4. Partner B asks a question from the worksheet; Partner B records on his/her own paper what Partner A says. Partner B coaches and/or praises a job well done.

5. Students say a parting gambit, raise their hand to indicate that they are in need of a new partner, and give a greeting gambit once they find a new partner.

6. Repeat steps 2-5 until all the problems are done.

▶ **Structure**
· Find Someone Who

▶ **Materials**
· 1 Blackline 5.2.3 per student
· 1 sheet of paper and pencil per student

Cooperative Learning and High School Geometry: Becky Bride
Kagan Publishing • 1 (800) WEE CO-OP • www.KaganOnline.com

205

Chapter 5: Polygons & Quadrilaterals

Lesson Two

ACTIVITY 1 VOCABULARY

Structure: RallyRobin

POLYGONS & QUADRILATERALS

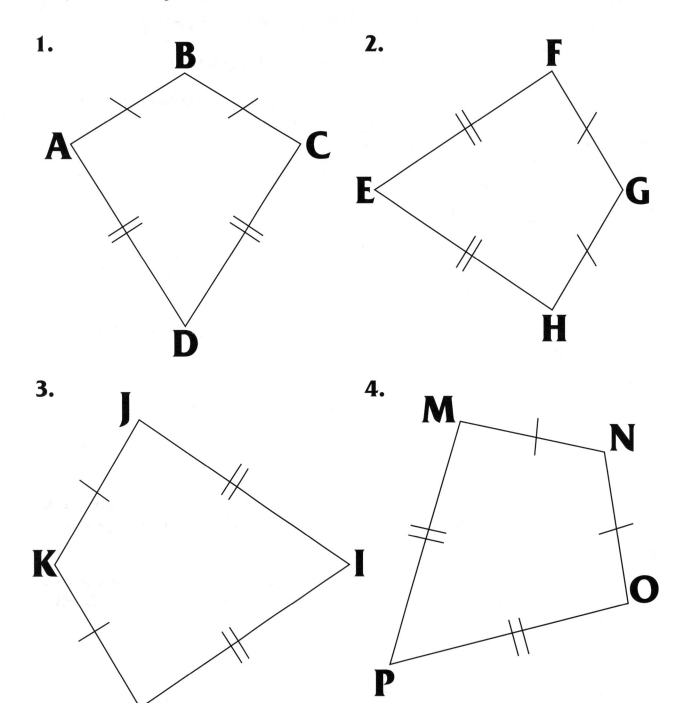

Cooperative Learning and High School Geometry: Becky Bride
Kagan Publishing • 1 (800) WEE CO-OP • www.KaganOnline.com

2 EXPLORING PROPERTIES OF KITES

Directions for Documenting the Investigation

To patty paper construct a kite for your investigations, do the following:

1. Using a straightedge, draw an obtuse angle on a sheet of patty paper with one side longer than the other. Label it as shown.

A < B
    D

2. Fold the patty paper so the fold of the patty paper contains points B and D. Using a straightedge, trace the angle onto the side of the patty paper that does not contain the angle.

3. Using a straightedge, draw segments $\overline{BC}$ and $\overline{CD}$. Label the angles in the kite like the angles are labeled on the transparency.

For each possible property investigated, do each of the following:

1. Describe the process you used to investigate the possible property. Be specific and detailed.

2. If, based on your investigation, the possible property appears to be false, check with your teammates to see what their results were. Explain why the possible property appears to be false.

3. If, based on your investigation, the possible property appears to be true, check with your teammates to see what their results were. If their results concur with yours, then write the property in the form of a conjecture.

Cooperative Learning and High School Geometry: Becky Bride
Kagan Publishing • 1 (800) WEE CO-OP • www.KaganOnline.com

207

ACTIVITY
2

EXPLORING PROPERTIES OF KITES

POLYGONS & QUADRILATERALS

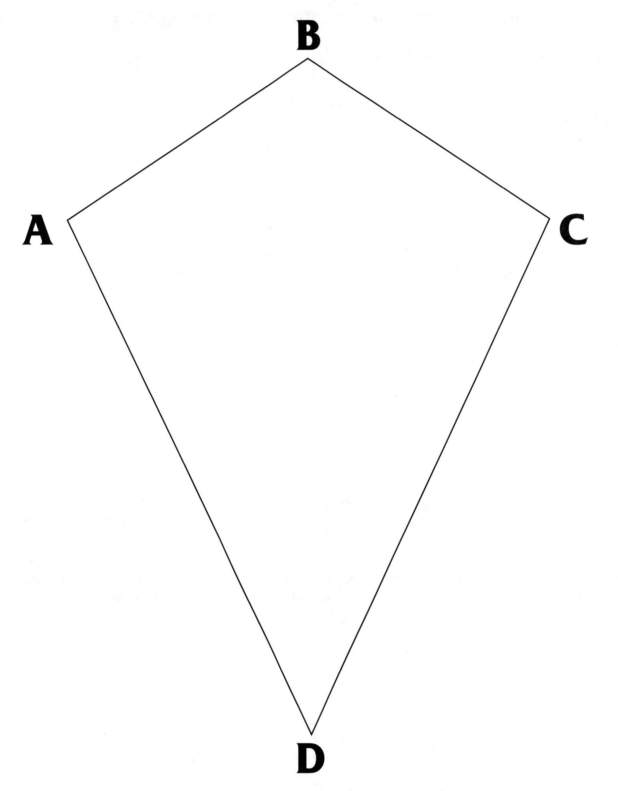

Cooperative Learning and High School Geometry: Becky Bride
Kagan Publishing • 1 (800) WEE CO-OP • www.KaganOnline.com

ACTIVITY

2 EXPLORING PROPERTIES OF KITES

1 | **2**

3 | **4**

Cooperative Learning and High School Geometry: Becky Bride
Kagan Publishing • 1 (800) WEE CO-OP • www.KaganOnline.com

209

Transparency 5.2.2c

EXPLORING PROPERTIES OF KITES

5   7

6   8

Cooperative Learning and High School Geometry: Becky Bride
Kagan Publishing • 1 (800) WEE CO-OP • www.KaganOnline.com

ARITHMETIC, ALGEBRA, AND KITES

Structure: Find Someone Who

KITE is a kite with ∠KIT and ∠KET the vertex angles. *The diagram is not drawn to scale.*

1. If m∠KIT = 82° then m∠8 = ?

2. If KT = 34 mm then KS = ?

3. If m∠IKE = 110° then m∠ITE = ?

4. If m∠3 = 35° then m ∠KET = ?

5. If m∠10 = 6x - 6, find x.

6. If KS = 3x + 1 and KT = 8x - 18 find x.

7. If m∠KIT = 12x - 8 and m∠8 = 3x + 26, find m∠7.

8. If m ∠3 = 5x + 7 and m∠4 = 9x - 21, find m∠KET.

9. If m∠1 = 4x + 1 and m ∠6 = 6x - 13, find x.

10. m∠IKE = 11x + 5 and m∠ITE = 6x + 50, find x.

Answers:
1. 41°
2. 17
3. 110°
4. 70°
5. 16
6. 10
7. 56°
8. 84°
9. 7
10. 9

Cooperative Learning and High School Geometry: Becky Bride
Kagan Publishing • 1 (800) WEE CO-OP • www.KaganOnline.com

211

LESSON 3
TRAPEZOIDS

A prerequisite to this lesson is that students be able to identify the bases and base angles of a trapezoid. Also students should know what the non-base angles are. This will help them articulate their summaries for the exploratory exercises in this lesson. The lesson begins with an exploratory exercise for the students to discover that non-base angles of a trapezoid are supplementary. An activity to process this concept follows. Students will explore the properties of isosceles trapezoids next and will need to know which sides of an isosceles trapezoid are the legs. An activity follows that processes these properties. The final exploratory exercise involves midsegments of a trapezoid. It is followed by two activities to process these concepts.

ACTIVITY
1 EXPLORING PROPERTIES OF TRAPEZOIDS

▶ **Materials**
- 1 Blackline 5.3.1 per student
- 1 protractor per student
- 1 sheet of paper and pencil per pair of students
- 1 straightedge per student

Have students complete Blackline 5.3.1. Formal proof may then follow.

ACTIVITY
2 ARITHMETIC, ALGEBRA, AND TRAPEZOIDS

▶ **Structure**
- RallyCoach

▶ **Materials**
- 1 Blackline 5.3.2 per pair of students
- 1 sheet of paper and pencil per pair of students

1. Student B supplies one sheet of paper, folded in half lengthwise. Each member of the pair writes his/her name at the top of 1 column.

2. Student B does problem one recording his/her work on his/her side of the paper while Student A watches, checks the work, and coaches if necessary.

3. Repeat step 2, reversing roles until all the problems are done.

Cooperative Learning and High School Geometry: Becky Bride
Kagan Publishing • 1 (800) WEE CO-OP • www.KaganOnline.com

ACTIVITY

3 EXPLORING PROPERTIES OF ISOSCELES TRAPEZOIDS

Have students complete
Blackline 5.3.3.

▶ **Materials**
- 1 Blackline 5.3.3 per student
- 1 sheet of paper and pencil
  per student
- 1 compass per student
- 1 straightedge per student

ACTIVITY

4 PROCESSING PROPERTIES OF ISOSCELES TRAPEZOIDS

1. Student A supplies one
sheet paper, folded in half
lengthwise with his/her name
in one column and a partner's
name in the other column.

2. Student B is the first boss
and Student A is the first
secretary.

3. As the boss, Student B tells
Student A how to do the
problem. Student A,
the secretary, records what
Student B says in Student B's
column of the paper.

4. If the boss makes a mistake,
then the secretary coaches and
praises once the boss does it
correctly. Otherwise, the
secretary praises the boss.

5. Reverse roles for each
problem and repeat steps 3
and 4.

▶ **Structure**
- Boss/Secretary

▶ **Materials**
- 1 Blackline 5.3.4 per pair of
  students
- 1 sheet of paper and pencil
  per pair of students

ACTIVITY

5 EXPLORING MIDSEGMENTS OF TRAPEZOIDS

Have students complete
Blackline 5.3.5.

▶ **Materials**
- 1 Blackline 5.3.5 per student
- 1 straightedge per student
- 2 sheets of patty paper per
  student

Chapter 5: Polygons & Quadrilaterals

L e s s o n   T h r e e

Cooperative Learning and High School Geometry: Becky Bride
Kagan Publishing • 1 (800) WEE CO-OP • www.KaganOnline.com

213

6 ARITHMETIC AND MIDSEGMENTS

▶ **Structure**
  · Pairs Check

▶ **Materials**
  · 1 Blackline 5.3.6 per pair of students
  · 1 sheet of paper and pencil per pair of students

1. Student B supplies one sheet of paper, folded in half lengthwise. Each member of the pair writes his/her name at the top of one column.

2. Student B does problem 1, recording his/her work on his/her side of the paper while Student A watches and coaches if necessary.

3. Student A checks Student B's work, coaches and/or praises. Then Student A does problem 2 on his/her side of the paper.

4. Student B checks Student A's work, coaches and/or praises.

5. After every 2 problems the pair checks their answers with the other pair in their team, coaching and/or praising each others' work.

6. Repeat steps 2-5, reversing roles until all the problems are done.

ACTIVITY

7 ALGEBRA AND MIDSEGMENTS

▶ **Structure**
  · RallyTable

▶ **Materials**
  · Blackline 5.3.7
  · 1 sheet of paper and pencil per pair of students

1. Student A does problem 1, writing in his/her column of the paper.

2. Student B coaches and/or praises Student A for a job well done and does the next problem, writing in his/her column of the paper.

3. Student A coaches and/or praises Student B for a job well done.

4. Repeat steps 1-3, alternating students for the remainder of the questions.

Chapter 5: Polygons & Quadrilaterals
Lesson Three

214

Cooperative Learning and High School Geometry: Becky Bride
Kagan Publishing · 1 (800) WEE CO-OP · www.KaganOnline.com

EXPLORING PROPERTIES OF TRAPEZOIDS

1. Using a straightedge, draw segments on both sides of the straightedge that are unequal in length. The two segments drawn are parallel.

2. Form a trapezoid with the two segments, labeling it ABCD such that segment $\overline{AB}$ and segment $\overline{CD}$ are the parallel sides.

3. Measure each angle and record those measurements.

4. What is the sum of ∠A and ∠D?
   What is the sum of ∠B and ∠C?

5. Describe the relationship between each pair of consecutive non-base angles.

6. Use same side interior angles to explain why this relationship exists.

Cooperative Learning and High School Geometry: Becky Bride
Kagan Publishing • 1 (800) WEE CO-OP • www.KaganOnline.com

215

ACTIVITY 2 ARITHMETIC, ALGEBRA, AND TRAPEZOIDS

Structure: RallyCoach

For each problem, find the value of x. *Diagrams are not drawn to scale and extraneous information is given. Round answers to the nearest tenth.*

1.

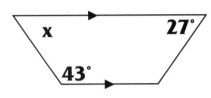

2.

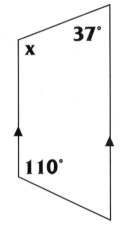

3.

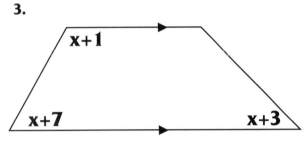

4.

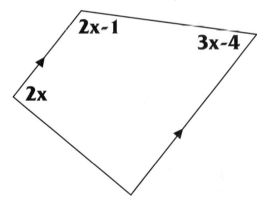

5.

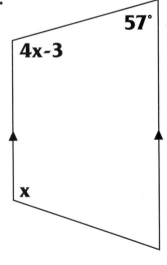

6.

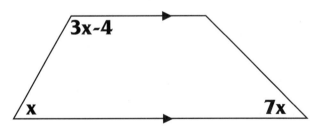

Answers:
1. 137°
2. 143°
3. 86
4. 37
5. 31.5
6. 46

Cooperative Learning and High School Geometry: Becky Bride
Kagan Publishing • 1 (800) WEE CO-OP • www.KaganOnline.com

1. Using a straightedge, draw a segment on one side of the straightedge, labeling the end-points A and B and a line on the other side of the straightedge. This ensures parallel lines.

2. Place the compass point on endpoint A and open the compass so the pencil point lies below the parallel segment. Draw an arc to the left of point A that intersects the parallel segment (extend the segment using a straightedge if necessary). Label the point of intersection of the arc and line point D.

3. Keeping the compass opening the same, place the compass point on endpoint B and draw an arc to the right of point B that intersects the parallel segment (extend the segment using a straightedge, if necessary). Label the point of intersection of the arc and segment point C. Join points A and D with a segment and join points B and C with a segment. The trapezoid is an isosceles trapezoid because segments $\overline{AD}$ and $\overline{BC}$ were constructed equal.

4. What appears to be true about each pair of base angles—∠A and ∠B; ∠C and ∠D? Trace ∠A onto a sheet of patty paper. Place it on ∠B. Trace ∠C onto a sheet of patty paper. Place it on ∠D. What is the relationship of each pair of base angles of an isosceles trapezoid?

5. Draw in the diagonals of trapezoid ABCD. What appears to be true? Trace $\overline{AC}$ onto a sheet of patty paper and place $\overline{AC}$ on top of $\overline{BD}$. What is the relationship of $\overline{AC}$ and $\overline{BD}$?

6. Summarize your findings in two complete sentences.

ACTIVITY 4 PROCESSING PROPERTIES OF ISOSCELES TRAPEZOIDS

Structure: Boss/Secretary

For each problem, find the value of x. *The diagrams are not drawn to scale.*

1.
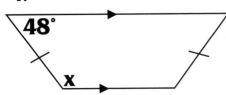

2.
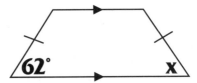

3.
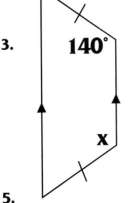

4.
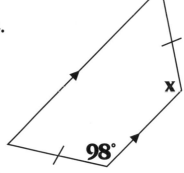

5.
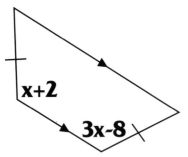

6.
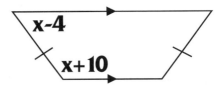

7.
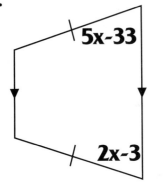

8.
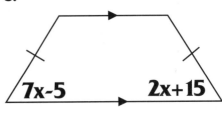

Answers: 1. 132° 2. 62° 3. 140° 4. 98° 5. 5 6. 87 7. 10 8. 4

Cooperative Learning and High School Geometry: Becky Bride
Kagan Publishing • 1 (800) WEE CO-OP • www.KaganOnline.com

EXPLORING MIDSEGMENTS OF TRAPEZOIDS

1. Construct a trapezoid on a sheet of patty paper using both sides of a straightedge to get the parallel sides. Label the trapezoid ABCD with $\overline{AB} \parallel \overline{DC}$.

2. Patty paper pinch the midpoints of the non parallel sides. Label the midpoints of $\overline{AD}$ and $\overline{BC}$, M and S respectively.

3. Connect points M and S with a segment. $\overline{MS}$ is the midsegment of trapezoid ABCD.

4. Trace ∠D and ∠C onto another sheet of patty paper. Place ∠D on top of ∠AMS. What is their relationship?

5. Place ∠C on top of ∠BSM. What is their relationship?

6. What do the answers to steps 4 and 5 imply about segments $\overline{MS}$ and $\overline{DC}$? Explain.

7. Since $\overline{AB} \parallel \overline{DC}$ (because quadrilateral ABCD is a trapezoid), what is the relationship between $\overline{MS}$ and $\overline{AB}$?

8. On the sheet of patty paper construct a segment whose length is AB + CD.

9. Compare the segment whose length is AB + CD to the length of the midsegment $\overline{MS}$. How many midsegments does it take to equal the segment whose length is AB + CD?

10. Write in words the relationships between the midsegment of a trapezoid and its bases.

Cooperative Learning and High School Geometry: Becky Bride
Kagan Publishing • 1 (800) WEE CO-OP • www.KaganOnline.com

219

ACTIVITY
6

ARITHMETIC AND MIDSEGMENTS

Structure: Pairs Check

$\overline{MN}$ is a midsegment in each trapezoid below. Find the value of all variables.
Note: the diagrams are not drawn to scale. Round answers to the nearest tenth.

1.
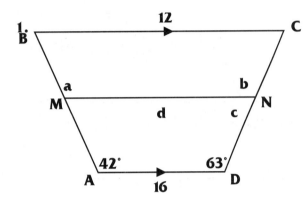

2.
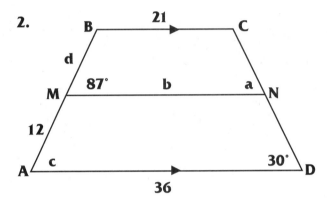

3.
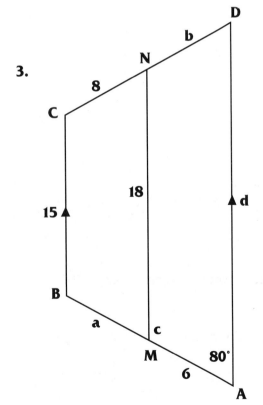

4.
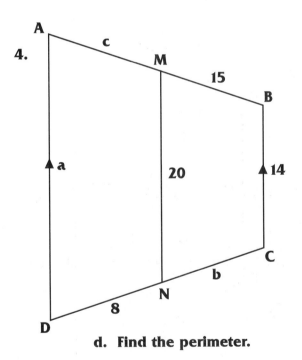

d. **Find the perimeter.**

Answers:
1. 42°; 63°; 117°; 14
2. 30°; 28.5°; 87°
3. 6; 8; 100°; 21
4. 26; 8; 15; 86

220

Cooperative Learning and High School Geometry: Becky Bride
Kagan Publishing • 1 (800) WEE CO-OP • www.KaganOnline.com

ACTIVITY

7 ALGEBRA AND MIDSEGMENTS

Structure: RallyTable

$\overline{MN}$ is a midsegment in each trapezoid below. Find the value of x.
Note: The diagram is not drawn to scale. Round answers to the nearest tenth.

1.

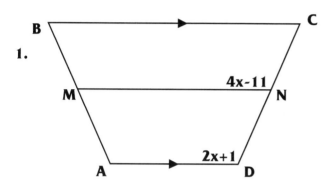

2.

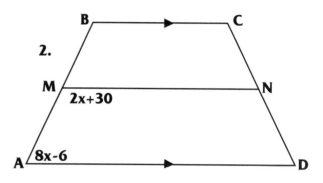

3.

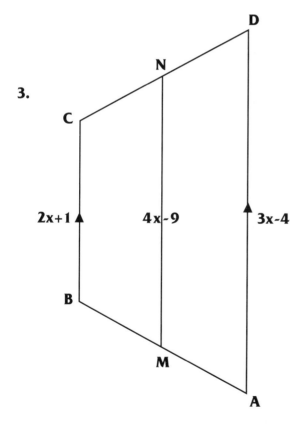

4.

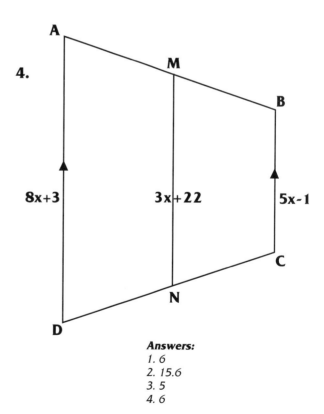

Answers:
1. 6
2. 15.6
3. 5
4. 6

Cooperative Learning and High School Geometry: Becky Bride
Kagan Publishing • 1 (800) WEE CO-OP • www.KaganOnline.com

221

LESSON 4
PARALLELOGRAMS

The first activity in this lesson is an exploratory one, in which teams, and then the class, will determine what explorations will take place. It demonstrates to students how mathematics has evolved. This first phase can lead to ideas that textbooks don't necessarily cover. Students will form conjectures from some of the ideas and may discard others due to counterexamples. All of this is valuable. The following properties of parallelograms must be investigated: discovering that opposite angles are congruent, that diagonals bisect each other, and that opposite sides are congruent. Students should generate these, and more should be encouraged. The parallelogram transparency and its overlay were designed to maximize the number of possible relationships that students see. At this stage, encourage the students to state the relationships in general terms (opposite angles are equal) and then include the specific angles or segments they will work with to test the relationship ($\angle B \cong \angle D$).

The second phase is the actual exploration of the ideas generated, which could lead to formulation of conjectures. Since this exploratory activity is so open-ended, the students will be asked to describe the process they went through to test a relationship, and the results of their test, and finally to form a conjecture if the investigation supported the relationship studied.

The final phase includes formal proof of the conjectures. The level of the student you teach will determine how involved you want the final phase to be. Kagan Structures will be used for the first two phases, while the third phase is done as a class.

Following the exploratory activity, there are two activities to process the properties of parallelograms and one activity to process how to determine if a quadrilateral is a parallelogram.

ACTIVITY
1
EXPLORING PARALLELOGRAMS

▶ **Materials**
• 1 sheet of patty paper per student
• Transparency 5.4.1a and 5.4.1b
• 1 Blackline 5.4.1 per student
• 1 straightedge per student
• 1 protractor per student if not using patty paper
• 1 sheet of paper for the team
• 1 pencil and sheet of paper per student

Phase 1
1. Have teams discuss what they already know about a parallelogram, based on its definition. Use the Stand-N-

Share structure to report the results of the team discussions, writing the results on the board. Tell students these properties need no investigation because they are true, based on the definition.

2. Place Transparency 5.4.1a on the overhead and ask each team to list possible properties that may be true about parallelogram ABCD. Students will take turns recording the possible properties on their team's sheet of paper. Remind students to write each as a gener-

al statement about parallelograms then include specific angles or segments that can be investigated to test the possible properties.

3. To merge the team's properties into a class list, the Stand-N-Share structure can be used. All students stand. One team is chosen and the teammate with the paper reads one of the team's properties. The students with the team paper in the other teams check off the property if it is on their sheet, otherwise they add it to

Continued on next page

Cooperative Learning and High School Geometry: Becky Bride
Kagan Publishing • 1 (800) WEE CO-OP • www.KaganOnline.com

their team paper. The papers rotate to the next student in a clockwise direction and the process begins again. It is important for the teacher to list the properties on the board as a master list. This master list will be the order in which the properties will be investigated. The Stand-N-Share structure ends when all possible properties that students generated are on the board.

4. Place Transparency 5.4.1b over 5.4.1a and repeat steps 2-3.

Phase 2

1. Each student now investigates all the possible properties listed on the board (also on their team sheets) that the class created. Blackline 5.4.1 describes what must be recorded for each possible property investigated. Have the students investigate the possible properties in the order that they are written on the board. This will make it easier for students and teams to cross reference with each other.

2. As a class, discuss which possible properties seem to be true, based on their investigations. Come to a consensus on the wording of each conjecture.

Phase 3

As a class, formally prove each conjecture that was written.

ACTIVITY 2
PROCESSING PROPERTIES OF THE ANGLES OF A PARALLELOGRAM

1. Students mix in the class, keeping a hand raised until they find a new partner who is not a teammate. They greet each other with a gambit.

2. In pairs, Partner A asks a question from the worksheet; Partner B explains how to solve the problem as Partner A records what Partner B has said on his/her own worksheet.

3. Partner B checks and initials the problem.

4. Partner B asks a question from the worksheet; Partner B records what Partner A says on Partner B's worksheet.

5. Partner A checks and initials the diagram.

6. Partners shake hands, give a goodbye gambit, part, and raise a hand again as they search for a new partner.

7. Students repeat steps 1-6 until their worksheets are complete.

8. When their worksheets are completed, students sit down; seated students can be approached by others as a resource. Students cannot pair with the same student twice.

▶ **Structure**
• Find Someone Who

▶ **Materials**
• 1 Blackline 5.4.2 and pencil per student

9. In teams, students compare answers; if there is disagreement or uncertainty they raise four hands to ask a team question.

Answers:
1. $x = 37°$; $y = 143°$
2. $x = 108°$; $y = 72°$
3. $x = 111°$; $y = 69°$
4. $x = 87°$; $y = 93°$
5. $x = 9$;
6. $x = 15.6$
7. $x = 14$
8. $x = 6$

Cooperative Learning and High School Geometry: Becky Bride
Kagan Publishing • 1 (800) WEE CO-OP • www.KaganOnline.com

223

PROCESSING ALL
PROPERTIES OF PARALLELOGRAMS

▶ **Structure**
  • Boss/Secretary

▶ **Materials**
  • 1 Blackline 5.4.3 per pair of students
  • 1 sheet of paper and pencil per pair of students

1. Student A supplies one sheet paper, folded in half lengthwise with his/her name in one column and a partner's name in the other column.

2. Student B is the first boss and Student A is the first secretary.

3. As the boss, Student B tells Student A how to do the problem. Student A, the secretary, records what Student B says in Student B's column of the paper.

4. If the boss makes a mistake, then the secretary coaches and praises once the boss does it correctly. Otherwise, the secretary praises the boss.

5. Reverse roles for each problem and repeat steps 3 and 4.

AM I A PARALLELOGRAM?

▶ **Structure**
  • Fan-N-Pick

▶ **Materials**
  • 1 set of Fan-N-Pick cards per team (Blackline 5.4.4)
  • 1 Transparency 5.4.4
  • 1 sheet of paper/pencil per team

1. Student 1 fans the cards face down.

2. Student 2 picks a card and reads it to Student 3.

3. Student 3 states whether or not the quadrilateral is a parallelogram and states the definition, postulate, or theorem that justifies it.

4. Student 4 coaches and/or praises Student 3 and then records the answer with justification on the team paper.

5. Cards are passed to the next person in a clockwise direction and steps 1-4 begin again, rotating roles to the next student in the clockwise direction. This process is repeated for a specific time limit or until cards are exhausted.

Chapter 5: Polygons & Quadrilaterals
Lesson four

Cooperative Learning and High School Geometry: Becky Bride
Kagan Publishing • 1 (800) WEE CO-OP • www.KaganOnline.com

ACTIVITY

1 EXPLORING PARALLELOGRAMS

Cooperative Learning and High School Geometry: Becky Bride
Kagan Publishing • 1 (800) WEE CO-OP • www.KaganOnline.com

225

1 EXPLORING PARALLELOGRAMS

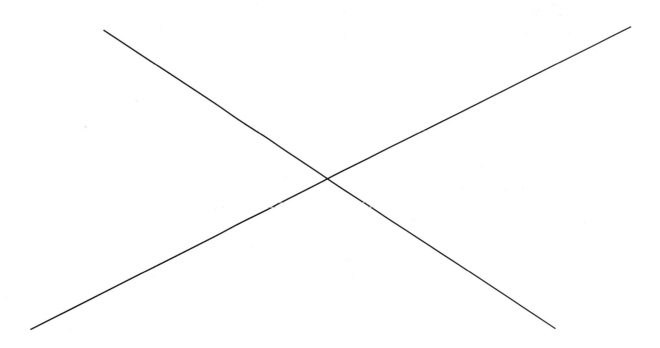

Cooperative Learning and High School Geometry: Becky Bride
Kagan Publishing • 1 (800) WEE CO-OP • www.KaganOnline.com

ACTIVITY

1

EXPLORING PARALLELOGRAMS

Directions for Documenting the Investigation

1. Using a straightedge, draw two parallel segments, one on each side of the straightedge. Using two straightedges put together, place them over the two parallel segments at a slant and draw two more parallel segments, one on the outside of each straightedge intersecting each parallel segment. Mark the four points of intersection A, B, C, and D like the figure below. Quadrilateral ABCD is a parallelogram because each pair of opposite sides is parallel.

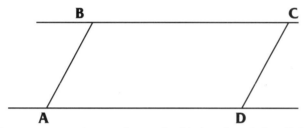

For each possible property investigated, do each of the following:

1. Describe the process you used to investigate the possible property. Be specific and detailed.

2. If, based on your investigation, the possible property appears to be false, check with your teammates and see what their results were. Explain why the possible property appears to be false.

3. If, based on your investigation, the possible property appears to be true, check with your teammates to see what their results were. If their results concur with your results, then write the property in the form of a conjecture.

Cooperative Learning and High School Geometry: Becky Bride
Kagan Publishing • 1 (800) WEE CO-OP • www.KaganOnline.com

227

PROCESSING PROPERTIES OF THE ANGLES OF A PARALLELOGRAM

ACTIVITY **2**

Structure: Find Someone Who

Show all work neatly. The following figures are parallelograms. Find the value of each variable. *They are not drawn to scale. Round answers to the nearest tenth.*

1.
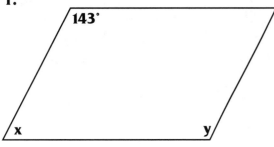

2.
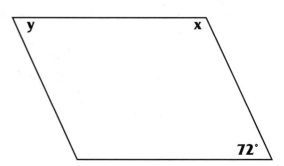

3.
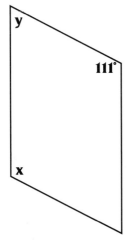

4.
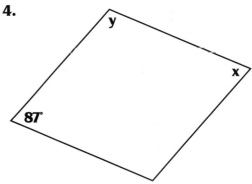

5.
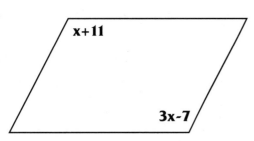

6.
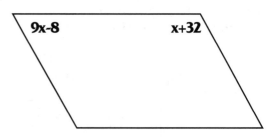

7.
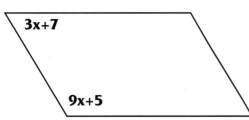

8.
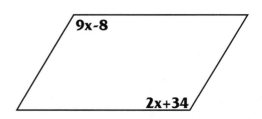

Cooperative Learning and High School Geometry: Becky Bride
Kagan Publishing • 1 (800) WEE CO-OP • www.KaganOnline.com

ACTIVITY 3 PROCESSING ALL PROPERTIES OF PARALLELOGRAMS

Structure: Boss/Secretary

Quadrilateral ABCD is a parallelogram. In addition to finding what is asked for, also state the postulate(s) or theorem(s) that justifies each answer. *The diagram is not drawn to scale.*

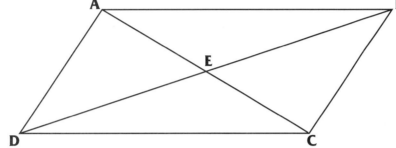

1. If AB = 12 and AE = 6, find DC and EC.

2. If AE = 9 and AD = 3, find AC and BC.

3. If BD = 14 and AB = 10, find BE and DC.

4. If m∠ADC = 42, find m ∠ABC and m∠DAB.

5. If AB = 2x + 1 and DC = 4x - 19, find x.

6. If BE = 6x + 1 and DE = 4x + 31, find x.

7. If AE = x + 1 and AC = 5x - 10, find x.

8. If AD = 7x - 9 and BC = 4x + 33, find x.

9. If AB = x + 3, BC = x - 4, and the perimeter of ABCD is 6x - 20, find x.

10. If AD = x - 2, DC = 3x + 1 and the perimeter of ABCD is 10x - 32, find x.

Answers:
1. DC = 12; EC = 6
2. AC = 18; BC = 3
3. BE = 7; DC = 10
4. m∠ABC = 42°;
*   m∠DAB=138°*
5. x = 10
6. x = 15
7. x = 4
8. x = 14
9. x = 9
10. x = 15

Cooperative Learning and High School Geometry: Becky Bride
Kagan Publishing • 1 (800) WEE CO-OP • www.KaganOnline.com

229

ACTIVITY

4

AM I A PARALLELOGRAM?

Structure: Fan-N-Pick

AB = CD; $\overline{AB} \parallel \overline{CD}$

Answer: Parallelogram; If 1 pair of
opposite sides of a quadrilateral are = and $\parallel$
then quadrilateral is a parallelogram

$\angle ABC \cong \angle CDA$
$\angle BCD \cong \angle BAD$

Answer: Parallelogram; If both pairs of opposite
angles are =, then quadrilateral is a parallelogram.

AB = CD; BC = AD

Answer: Parallelogram; If both pairs of opposite
sides are =, then quadrilateral is a parallelogram.

$\angle 1 \cong \angle 5$; $\angle 6 \cong \angle 2$

Answer: Parallelogram; definition of parallelogram
(both pairs of opposite sides are parallel).

E is the midpoint
of $\overline{BD}$ and $\overline{AC}$

Answer: Parallelogram; If the diagonals bisect
each other, then quadrilateral is a parallelogram.

$\angle ABC$ and $\angle DAB$
are supplementary;
$\angle BCD$ and $\angle CDA$
are supplementary

Answer: Parallelogram; Definition of parallelogram
(both pairs of opposite sides are parallel).

$\angle 7 \cong \angle 3$; BC = AD

Answer: Parallelogram; If 1 pair of opposite sides
are = and $\parallel$, then quadrilateral is a parallelogram.

BE = DE; CE = AE

Answer: Parallelogram; If the diagonals bisect
each other, then quadrilateral is a parallelogram.

Cooperative Learning and High School Geometry: Becky Bride
Kagan Publishing • 1 (800) WEE CO-OP • www.KaganOnline.com

ACTIVITY

4 AM I A PARALLELOGRAM?

Structure: Fan-N-Pick

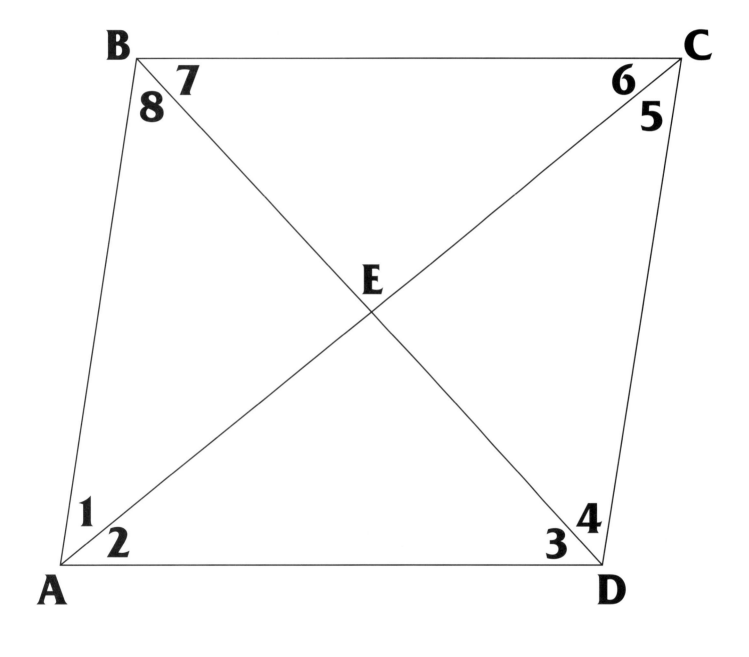

Cooperative Learning and High School Geometry: Becky Bride
Kagan Publishing • 1 (800) WEE CO-OP • www.KaganOnline.com

231

LESSON 5
RHOMBUS

The first activity in this lesson is an exploratory one, in which teams and then the class will determine what explorations will take place. It demonstrates to students how mathematics has evolved. This first phase can lead to ideas that textbooks don't necessarily cover. The students will form some of the ideas into conjectures, and may discard others due to counterexamples. All of this is valuable. The following properties of rhombus must be investigated: discovering that diagonals bisect opposite angles and that diagonals are perpendicular. Students should generate these, and more should be encouraged. At this stage, encourage the students to state the relationships in general terms (diagonals are perpendicular) and then include the specific angles or segments they will work with to test the relationship ($\overline{AC} \perp \overline{BD}$).

The second phase is the actual exploration of the ideas generated, which could lead to formulation of conjectures. Since this exploratory activity is so open-ended, the students will be asked to describe the process they went through to test a relationship and the results of their test, and finally to form a conjecture if the investigation supported the relationship studied.

The final phase includes formal proof of the conjectures. The level of the student you teach will determine how involved you want the final phase to be. Kagan Structures will be used for the first two phases while the third phase is done as a class.

Following the exploratory activity are two activities to process the properties of a rhombus.

Chapter 5: Polygons & Quadrilaterals
Lesson Five

232

Cooperative Learning and High School Geometry: Becky Bride
Kagan Publishing • 1 (800) WEE CO-OP • www.KaganOnline.com

EXPLORING PROPERTIES OF A RHOMBUS

▶ Materials
- 1 sheet of patty paper per student
- Transparency 5.5.1
- 1 Blackline 5.5.1 per student
- 1 straightedge per student
- 1 sheet of paper and pencil per student
- 1 sheet of paper for the team

Phase 1
1. Have teams discuss what they already know about a rhombus, based on its definition and the fact that it is a parallelogram. Use the Stand-N-Share structure to report the results of the team discussions, writing the results on the board. Tell students these properties need no investigation because they are true, based on the definition.

2. Place Transparency 5.5.1 on the overhead and ask each team to list possible properties that may be true about rhombus ABCD. Students will take turns recording the possible properties on their team sheet of paper. Remind students to write each as a general statement about the rhombus then include specific angles or segments that can be investigated to test the possible properties.

3. To merge the team's properties into a class list, the Stand-N-Share structure can be used. All students stand. One team is chosen and the teammate with the paper reads one of that team's properties. The students with the team paper in the other teams check off the property if it is on their sheet, otherwise they add it to their team paper. The papers rotate to the next student in a clockwise direction and the process begins again. It is important for the teacher to list the properties on the board as a master list. This master list will be the order in which the properties will be investigated. The Stand-N-Share structure ends when all possible properties that students generated are on the board.

Phase 2
1. Each student now investigates all the possible properties listed on the board (also on their team sheets) that the class created. Blackline 5.5.1 describes what must be recorded for each possible property investigated. Have the students investigate the possible properties in the order in which they are written on the board. This will make it easier for students and teams to cross reference with each other.

2. As a class, discuss which possible properties seem to be true, based on their investigations. Come to a consensus on the wording of each conjecture.

Phase 3
As a class, formally prove each conjecture that was written.

ARITHMETIC, ALGEBRA, AND THE RHOMBUS

1. Student A does problem 1, writing in his/her column of the paper and writing a postulate, definition, or theorem that justifies the work.

2. Student B coaches and/or praises Student A for a job well done and does the next problem, writing in his/her column of the paper and writing a postulate, definition or theorem that justifies the work.

3. Student A coaches and/or praises Student B for a job well done.

4. Repeat steps 1-3 alternating students for the remainder of the questions.

▶ Structure
- RallyTable

▶ Materials
- 1 Blackline 5.5.2 per pair of students
- 1 sheet of paper and pencil per pair of students

Cooperative Learning and High School Geometry: Becky Bride
Kagan Publishing • 1 (800) WEE CO-OP • www.KaganOnline.com

233

EXPLORING PROPERTIES
OF A RHOMBUS

The following figure is a rhombus.

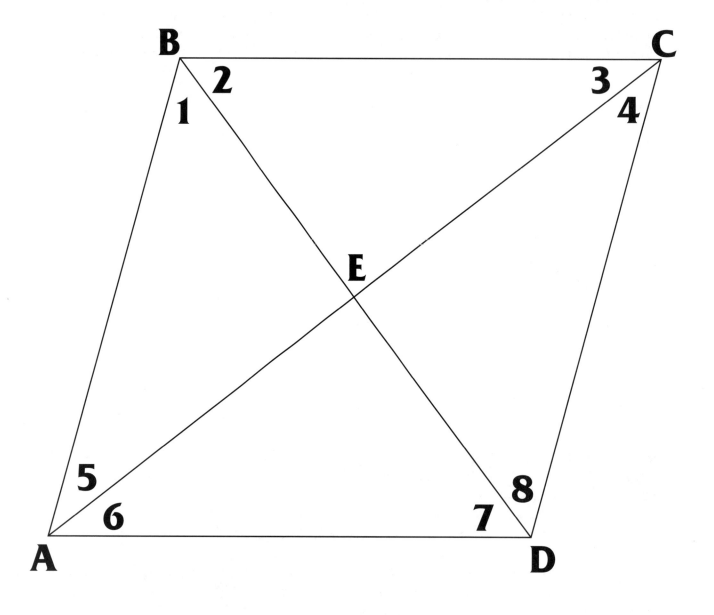

Cooperative Learning and High School Geometry: Becky Bride
Kagan Publishing • 1 (800) WEE CO-OP • www.KaganOnline.com

ACTIVITY 1 EXPLORING PROPERTIES OF A RHOMBUS

Directions for Documenting the Investigation

1. Using a straightedge, draw 2 parallel segments, one on each side of the straightedge. Using the same straightedge, place it over the 2 parallel segments at a slant and draw 2 more parallel segments, one on each side of the straightedge intersecting each parallel segment. Mark the 4 points of intersection A, B, C, and D like the figure shown below.

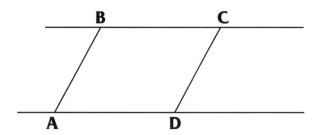

2. Draw in diagonals $\overline{AC}$ and $\overline{BD}$. Number the angles as they are numbered on the transparency.

For each possible property investigated do each of the following.

1. Describe the process you used to investigate the possible property. Be specific and detailed.

2. If, based on your investigation, the possible property appears to be false, check with your teammates and see what their results were. Explain why the possible property appears to be false.

3. If, based on your investigation, the possible property appears to be true, check with your other teammates to see what their results were. If their results concur with your results then write the property in the form of a conjecture.

Cooperative Learning and High School Geometry: Becky Bride
Kagan Publishing • 1 (800) WEE CO-OP • www.KaganOnline.com

235

ARITHMETIC, ALGEBRA, AND THE RHOMBUS

ACTIVITY 2

Structure: RallyTable

Show all work neatly on your own paper. ABCD is a rhombus.
The diagram is not drawn to scale.

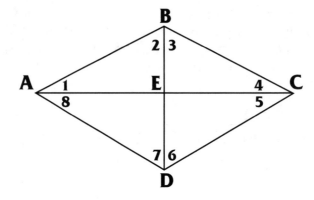

1. If AE = 8, then find AC.

2. If m∠1 = 82°, then find the m∠4.

3. If m∠ABC = 120°, then find the m∠2.

4. Find the m∠AEB.

5. If m∠8 = 2x + 11 and m∠5 = 4x - 19, find x.

6. If m∠2 = 3x - 4 and m∠ABC = 2x + 32, find x.

7. If m∠CED = 6x - 12, find x.

8. If BE = 3x + 1 and BD = 9x - 31, find x.

Answers:
1. 16
2. 82°
3. 60°
4. 90°
5. 15
6. 10°
7. 17
8. 11

Cooperative Learning and High School Geometry: Becky Bride
Kagan Publishing • 1 (800) WEE CO-OP • www.KaganOnline.com

LESSON 6
RECTANGLES

The first activity in this lesson explores the relationship of the diagonals of a rectangle. Students will use the distance formula to verify their findings and may need a review of this concept. This connects algebra to geometry. The next activity has students generate properties of rectangles based on the definition of rectangles and the fact that a rectangle is a parallelogram. The last activity processes all the properties of rectangles.

ACTIVITY

EXPLORING PROPERTIES OF RECTANGLES

Have students complete
Blackline 5.6.1.

▶ **Materials**
• 1 sheet of patty paper per student
• 1 Blackline 5.6.1 per student
• 1 straightedge per student
• 1 sheet of graph paper per student

ACTIVITY

WHAT ARE MY OTHER PROPERTIES?

1. Student 1 will fold the paper in fourths writing each teammate's name in one quadrant of the paper.

2. Student 2 will write one property of rectangles, based of the definition of a rectangle or the fact that a rectangle is a parallelogram, recording it in his/her quadrant of the paper, and draw a diagram to illustrate.

3. Student 3 will read what has been written on the paper, coach and/or praise his/her teammate and write another property recording it in his/her quadrant of the paper.

4. Repeat step 3 rotating to the next teammate each time until the team can no longer think of any properties.

Note:
This activity can be followed with the Stand-N-Share structure so that the teams will have all properties of rectangles in case they didn't come up with them all.

▶ **Structure**
• RoundTable

▶ **Materials**
• 1 sheet of paper and pencil per team.

Cooperative Learning and High School Geometry: Becky Bride
Kagan Publishing • 1 (800) WEE CO-OP • www.KaganOnline.com

237

3

ALGEBRA AND RECTANGLES

▶ **Structure**
  • Pairs Check

▶ **Materials**
  • 1 Blackline 5.6.3 per pair of students
  • 1 sheet of paper and pencil per pair of students

1. Student B supplies one sheet of paper folded in half lengthwise. Each member of the pair writes his/her name at the top of 1 column.

2. Student B does problem 1, recording his/her work on his/her side of the paper while Student A watches and coaches if necessary.

3. Student A checks Student B's work, coaches and/or praises. Then Student A does problem 2 on his/her side of the paper.

4. Student B checks Student A's work, coaches and/or praises.

5. After every two problems, the pair checks their answers with the other pair in their team, coaching and/or praising each others' work.

6. Repeat steps 2-5 reversing roles until all the problems are done.

4

SQUARES: STATE MY PROPERTIES

▶ **Structure**
  • Talking Chips

▶ **Materials**
  • 1 sheet of paper per team
  • 1 pencil/pen per student
  • 1 pencil/pen per team

1. Each student's pen or pencil is their talking chip. When a teammate wants to name a property of a square based on the definition, properties of parallelograms, rhombuses, or rectangles, the student will put his/her pencil in the middle of the table and name one. If the team agrees that it is a valid property and one that has not already been named, then that student will record the property on the team paper with the team pen/pencil, and draw a diagram to illustrate.

2. Only the teammates with a pen or pencil still in their hand may now offer another property, and step one is repeated.

3. Continue this process until all pens/pencils are in the middle of the table. At this point, each teammate picks up his/her pen/pencil and begins the process over again adding to what was already generated.

4. Give the students 4 minutes to do this activity.

Note:
This activity can be followed with the Stand-N-Share structure to share with the class all the properties that were found.

5

ALGEBRA AND SQUARES

▶ **Structure**
  • Boss/Secretary

▶ **Materials**
  • 1 Blackline 5.6.5 per pair of students
  • 1 sheet of paper and pencil per pair of students

1. Student A supplies one sheet paper, folded in half lengthwise with his/her name in one column and a partner's name in the other column.

2. Student B is the first boss and Student A is the first secretary.

3. As the boss, Student B tells Student A how to do the problem. Student A, the secretary, records what Student B says in Student B's column of the paper.

4. If the boss makes a mistake, then the secretary coaches and praises once the boss does it correctly. Otherwise, the secretary praises the boss.

5. Reverse roles for each problem and repeat steps 3 and 4.

Cooperative Learning and High School Geometry: Becky Bride
Kagan Publishing • 1 (800) WEE CO-OP • www.KaganOnline.com

1 EXPLORING PROPERTIES OF RECTANGLES

1. On a sheet of graph paper, using a straightedge, draw a rectangle. Draw in the diagonals of the rectangle. Label the rectangle ABCD.

2. Trace diagonal $\overline{AC}$ onto a sheet of patty paper. Lay it on top of diagonal $\overline{BD}$. What appears to be true about the diagonals of a rectangle?

3. Check with your teammates to see if they got similar results.

4. Write the ordered pairs of each vertex of your rectangle below.

      A   B   C   D

5. Using the distance formula, compute the length of each segment, showing your work below.

    AC =

    BD =

6. Did the calculations in step 5 verify the relationship of the diagonals you found in step 2?

7. In a complete sentence, summarize your findings.

Cooperative Learning and High School Geometry: Becky Bride
Kagan Publishing • 1 (800) WEE CO-OP • www.KaganOnline.com

239

ACTIVITY

3

ALGEBRA AND RECTANGLES

Structure: Pairs Check

Show all work neatly on your own paper. ABCD is a rectangle.
The diagram is not drawn to scale.

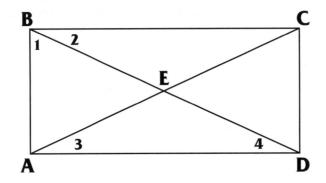

1. If BE = 5x - 3 and BD = 2x + 26, find x.

2. If BD = 8x - 7 and AC = 6x + 31, find x.

3. If m∠BAD = 3x - 15, find x.

4. If AB = 8x - 5 and CD = 3x + 20, find x.

5. If AB = 2x + 1, BC = 4x - 3, and the perimeter is 80 cm, find x, then find DC.

6. If AC = 9x - 14 and BD = 2x + 28, find x, then find BE.

7. If m∠1 = 3x - 7 and m∠2 = x + 41, find x, then find m∠4.

8. If m∠3 = 9x - 7 and m∠4 = x + 33, find x, then find m∠1.

Answers:
1. 4
2. 19
3. 35
4. 5
5. 7; 15
6. 6; 20
7. 14; 55°
8. 5; 52°

Cooperative Learning and High School Geometry: Becky Bride
Kagan Publishing • 1 (800) WEE CO-OP • www.KaganOnline.com

ACTIVITY 5

ALGEBRA AND SQUARES

Structure: Boss/Secretary

Show all work neatly on your own paper. ABCD is a square.
The diagram is not drawn to scale.

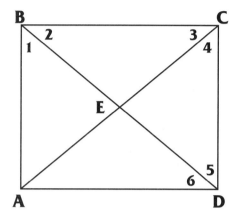

1. If m ∠3 = 4x - 7, find x.

2. If BE = x + 1 and BD = 4x - 20, find x, then find CE.

3. If AC = 12x - 5 and BD = 7x + 30, find x, then find DE.

4. If m∠BEC = 7x - 1, find x.

5. If AE = 2x + 3 and BE = 10x - 53, find x, then find AC.

6. If m∠6 = 2x - 1, find x.

7. If m∠BEA = 4x - 18, find x.

8. If AD = 3x - 1 and the perimeter of square ABCD is 140, find x, then find CD.

Answers:
1. 13
2. 11; 12
3. 7; 39.5
4. 13
5. 7; 34
6. 23
7. 27
8. 12; 35

Cooperative Learning and High School Geometry: Becky Bride
Kagan Publishing • 1 (800) WEE CO-OP • www.KaganOnline.com

241

LESSON 7
REVIEW

This lesson works on the interrelationships of the quadrilaterals studied. It has the students review all properties of all the quadrilaterals.

MAP THE QUADRILATERALS

▶ **Structure**
 • Team Word Web

▶ **Materials**
 • 1 large sheet of paper per team
 • different color pen/pencil for each student in a team

1. Each teammate signs his/her name in the upper right corner of the team paper with the color pen or pencil he/she is using.

2. One teammate writes "quadrilateral" in the center of the team paper in a rectangle.

3. Teammates RoundTable (take turns using their color pen or pencil), writing in the core concepts. Core concepts are placed in ovals connected by lines to the main idea.

4. Continuing in the RoundTable format, teammates add details and make bridges between related ideas.

Tips:
Teammates each have a different color to write with so that it is very apparent whether the participation was equal.

Step 4 can be done as a free-for-all with all teammates writing at the same time. If you are concerned that all won't get equal opportunity, use the RoundTable format.

Below is a sample of what a portion of the web could look like.

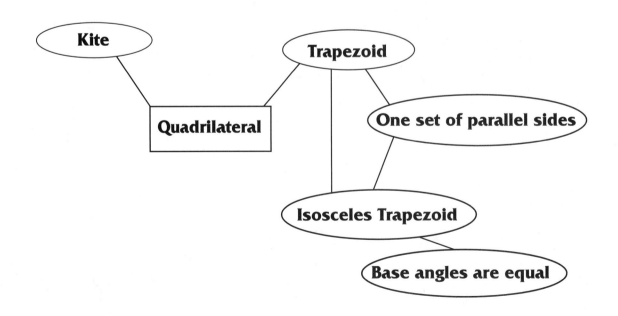

Cooperative Learning and High School Geometry: Becky Bride
Kagan Publishing • 1 (800) WEE CO-OP • www.KaganOnline.com

ACTIVITY

2

WHICH ONE IS FALSE?

1. All students write three statements involving quadrilaterals—two true and one false. Encourage students to write statements that require thought, such as, "All parallelograms have congruent diagonals."

2. One student stands and reads his/her three statements.

3. Individually, each seated teammate thinks about the three statements read and then writes down the number of the statement he/she thinks is false.

4. The seated teammates share and discuss their answers and come to a consensus as to which statement is false.

5. If the seated teammates are correct, the student standing praises them.

▶ **Structure**
· Find the Fiction

▶ **Materials**
· 1 sheet of paper and pencil per student

6. If the seated teammates are wrong, then the standing teammate coaches the team. The seated teammates then praise the standing teammate for challenging them.

7. Repeat steps 2-6 until each teammate has had a chance to read his/her statement.

ACTIVITY

3

ALWAYS, SOMETIMES, NEVER

1. Students mix in the class, keeping a hand raised until they find a new partner who is not a teammate. They greet their partners using a gambit.

2. In pairs, Partner A asks a question from the worksheet; Partner B answers the question explaining why he/she chose the answer. Partner A coaches and/or praises Partner B. Then Partner A records what Partner B has said on his/her own worksheet.

3. Partner B checks and initials the answer.

4. Partner B asks a question from the worksheet; Partner B records what Partner A says on Partner B's worksheet and coaches and/or praises Partner A.

5. Partner A checks and initials the answer.

6. Partners shake hands, give a goodbye gambit, part, and raise a hand again as they search for a new partner.

7. Students repeat steps 1-6 until their worksheets are complete.

8. When their worksheets are completed, students sit down; seated students can be approached by others as a resource. Students cannot pair with the same student twice.

▶ **Structure**
· Find Someone Who

▶ **Materials**
· 1 Blackline 5.7.3 per student
· 1 pencil per student

9. In teams, students compare answers; if there is disagreement or uncertainty, they raise four hands to ask a team question.

Answers:

1. S	8. N
2. N	9. S
3. S	10. S
4. S	11. A
5. S	12. N
6. N	13. N
7. A	14. S
	15. S

Cooperative Learning and High School Geometry: Becky Bride
Kagan Publishing • 1 (800) WEE CO-OP • www.KaganOnline.com

243

Chapter 5: Polygons & Quadrilaterals
Lesson Seven

ACTIVITY

4

IDENTIFY THE CATEGORIES

▶ **Structure**
- Fan-N-Pick

▶ **Materials**
- 1 set of Fan-N-Pick cards per team (Blackline 5.7.4)
- 1 sheet of paper and pencil for the team

Note:
Activity 4 is a higher level thinking activity. Each card has a Venn Diagram. The students are to identify the quadrilateral that is represented by each oval.

1. Student 1 fans the cards face down.

2. Student 2 picks a card, shows it to Student 3, and reads the categories.

3. Student 3 determines what quadrilateral each oval represents.

4. Student 4 coaches and/or praises Student 3.

5. Cards are passed to the next person in a clockwise direction and steps 1-4 begin again rotating roles to the next student in the clockwise direction. This process is repeated for a specific time limit or until cards are exhausted.

Cooperative Learning and High School Geometry: Becky Bride
Kagan Publishing • 1 (800) WEE CO-OP • www.KaganOnline.com

ALWAYS, SOMETIMES, NEVER

Structure: Find Someone Who

For each of the following, reply with always, sometimes, or never.

1. The diagonals of a parallelogram are _____ equal.

2. Both pairs of opposite angles of a kite are _____ equal.

3. The diagonals of a rectangle are _____ perpendicular.

4. The diagonals of a rhombus are _____ equal.

5. The diagonals of a trapezoid are _____ equal.

6. Trapezoids are _____ kites.

7. Two pairs of consecutive sides of a rhombus are _____ equal.

8. The diagonals of a trapezoid are _____ perpendicular.

9. Both pairs of opposite angles of a rectangle are _____ bisected.

10. The angles of a rhombus are _____ right angles.

11. The diagonals of a rhombus _____ bisect each other.

12. Kites _____ have one pair of congruent opposite angles.

13. Both pairs of opposite angles of a kite are _____ bisected by diagonals.

14. Trapezoids are _____ isosceles.

15. Parallelograms are _____ squares.

Cooperative Learning and High School Geometry: Becky Bride
Kagan Publishing • 1 (800) WEE CO-OP • www.KaganOnline.com

245

ACTIVITY 4

IDENTIFY THE CATEGORIES

Structure: Fan-N-Pick

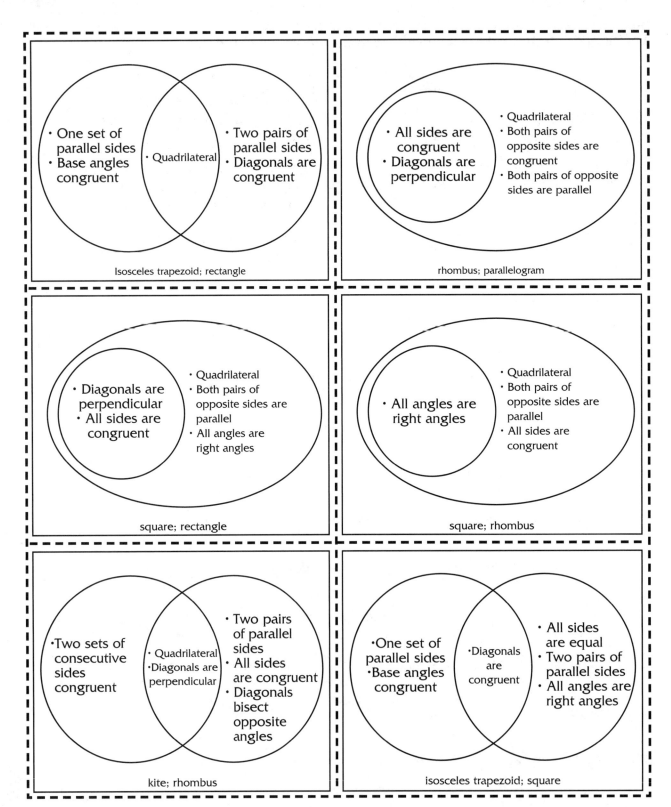

- One set of parallel sides
- Base angles congruent

· Quadrilateral

- Two pairs of parallel sides
- Diagonals are congruent

Isosceles trapezoid; rectangle

- All sides are congruent
- Diagonals are perpendicular

· Quadrilateral
· Both pairs of opposite sides are congruent
· Both pairs of opposite sides are parallel

rhombus; parallelogram

- Diagonals are perpendicular
- All sides are congruent

· Quadrilateral
· Both pairs of opposite sides are parallel
· All angles are right angles

square; rectangle

- All angles are right angles

· Quadrilateral
· Both pairs of opposite sides are parallel
· All sides are congruent

square; rhombus

·Two sets of consecutive sides congruent

· Quadrilateral
·Diagonals are perpendicular

- Two pairs of parallel sides
- All sides are congruent
- Diagonals bisect opposite angles

kite; rhombus

·One set of parallel sides
·Base angles congruent

·Diagonals are congruent

- All sides are equal
- Two pairs of parallel sides
- All angles are right angles

isosceles trapezoid; square

Cooperative Learning and High School Geometry: Becky Bride
Kagan Publishing • 1 (800) WEE CO-OP • www.KaganOnline.com

SIMILARITY

This chapter begins with a review of proportions and the algebra involved in solving proportions and then develops the concept of similar figures. The chapter ends with properties of similar triangles.

LESSON 1
PROPORTIONS

The purpose of this first lesson is to reinforce the concept of proportion. It begins with recognizing proportions, moves to the algebra involved in solving proportions and finishes with applications of proportions. The application activity is included to focus the students' attention on the fact that ratios must be set up similarly or they don't make sense. For example, if one half of the proportion was set up with number of bears to number of fish, then the other side of the proportion must have bears to fish also. This will help when the students begin writing proportions to find missing sides of similar figures. When students get to the ratio of similitude in Chapter 9, these prerequisite skills will also be important. If you have an honors group, this first lesson may not be necessary. For average and informal courses, it is a must.

ACTIVITY

1 RECOGNIZING PROPORTIONS

▶ **Structure**
• Fan-N-Pick

▶ **Materials**
• 1 set of Fan-N-Pick cards per 4 students. (Blackline 6.1.1)

1. Student 1 fans the cards face down.

2. Student 2 picks a card and reads it to Student 3.

3. Student 3 determines if the two ratios can form a proportion and explains why.

4. Student 4 augments and praises.

5. Cards are passed to the next person in the clockwise direction and steps 1-4 begin again, rotating roles to the next person in the clockwise direction. This process is repeated for a specific time limit or until cards are exhausted.

Tips:
Instead of four students working with a set of cards, each pair of students could work with a set of cards. This would increase participation to 50 percent.

Use one sheet of paper, which is passed from person to person for recording of the problems.

For individual accountability, have each student initial his/her problem, use a different color pencil, or write on only 1 quadrant of the paper.

Students can do this with replacement of the cards or without replacement of the cards.

Cooperative Learning and High School Geometry: Becky Bride
Kagan Publishing • 1 (800) WEE-CO-OP • www.KaganOnline.com

ACTIVITY

2

SOLVING PROPORTIONS

1. Student A supplies one sheet paper, folded in half lengthwise with his/her name in one column and a partner's name in the other column.

2. Student B is the first boss and Student A is the first secretary.

3. As the boss, Student B tells Student A how to do the problem. Student A, the secretary, records what Student B says in Student B's column of the paper.

4. If the boss makes a mistake, then the secretary coaches and praises once the boss does it correctly. Otherwise, the secretary praises the boss.

5. Reverse roles for each problem and repeat steps 3 and 4.

▶ **Structure**
· Boss/Secretary

▶ **Materials**
· Transparency 6.1.2
· 1 sheet of paper/pencil per pair of students

ACTIVITY

3

APPLICATIONS OF PROPORTIONS

Note:

Activity 3 gives students practice setting up proportions correctly. The first step of the Simultaneous RoundTable asks the student to determine how the ratios will be written. If a word problem involved the number of cups of flour needed to make a certain number of cookies, then the first step requires to student to decide whether the ratios will be written flour to cookies or cookies to flour. The student writes down his/her decision so the next student writes each ratio in that format. This reinforces the need to set up ratios the same way for each side of a proportion.

1. Each student supplies one sheet of paper.

2. Student 1 writes problem 1, Student 2 writes problem 2, Student 3 writes problem 3, and Student 4 writes problem 4 on his/her paper.

3. Each student determines how the ratios will be set up for the problem on his/her paper and writes down the decision. They initial their work then pass the papers to the next person in a clockwise direction.

4. On the paper just received, each student checks to see how to write the ratios, and then writes a proportion to solve the problem accordingly. Students initial their work and pass the papers to the next person in a clockwise direction.

5. On the paper just received, each student checks the previous work, coaches if necessary, and then solves the proportion. Students initial their

work and pass the papers to the next person in a clockwise direction.

6. On the paper just received, each student checks the previous work, coaches if necessary, and then writes a complete sentence to answer the problem. Students initial their work.

▶ **Structure**
· Simultaneous RoundTable

▶ **Materials**
· Transparencies 6.1.3a and 6.1.3b
· 1 sheet of paper/pencil per student

Cooperative Learning and High School Geometry: Becky Bride
Kagan Publishing · 1 (800) WEE-CO-OP · www.KaganOnline.com

249

1 RECOGNIZING PROPORTIONS

Structure: Fan-N-Pick

Do the following
ratios form a proportion?

$$\frac{2}{3} \;,\; \frac{16}{24}$$

Answer: yes

Do the following
ratios form a proportion?

$$\frac{9}{5} \;,\; \frac{10}{18}$$

Answer: no

Do the following
ratios form a proportion?

$$\frac{7}{4} \;,\; \frac{21}{14}$$

Answer: no

Do the following
ratios form a proportion?

$$\frac{8}{7} \;,\; \frac{24}{21}$$

Answer: yes

Do the following
ratios form a proportion?

$$\frac{3}{2x + 6} \;,\; \frac{6}{4x + 12}$$

Answer: yes

Do the following
ratios form a proportion?

$$\frac{2x}{x^2y} \;,\; \frac{8y}{4xy^3}$$

Answer: no

Do the following
ratios form a proportion?

$$\frac{4mn^2}{2m^4n} \;,\; \frac{8n^4}{2}$$

Answer: no

Do the following
ratios form a proportion?

$$\frac{3}{x} \;,\; \frac{9x - 12y}{3x^2 - 4xy}$$

Answer: yes

Cooperative Learning and High School Geometry: Becky Bride
Kagan Publishing • 1 (800) WEE-CO-OP • www.KaganOnline.com

ACTIVITY 2

SOLVING PROPORTIONS

Structure: Boss/Secretary

Solve for x.

1. $\dfrac{2x+3}{5} = \dfrac{4}{9}$

2. $\dfrac{7}{x+1} = \dfrac{2}{3}$

3. $\dfrac{3}{10} = \dfrac{3x-4}{7x+1}$

4. $\dfrac{5}{2x-4} = \dfrac{9}{3x+1}$

Answers:

1. $\dfrac{-7}{18}$

2. $\dfrac{19}{2}$

3. $\dfrac{43}{9}$

4. $\dfrac{41}{3}$

Cooperative Learning and High School Geometry: Becky Bride
Kagan Publishing • 1 (800) WEE-CO-OP • www.KaganOnline.com

251

APPLICATIONS OF PROPORTIONS

Structure: Simultaneous RoundTable

1. A recipe for 3 dozen cookies calls for 4 cups of flour. How much flour is needed to make 5 dozen cookies?

2. A certain medication calls for 250 mg for every 75 lbs. of body weight. How many milligrams of medication should a 220-lb person take?

3. A 2-inch wound requires 9 inches of suture thread. How long of a thread should a nurse have ready to close a 5-inch wound?

4. An apartment building has 24 identical apartments. It took 42.7 gallons of paint to paint 3 apartments. How many gallons of paint are needed to paint 21 apartments?

Answers: *1. 6.7 cups 2. 733.3 mg 3. 22.5 inches 4. 298.9 gallons*

Cooperative Learning and High School Geometry: Becky Bride
Kagan Publishing • 1 (800) WEE-CO-OP • www.KaganOnline.com

APPLICATIONS OF PROPORTIONS

Structure: Simultaneous RoundTable

Directions: *Round Answers to the nearest tenth*

a) Determine how the ratios will be set up for your problem and record your decision. Initial your work and pass your paper to the next person in a clockwise direction.

b) Write a proportion to solve the problem setting up each ratio as determined in step a). Initial your work and pass your paper to the next person in a clockwise direction.

c) Check the proportion, coach if necessary, then solve the proportion. Initial your work and pass your paper to the next person in a clockwise direction.

d) Write a complete sentence to answer the problem. Initial your work.

Cooperative Learning and High School Geometry: Becky Bride
Kagan Publishing • 1 (800) WEE-CO-OP • www.KaganOnline.com

253

LESSON 2
SIMILAR FIGURES

This lesson begins with an exploratory activity so students can discover the two properties of similar figures. Because the distance formula is used it may need to be reviewed. This is done before similar figures are defined. When the students are finished, they should know that corresponding angles are equal and corresponding sides are in proportion. The second activity has students process the properties just learned. The third activity is more processing but has the students view the concept from a different angle, which deepens their understanding. In the fourth activity students, will find lengths of missing sides of similar figures.

ACTIVITY
1 EXPLORING SIMILARITY

▶ **Materials**
- 1 Blackline 6.2.1 per student
- 1 straightedge
- 1 protractor or sheet of patty paper per student
- 1 sheet of graph paper per student

Have the students write the ratios using unsimplified radicals. Then have the students simplify each ratio using a cal-

culator. This will minimize the rounding error.

Have students complete Blackline 6.2.1. To determine whether the corresponding angles are equal, students can measure the angles with a protractor or use patty paper to trace the angles of one figure and compare them to the

corresponding angles of the other figure. The activity has the students use patty paper because it is quicker, but protractors would work just fine. It's beneficial to discuss an acceptable range of decimal places to show the equality of the ratios.

ACTIVITY
2 ARE THE FIGURES SIMILAR?

▶ **Structure**
- RallyTable

▶ **Materials**
- 1 Blackline 6.2.2 per pair of students
- 1 sheet of paper/pencil per pair of students

1. Student A supplies a sheet of paper, folds it in half lengthwise and writes his/her name in one column. Student B writes his/her name at the top of the other column.

2. On his/her side of the paper, Student B writes the ratios of the corresponding sides for problem 1 then determines if the sides are proportional. Next, he/she determines if the corresponding angles are equal. From those results Student B explains why the figures are or are not similar and records his/her findings.

3. Student A checks Student B's work and coaches and/or praises a job well done.

4. Repeat steps 2 and 3 for the other problems rotating roles each problem.

Cooperative Learning and High School Geometry: Becky Bride
Kagan Publishing • 1 (800) WEE-CO-OP • www.KaganOnline.com

ACTIVITY

3

FIND THE SIMILAR FIGURE

Note:
Activity 3 requires the students to write problems both with figures that meet the two properties of similar figures and with figures that don't meet the properties. This makes the student view the concept from a different angle, deepening the understanding. No blackline master is necessary.

1. Each teammate makes three problems each with two pairs of figures that look similar.

2. For each problem, each teammate will put angle measures and side lengths on each diagram, making sure in two problems the figures are not similar and one problem has similar figures.

3. Student 1 stands and shows his/her teammates the problems he/she wrote.

4. Individually, each teammate determines which pair of figures is similar and records it on their paper.

5. The teammates discuss their answers and try to reach a consensus as to which problem has similar figures.

6. If the teammates get it right, then the team celebrates. Otherwise, the student coaches the teammates until they find the correct one. Then they celebrate.

7. Repeat steps 3-6 for each remaining teammate.

▶ **Structure**
· Variation of Find the Fiction

▶ **Materials**
· 1 sheet of paper/pencil per student

Below is a sample problem.

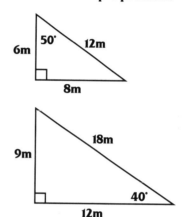

ACTIVITY

4

FINDING SIDES OF SIMILAR FIGURES

Note:
This activity could use a variety of structures. RallyCoach is the structure explained but Boss/Secretary, PairsCheck, or RallyTable could be as easily used.

1. Student B supplies one sheet of paper, folded in half lengthwise. Each member of the pair writes his/her name at the top of one column.

2. Student B does problem one recording his/her work on his/her side of the paper while Student A watches, checks the work, and coaches if necessary.

3. Repeat step 2, reversing roles until all the problems are done.

▶ **Structure**
· RallyCoach

▶ **Materials**
· 1 Blackline 6.2.4 per pair of students
· 1 sheet of paper/pencil per pair of students

Cooperative Learning and High School Geometry: Becky Bride
Kagan Publishing • 1 (800) WEE-CO-OP • www.KaganOnline.com

255

1 EXPLORING SIMILARITY

1. On a sheet of graph paper, plot the following points: Q(-9, -6), U(-6, 6), A(9, 6), and D(12, -9) on a coordinate plane. Join the points to form quadrilateral, QUAD.

2. On the same coordinate plane, plot the points S(-6, -4), I(-4, 4), M(6, 4), and L(8, -6). Join the points to form quadrilateral, SIML.

3. Trace quadrilateral, QUAD, on a piece of patty paper. Compare the corresponding angles of quadrilateral, QUAD, with quadrilateral, SIML. How do the corresponding angles compare?

4. Using the distance formula, compute the following lengths. Leave answers in radical form and show work.

QU =   SI =

UA =   IM =

AD =   ML =

DQ =   LS =

5. Using your answers from step 2, write the following ratios and then simplify each ratio to a decimal:

$\dfrac{QU}{SI}$ = ? $\dfrac{UA}{IM}$ = ? $\dfrac{AD}{ML}$ = ? $\dfrac{QD}{SL}$ = ?

6. What is the significance of the ratios in step 5? Can any of the ratios be written as a proportion? Explain.

7. Based on your investigation, what two properties do you believe similar figures have?

Cooperative Learning and High School Geometry: Becky Bride
Kagan Publishing • 1 (800) WEE-CO-OP • www.KaganOnline.com

ACTIVITY

2 ## ARE THE FIGURES SIMILAR?

Structure: RallyTable

For each pair of figures, determine if the figures are or are not similar. Explain your reasoning.

1. The figures are rectangles.

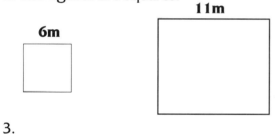

22cm

12cm

11cm

7cm

2. The figures are squares.

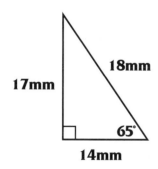

6m

11m

3.

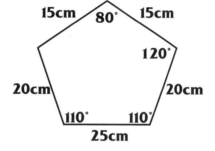

6cm   6cm

120° 120°

8cm   8cm

110° 110°

10cm

15cm 80° 15cm

120°

20cm   20cm

110° 110°

25cm

4.

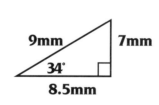

18mm

17mm

65°

14mm

9mm   7mm

34°

8.5mm

Answers:
1. *not similar*
2. *similar*
3. *similar*
4. *not similar*

Cooperative Learning and High School Geometry: Becky Bride
Kagan Publishing • 1 (800) WEE-CO-OP • www.KaganOnline.com

257

ACTIVITY 4 FINDING SIDES OF SIMILAR FIGURES

Structure: RallyCoach

For the following problems, the figures are similar. Find the value of each variable. The figures are not drawn to scale. *Round your answers to the nearest tenth.*

1.

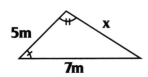

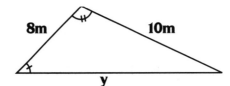

2.

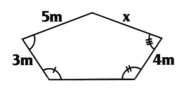

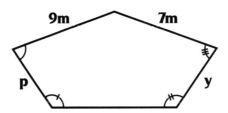

3.

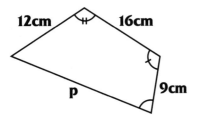

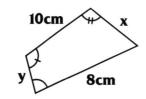

4.

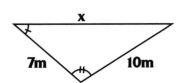

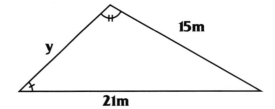

Answers:
1. x = 6.3; y = 11.2
2. x = 3.9; y = 7.2; p = 5.4
3. x = 7.5; y = 5.6; p = 12.8
4. x = 14; y = 10.5

Cooperative Learning and High School Geometry: Becky Bride
Kagan Publishing • 1 (800) WEE-CO-OP • www.KaganOnline.com

LESSON 3

POSTULATES AND THEOREMS OF SIMILAR TRIANGLES

This lesson contains exploratory activities for SSS~, AA~, and SAS~. Then there are two activities to process these, the last one requiring students to find missing values of angles and side lengths.

EXPLORING THE SSS SIMILARITY THEOREM

Have each student complete the exploratory activity on Blackline 6.3.1.

▶ **Materials**
  • 1 ruler per student
  • 1 piece of patty paper per student
  • 1 piece of graph paper per student
  • 1 Blackline 6.3.1 per student

ACTIVITY

EXPLORING THE AA SIMILARITY POSTULATE

Have each student complete the exploratory activity on Blackline 6.3.2.

▶ **Materials**
  • 1 ruler per student
  • 1 compass or piece of patty paper per student
  • 1 Blackline 6.3.2 per student

ACTIVITY

EXPLORING THE SAS SIMILARITY THEOREM

Have each student complete the exploratory activity on Blackline 6.3.3.

▶ **Materials**
  • 1 ruler per student
  • 1 piece of patty paper per student
  • 1 Blackline 6.3.3 per student

Cooperative Learning and High School Geometry: Becky Bride
Kagan Publishing • 1 (800) WEE-CO-OP • www.KaganOnline.com

259

Chapter 6: Similarity Lesson Three

4

PROCESSING AA~, SSS~, AND SAS~

▶ **Structure**
- RallyTable

▶ **Materials**
- 1 Blackline 6.3.4 per pair of students
- 1 sheet of paper and pencil per pair of students

1. Student A does problem 1, writing in his/her column of the paper.

2. Student B coaches and/or praises Student A for a job well done and does the next problem, writing in his/her column of the paper.

3. Student A coaches and/or praises Student B for a job well done.

4. Repeat steps 1-3, alternating students for the remainder of the questions.

Answers:
1) SSS~ 2) AA~ 3) AA~
4) SAS~ 5) AA~   6) SSS~

5

APPLYING AA~, SSS~, AND SAS~

▶ **Structure**
- Boss/Secretary

▶ **Materials**
- 1 Blackline 6.3.5 per pair of students
- 1 sheet of paper and pencil per pair of students

1. Student A supplies one sheet paper, folded in half lengthwise with his/her name in one column and a partner's name in the other column.

2. Student B is the first boss and Student A is the first secretary.

3. As the boss, student B tells Student A how to do the problem. Student A, the secretary, records what Student B says in Student B's column of the paper.

4. If the boss makes a mistake, then the secretary coaches and praises once the boss does it correctly. Otherwise, the secretary praises the boss.

5. Reverse roles for each problem and repeat steps 3 and 4.

Answers:
1) AA~; 13.8   2) SAS~; 8
3) AA~; 18.3   4) AA~; 8.6
5) AA~; 10.6   6) AA~; 13.4

AA~ is used often in this last activity because solving for x is so much more interesting.

Chapter 6: Similarity
Lesson Three

260

Cooperative Learning and High School Geometry: Becky Bride
Kagan Publishing • 1 (800) WEE-CO-OP • www.KaganOnline.com

1 EXPLORING THE SSS SIMILARITY THEOREM

1. On a sheet of graph paper, plot the points A(-2, -1), B(-2, 3), and C(4, -1). Using a ruler, connect the points to form a triangle.

2. The coordinates of point D are the coordinates of point A, multiplied by 2. The coordinates of point E are the coordinates of point B, multiplied by 2. The coordinates of point F are the coordinates of point C, multiplied by 2. Write the coordinates of D, E, and F below.

3. Plot points D, E, and F. Using a ruler, connect these points to form a triangle.

4. By counting, calculate the lengths of $\overline{AB}$, $\overline{AC}$, $\overline{DE}$, and $\overline{DF}$. Use the distance formula to calculate the lengths of $\overline{BC}$ and $\overline{EF}$.

   AB =   AC =   DE =   DF =   BC =   EF =

5. Write the following ratios in simplest form.

   $\dfrac{AB}{DE}$ = $\dfrac{AC}{DF}$ = $\dfrac{BC}{EF}$ =

6. Are the sides in proportion? Explain your answer. Did multiplying the coordinates by a factor of 2 guarantee proportional sides?

7. Trace △ABC onto a sheet of patty paper. Using the patty paper compare the corresponding angles. Are they congruent?

8. Based on your answers from questions 6 and 7 are the triangles similar? Explain your answer.

Cooperative Learning and High School Geometry: Becky Bride
Kagan Publishing • 1 (800) WEE-CO-OP • www.KaganOnline.com

261

ACTIVITY 2

EXPLORING THE AA SIMILARITY POSTULATE

1. Using a ruler, draw a triangle on a sheet of paper and label it △DEF.

2. On a sheet of patty paper, using a ruler, trace ∠D, making the sides extra long, and label it ∠G.

3. Place the patty paper over ∠D so that ∠G lies on top of ∠D. On the ray of ∠G that corresponds to $\overrightarrow{DE}$, place a point H so that DE ≠ GH.

patty paper ⟶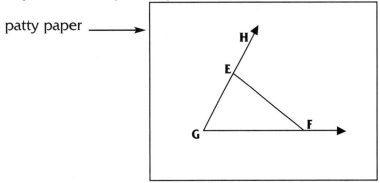

4. Slide the patty paper along $\overline{DE}$ until point H lies on top of point E. Trace along $\overline{EF}$, extending it until it intersects the other ray of ∠G. Mark the point of intersection J.

patty paper ⟶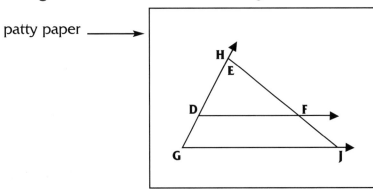

5. △GHJ was constructed so that ∠G ≅ ∠D and ∠E ≅ ∠H. Slide the patty paper or use a protractor to check to see if ∠F ≅ ∠J.

6. Find the lengths of segments $\overline{DE}$, $\overline{EF}$, $\overline{DF}$, $\overline{GH}$, $\overline{HJ}$, and $\overline{GJ}$.

   DE =   EF =   DF =   GH =   HJ =   GJ =

7. Write the following ratios in simplest form.

   $\dfrac{DE}{GH} =$ $\dfrac{EF}{HJ} =$ $\dfrac{DF}{GJ} =$

8. Is △DEF similar to △GHJ? Explain your answer.

Cooperative Learning and High School Geometry: Becky Bride
Kagan Publishing • 1 (800) WEE-CO-OP • www.KaganOnline.com

ACTIVITY 3 EXPLORING THE SAS SIMILARITY THEOREM

1. Using a ruler, draw a triangle on a sheet of paper and label it △ABC.

2. On a sheet of patty paper trace ∠A and label it ∠D.

3. Measure $\overline{AB}$ and $\overline{AC}$ and record your measurements below.
   AB =   AC =

4. On one of the rays of ∠D, locate point E such that DE = $\frac{1}{2}$ AB.

5. On the other ray of ∠D, locate point F such that DF = $\frac{1}{2}$ AC.

6. Connect points E and F to form △DEF.

7. Find the lengths of $\overline{BC}$ and $\overline{EF}$.
   BC=   EF=

8. Write the following ratios in simplest form.
   $\frac{AB}{DE}$ = $\frac{BC}{EF}$ = $\frac{AC}{DF}$ =

9. Are the sides of the two triangles proportional?

10. Use patty paper or a protractor to determine if corresponding angles are congruent.

11. Are the two triangles similar? Explain your answer.

Cooperative Learning and High School Geometry: Becky Bride
Kagan Publishing • 1 (800) WEE-CO-OP • www.KaganOnline.com

263

PROCESSING AA~, SSS~, AND SAS~

Structure: RallyTable

Determine if the following triangles are similar. If they are similar, give the postulate or theorem that supports your claim. *The diagrams are not drawn to scale.*

1.

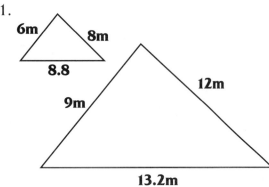

2.

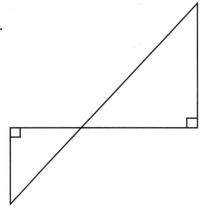

3.

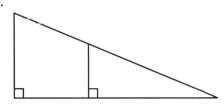

4.

5.

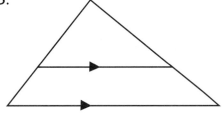

6.

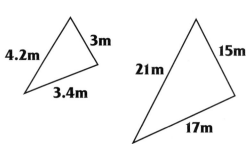

Cooperative Learning and High School Geometry: Becky Bride
Kagan Publishing • 1 (800) WEE-CO-OP • www.KaganOnline.com

ACTIVITY

5 | APPLYING AA~, SSS~, AND SAS~

Structure: Boss/Secretary

Determine if the triangles are similar and state the postulate or theorem that justifies your answer. If the triangles are similar, find the value of x. All lengths are in centimeters. Diagrams are not drawn to scale. Round answers to the nearest tenth.

1.

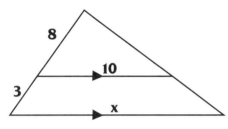

2.

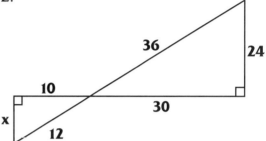

3.

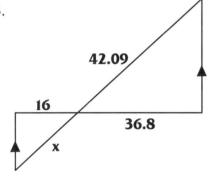

4.

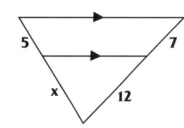

5.

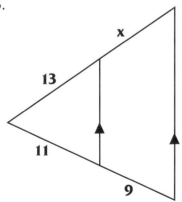

6.

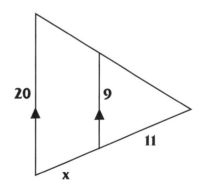

Cooperative Learning and High School Geometry: Becky Bride
Kagan Publishing • 1 (800) WEE-CO-OP • www.KaganOnline.com

265

PYTHAGOREAN THEOREM AND SPECIAL RIGHT TRIANGLES

This chapter has exploratory activities for the Pythagorean Theorem and its converse. It also includes activities to process each of these concepts. The chapter begins with a review of radicals and solving simple quadratic equations. If students are not required to put their answers in simplest radical form, this lesson is not necessary. All students will benefit from this review if simplest radical form is a requirement. This is yet another opportunity to reinforce algebraic concepts.

LESSON 1
RADICAL REVIEW

This lesson is designed to reinforce algebra skills necessary for this chapter. It begins with an activity that requires students to line up in ascending order, according to the numerical value of the expression on the card they are holding. Whole numbers and simplified square roots are on the cards. The purpose of this activity is to deepen the students' number sense with regard to square roots.

The next two activities progress from simplifying radicals to simplifying radicals by rationalizing the denominator. This skill is necessary when students work with the special right triangles. Finally, the lesson concludes with solving simple quadratic equations required when using the Pythagorean Theorem.

This first activity is not an easy one. Calculators are not to be used. A deeper understanding of radicals is the goal. If a student had the radical $\sqrt{10}$, the student would need to determine which perfect squares 10 falls between: 9 and 16. Therefore, the square root of 10 must fall between 3 and 4. Since 10 is very close to 9 it would be smaller than the square root of 14.

ACTIVITY

NUMBER SENSE WITH RADICALS

▶ **Structure**
  · Mix-Pair-Discuss followed by Line Up

▶ **Materials**
  · 1 set of Line Up cards (Blackline 7.1.1)

Phase 1: Mix-Pair-Discuss
1. Teacher distributes one card per student.

2. Students get up and mix to find a classmate who is not a teammate, greet each other and pair.

3. One student asks his/her partner what two whole numbers the expression on his/her card falls between.

4. Partner responds.

5. Student coaches and praises or praises.

6. Reverse roles and repeat steps 3-5.

7. The students trade cards.

8. Following a gambit, pairs depart to find someone else to pair with and repeat steps 2-7.

9. Teacher calls time and students stop mixing.

Tips:
Play music to signal the start and stop of the Mix-Pair-Discuss.

Model the Mix-Pair-Discuss and ask a student to repeat your directions to see if they were clearly communicated.

As students look for a partner, they can put their hands up to signal that they are available.

Note:
Blackline 7.1.1 is designed so that the radicals are listed in ascending order. This can be used as your answer key.

Phase 2: Line Up
1. Students look at the card they are holding and mentally determine which pair of whole numbers their expression falls between.

2. Students line up in numerical order, according to the numerical value of the expression on their card. Once they determine which whole numbers they fall between, they must order themselves with the other radicals that fall between the same two whole numbers.

Cooperative Learning and High School Geometry: Becky Bride
Kagan Publishing • 1 (800) WEE CO-OP • www.KaganOnline.com

SIMPLIFYING RADICALS

1. Student A supplies one sheet paper, folded in half lengthwise with his/her name in one column and a partner's name in the other column.

2. Student B is the first boss and Student A is the first secretary.

3. As the boss, Student B tells Student A how to do the problem. Student A, the secretary, records what Student B says in Student B's column of the paper.

4. If the boss makes a mistake, then the secretary coaches and praises once the boss does it correctly. Otherwise, the secretary praises the boss.

5. Reverse roles for each problem and repeat steps 3 and 4.

▶ **Structure**
• Boss/Secretary

▶ **Materials**
• 1 Blackline 7.1.2 per pair of students
• 1 sheet of paper and pencil per pair of students

SIMPLIFYING RADICALS BY RATIONALIZING THE DENOMINATOR

1. Student B supplies one sheet of paper, folded in half lengthwise. Each member of the pair writes his/her name at the top of one column.

2. Student B does problem 1, recording his/her work on his/her side of the paper while Student A watches and coaches if necessary.

3. Student A checks Student B's work, coaches and/or praises. Then Student A does problem 2 on his/her side of the paper.

4. Student B checks Student A's work, coaches and/or praises.

5. After every two problems the pair checks their answers with the other pair in their team, coaching and/or praising each others' work.

6. Repeat steps 2-5, reversing roles, until all the problems are done.

▶ **Structure**
• Pairs Check

▶ **Materials**
• 1 Blackline 7.1.3 per pair of students
• 1 sheet of paper and pencil per pair of students

Chapter 7: Pythagorean Theorem and Special Right Triangles

Lesson One

Cooperative Learning and High School Geometry: Becky Bride
Kagan Publishing • 1 (800) WEE CO-OP • www.KaganOnline.com

269

SOLVING SIMPLE QUADRATIC EQUATIONS

▶ **Structure**
  · Simultaneous RoundTable

▶ **Materials**
  · Transparencies 7.1.4a and 7.1.4b
  · 1 sheet of paper and pencil per student

1. Teammate 1 writes problem 1 on his/her paper, Teammate 2 writes problem 2, Teammate 3 writes problem 3, and Teammate 4 writes problem 4.

2. Each teammate does one step to solve for x. They initial their work and pass the paper to the next person in a clockwise direction.

3. On the paper just received, each teammate checks the previous teammate's work, coaches and/or praises, and then does one more step to solve the equation. They initial their work and pass the paper to the next person in a clockwise direction.

4. On the paper just received, each teammate checks the previous teammate's work, coaches and/or praises, and then finishes solving the equation. They initial their work and pass the paper to the next person in a clockwise direction.

5. On the paper they receive, the student checks the previous work and coaches if necessary. Then the student signs the paper, indicating his/her approval of all the work done.

Tips:
Model this process for students. Each teammate could write in a different color rather than initial work.

1 NUMBER SENSE WITH RADICALS

Structures: Mix-Pair-Discuss and Line Up

$\sqrt{2}$	4	$\sqrt{30}$
$\sqrt{3}$	$\sqrt{17}$	$4\sqrt{2}$
$\sqrt{21}$	$3\sqrt{2}$	34
$\sqrt{5}$	$\sqrt{19}$	6
$\sqrt{7}$	$2\sqrt{5}$	$2\sqrt{10}$
$2\sqrt{2}$	$\sqrt{23}$	$2\sqrt{11}$
3	$2\sqrt{6}$	7
$\sqrt{10}$	5	$2\sqrt{13}$
$\sqrt{11}$	$\sqrt{26}$	$2\sqrt{15}$
$2\sqrt{3}$	$3\sqrt{3}$	8
$\sqrt{13}$	$2\sqrt{7}$	$3\sqrt{7}$
$\sqrt{15}$	$\sqrt{29}$	9

Cooperative Learning and High School Geometry: Becky Bride
Kagan Publishing • 1 (800) WEE CO-OP • www.KaganOnline.com

271

2 SIMPLIFYING RADICALS

Structure: Boss/Secretary

Simplify each radical.

1. $\sqrt{50}$

6. $\sqrt{80x^{16}}$

2. $\sqrt{72}$

7. $3\sqrt{12x^3y^4}$

3. $3\sqrt{18}$

8. $-5\sqrt{16x^8y^7}$

4. $2\sqrt{27}$

9. $-7\sqrt{45m^{10}n^3}$

5. $\sqrt{125y^9}$

10. $-3\sqrt{24x^9y^{20}}$

Answers
1. $5\sqrt{2}$
2. $6\sqrt{2}$
3. $9\sqrt{2}$
4. $6\sqrt{3}$
5. $5y^4\sqrt{5y}$
6. $4x^8\sqrt{5}$
7. $6xy^2\sqrt{3x}$
8. $-20x^4y^3\sqrt{y}$
9. $-21m^5n\sqrt{5n}$
10. $-6x^4y^{10}\sqrt{6x}$

Cooperative Learning and High School Geometry: Becky Bride
Kagan Publishing • 1 (800) WEE CO-OP • www.KaganOnline.com

ACTIVITY 3 SIMPLIFYING RADICALS BY RATIONALIZING THE DENOMINATOR

Structure: Pairs Check

1. $\sqrt{\dfrac{2}{3}}$

2. $\sqrt{\dfrac{5}{6}}$

3. $\sqrt{\dfrac{7}{8}}$

4. $\sqrt{\dfrac{5}{12}}$

5. $\dfrac{3\sqrt{6}}{\sqrt{2}}$

6. $\dfrac{-4\sqrt{3}}{\sqrt{18}}$

7. $\dfrac{8\sqrt{3}}{\sqrt{12}}$

8. $\dfrac{2\sqrt{8}}{3\sqrt{6}}$

9. $\dfrac{-4\sqrt{3}}{\sqrt{15}}$

10. $\dfrac{-9\sqrt{7}}{\sqrt{12}}$

Answers:

1. $\dfrac{\sqrt{6}}{3}$

2. $\dfrac{\sqrt{30}}{6}$

3. $\dfrac{\sqrt{14}}{4}$

4. $\dfrac{\sqrt{15}}{6}$

5. $3\sqrt{3}$

6. $\dfrac{-2\sqrt{6}}{3}$

7. 4

8. $\dfrac{4\sqrt{3}}{9}$

9. $\dfrac{-4\sqrt{5}}{5}$

10. $\dfrac{-3\sqrt{21}}{2}$

Cooperative Learning and High School Geometry: Becky Bride
Kagan Publishing • 1 (800) WEE CO-OP • www.KaganOnline.com

273

SOLVING SIMPLE
QUADRATIC EQUATIONS

Structure: Simultaneous RoundTable

Solve each equation and put answers in simplest radical form.

1. $2x^2 + 7 = 23$

2. $3x^2 - 6 = 129$

3. $4x^2 - 5 = 91$

4. $2x^2 + 7 = 71$

Answers:
1. $\pm 2\sqrt{2}$
2. $\pm 3\sqrt{5}$
3. $\pm 2\sqrt{6}$
4. $\pm 4\sqrt{2}$

Cooperative Learning and High School Geometry: Becky Bride
Kagan Publishing • 1 (800) WEE CO-OP • www.KaganOnline.com

ACTIVITY 4 SOLVING SIMPLE QUADRATIC EQUATIONS

Structure: Simultaneous RoundTable

1. Do one step to solve for x. Initial your work and pass the paper to the next person in a clockwise direction.

2. On the paper just received, check the previous teammate's work, coach and/or praise, and then do one more step to solve the equation. Initial your work and pass the paper to the next person in a clockwise direction.

3. On the paper just received, check the previous teammate's work, coach and/or praise, and then finish solving the equation. Initial your work and pass the paper to the next person in a clockwise direction.

4. On the paper just received, check the previous work and coach if necessary. Then sign the paper indicating your approval of all the work done.

Cooperative Learning and High School Geometry: Becky Bride
Kagan Publishing • 1 (800) WEE CO-OP • www.KaganOnline.com

275

LESSON 2
PYTHAGOREAN THEOREM AND ITS CONVERSE

This lesson contains two exploratory activities—one for the Pythagorean Theorem and the other for its converse. Following each are activities to process each concept. The exploratory activity for the Pythagorean Theorem emphasizes how the Pythagoreans visualized mathematics. They thought about all mathematics in terms of geometric shapes. So, to them, the area of the square on one leg of the right triangle plus the area of the square on the other leg of the right triangle literally equaled the area of the square on the hypotenuse of the right triangle.

ACTIVITY 1
EXPLORING THE PYTHAGOREAN THEOREM

▶ **Materials**
- 1 Blackline 7.2.1 per student
- 1 sheet of paper and pencil per student
- 1 pair of scissors per student
- 1 tape dispenser per team

Have students complete Blackline 7.2.1.

Note:
Make copies of the diagram on a separate sheet of paper or copy the activity on 2 pieces of paper, so as the students cut out the

necessary parts of the diagram without cutting through the questions on the backside of the paper.

ACTIVITY 2
PROCESSING THE PYTHAGOREAN THEOREM

▶ **Structure**
- Simultaneous RoundTable

▶ **Materials**
- Transparencies 7.2.2a and 7.2.2b
- 1 sheet of paper and pencil per student

1. To begin, Teammate 1 writes problem 1, Teammate 2 writes problem 2, Teammate 3 writes problem 3, and Teammate 4 writes problem 4 on his/her sheet of paper.

2. Each teammate writes the Pythagorean formula on his/her paper, initials the formula, and passes the paper to the next person in a clockwise direction.

3. Each teammate checks the previous work, coaches and/or praises his/her teammate for a job well done. Each teammate substitutes the appropriate values into the Pythagorean formula, initials the equation, and passes the paper to the next person in a clockwise direction.

4. Each teammate checks the previous work, coaches and/or praises his/her teammate for a job well done. Each teammate solves the equation on his/her paper putting his/her answer in simplest radical form, initials the work, and passes the paper to the next person in a clockwise direction.

5. Each teammate checks all the previous work and coaches and/or praises his/her teammate for a job well done. Each teammate signs the paper indicating his/her approval of all work done.

Cooperative Learning and High School Geometry: Becky Bride
Kagan Publishing • 1 (800) WEE CO-OP • www.KaganOnline.com

3 ADVANCED PROCESSING OF THE PYTHAGOREAN THEOREM

1. Student A supplies one sheet paper, folded in half lengthwise with his/her name in one column and a partner's name in the other column.

2. Student B is the first boss and Student A is the first secretary.

3. As the boss, Student B tells Student A how to do the problem. Student A, the secretary, records what Student B says in Student B's column of the paper.

4. If the boss makes a mistake, then the secretary coaches and praises once the boss does it correctly. Otherwise, the secretary praises the boss.

5. Reverse roles for each problem and repeat steps 3 and 4.

▶ **Structure**
 · Boss/Secretary

▶ **Materials**
 · 1 Blackline 7.2.3 per pair of students
 · 1 sheet of paper and pencil per pair of students

4 APPLICATIONS OF THE PYTHAGOREAN THEOREM

1. Student B supplies one sheet of paper, folded in half lengthwise. Each member of the pair writes his/her name at the top of one column.

2. Student B does problem one recording his/her work on his/her side of the paper while Student A watches, checks the work, and coaches if necessary.

3. Repeat step 2, reversing roles, until all the problems are done.

▶ **Structure**
 · RallyCoach

▶ **Materials**
 · 1 Blackline 7.2.4 per pair of students
 · 1 sheet of paper and pencil per pair of students

Chapter 7: Pythagorean Theorem and Special Right Triangles

L e s s o n   T w o

Cooperative Learning and High School Geometry: Becky Bride
Kagan Publishing • 1 (800) WEE CO-OP • www.KaganOnline.com

277

ACTIVITY

5

EXPLORING THE CONVERSE OF THE PYTHAGOREAN THEOREM

▶ Materials
- 1 Blackline 7.2.5 per student
- 1 sheet of paper and pencil per student
- 1 ruler and compass per student
- 1 protractor or sheet of patty paper per student

Have students complete Blackline 7.2.5.

ACTIVITY

6

FIND THE RIGHT TRIANGLE

▶ Structure
- Variation of Find the Fiction

▶ Materials
- 1 sheet of paper and pencil per student

1. All students write three trios of segment lengths—two that don't form a right triangle and one that does form a right triangle.

2. One student stands and reads three trios of segments or shows the teammates the three trios.

3. The seated teammates individually determine which two trios form a right triangle.

4. The seated teammates show each other their answers, and come to a consensus as to which trio forms a right triangle.

5. If the seated teammates are correct, the student standing praises them.

6. If the seated teammates are wrong, then the standing teammate coaches the team. The seated teammates then praise the standing teammate for challenging them.

7. Repeat steps 2-6 until each teammate has had a chance to read his/her trios of segments.

Cooperative Learning and High School Geometry: Becky Bride
Kagan Publishing • 1 (800) WEE CO-OP • www.KaganOnline.com

1 EXPLORING THE PYTHAGOREAN THEOREM

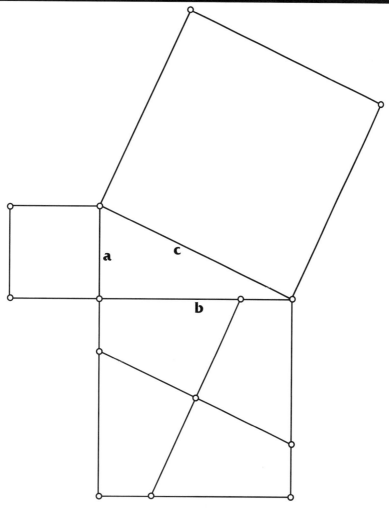

1. What are the lengths of all the sides of the smallest square? To which side of the triangle does this length correspond, a leg or a hypotenuse?

2. Write an expression for the area of the small square.

3. What are the lengths of all the sides of the medium square? To which side of the triangle does this length correspond, a leg or a hypotenuse?

4. Write an expression for the area of the medium square.

5. What are the lengths of all the sides of the largest square? To which side of the triangle does this length correspond, a leg or a hypotenuse?

Cooperative Learning and High School Geometry: Becky Bride
Kagan Publishing • 1 (800) WEE CO-OP • www.KaganOnline.com

279

6. Write an expression for the area of the largest square.

7. Cut out the small square.

8. Cut out the medium square and cut the square into 4 congruent pieces by cutting on the segments already drawn inside the square.

9. Taking the small square and the 4 congruent pieces of the medium square, place them in the large square on the hypotenuse of the triangle, so that the five pieces completely cover the large square with no gaps or overlaps. Tape in place.

10. What you have demonstrated is that the area of the small square together with the area of the medium square is equal to the area of the large square. Write this relationship using the expressions developed in steps 2, 4, and 6.

11. Summarize your findings in a complete sentence.

Cooperative Learning and High School Geometry: Becky Bride
Kagan Publishing • 1 (800) WEE CO-OP • www.KaganOnline.com

ACTIVITY 2
PROCESSING THE PYTHAGOREAN THEOREM

Structure: Simultaneous RoundTable

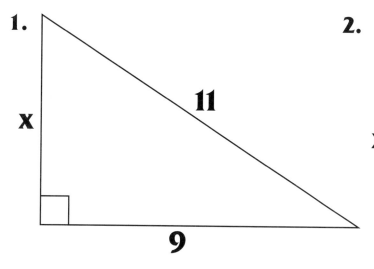

1.

x

11

9

2.

10

x

20

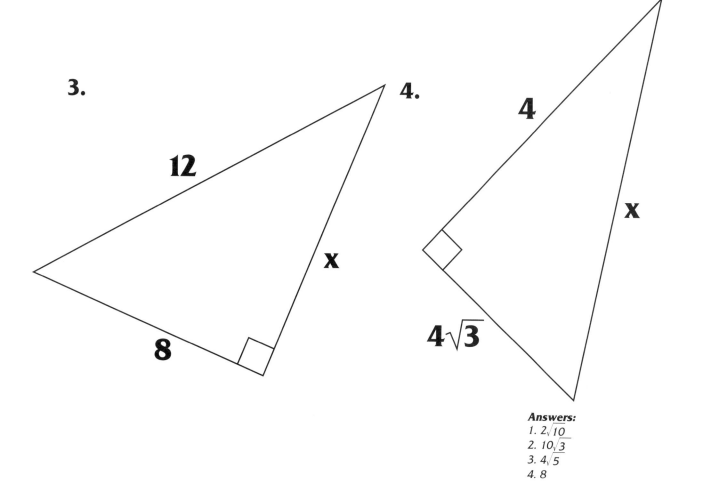

3.

12

8

x

4.

4

x

$4\sqrt{3}$

Answers:
1. $2\sqrt{10}$
2. $10\sqrt{3}$
3. $4\sqrt{5}$
4. 8

Cooperative Learning and High School Geometry: Becky Bride
Kagan Publishing • 1 (800) WEE CO-OP • www.KaganOnline.com

ACTIVITY 2 PROCESSING THE PYTHAGOREAN THEOREM

Structure: Simultaneous RoundTable

1. Write the Pythagorean formula on your paper, initial the formula, and pass the paper to the next person in a clockwise direction.

2. Check the previous work and coach and/or praise your teammate for a job well done. Substitute the appropriate values into the Pythagorean formula, initial the equation, and pass the paper to the next person in a clockwise direction.

3. Check the previous work and coach and/or praise your teammate for a job well done. Solve the equation on your paper, putting your answer in simplest radical form. Initial the work, and pass the paper to the next person in a clockwise direction.

4. Check all the previous work and coach and/or praise your teammate for a job well done. Sign the paper, indicating your approval of all work done.

Cooperative Learning and High School Geometry: Becky Bride
Kagan Publishing • 1 (800) WEE CO-OP • www.KaganOnline.com

ADVANCED PROCESSING OF
THE PYTHAGOREAN THEOREM

Structure: Boss/Secretary

Find the value of all variables. All answers must be in simplest radical form.

1.

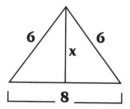

2.

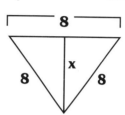

3.

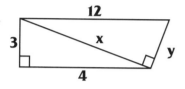

4.

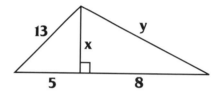

5.

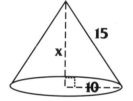

6.

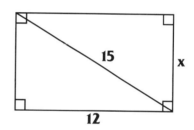

7.

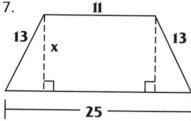

8.

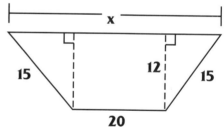

9.

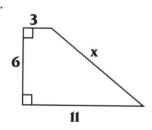

10.

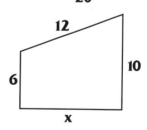

Answers:
1. $2\sqrt{5}$
2. $4\sqrt{3}$
3. $5; \sqrt{119}$
4. $12; 4\sqrt{13}$
5. $5\sqrt{5}$
6. 9
7. $2\sqrt{30}$
8. 38
9. 10
10. $8\sqrt{2}$

Cooperative Learning and High School Geometry: Becky Bride
Kagan Publishing • 1 (800) WEE CO-OP • www.KaganOnline.com

283

ACTIVITY 4
APPLICATIONS OF THE PYTHAGOREAN THEOREM

Structure: RallyCoach

For each problem, a) draw a diagram, b) write an equation, c) solve the equation, d) write the answer, using a complete sentence. *Round answers to the nearest tenth.*

1. Jose's school is 2 miles north of his house and the soccer fields are 3 miles east of his house. What is the distance from Jose's school to the soccer fields?

2. A 10-foot ladder is placed against a house. If the base of the ladder is 3.5 feet from the base of the house, how high does the ladder reach on the house?

3. One end of a guy wire will attach to a telephone pole 10 feet above the ground. The other end of the guy wire will attach to a bracket located 30 feet from the base of the pole. How long of a guy wire is needed?

4. Find the length of the diagonal of a box whose length is 10 inches, width is 8 inches, and height is 6 inches.

Answers:
1. 3.6 mi
2. 9.4 ft
3. 31.6 ft
4. 14.1 in

Cooperative Learning and High School Geometry: Becky Bride
Kagan Publishing • 1 (800) WEE CO-OP • www.KaganOnline.com

EXPLORING THE CONVERSE OF THE PYTHAGOREAN THEOREM

1. *Student 1:* Draw three segments on a sheet of paper whose lengths are 3 cm, 4 cm, and 5cm respectively. *Student 2:* Draw three segments on a sheet of paper whose lengths are 6 cm, 8cm, and 10 cm respectively. *Student 3*: Draw three segments on a sheet of paper whose lengths are 5 cm, 12 cm, and 13 cm, respectively. *Student 4:* Draw 3 segments on a sheet of paper whose lengths are 8 mm, 15 mm, and 17 cm, respectively.

2. Construct a triangle, using a compass and straightedge, that has sides the lengths of your three segments.

3. Using a sheet of patty paper or a protractor, determine if your triangle has a right angle. State your findings.

4. Consult your teammates to see if their triangles were right triangles. State your findings.

5. Substitute your segment lengths into the Pythagorean formula and see if a true statement (left side equals the right side) is formed. State your findings.

6. Consult your teammates to see if their segment lengths worked in the Pythagorean formula. State your findings.

7. If the lengths of three sides of a triangle satisfy the Pythagorean formula, does this guarantee a right triangle? Explain.

8. Summarize your findings in a complete sentence.

Cooperative Learning and High School Geometry: Becky Bride
Kagan Publishing • 1 (800) WEE CO-OP • www.KaganOnline.com

285

LESSON 3
SPECIAL RIGHT TRIANGLES

Students' understanding of 30-60-90 and 45-45-90 triangles is important for trigonometry, ACT and SAT tests. In this lesson, there are two derivation activities for the students to derive the ratios of the sides of each special triangle. Two activities have been included to process each. The lesson ends with applications of these triangles.

For Activities 5 and 6 the triangles have not been drawn to scale. When students work with these triangles in trigonometry, they will be drawing hand sketches with reference angles 30 or 60. It is very likely that in their hand sketches the shortest leg may not be opposite the 30° angle. If students learn that the ratio of the sides in a 30-60-90 triangle in ascending order is (relying on degrees not the diagram) x, $x\sqrt{3}$, and $2x$ and that the smallest side is opposite the smallest angle etc., then students will be successful with these triangles in spite of the drawing. Therefore, the triangles are purposely not drawn to scale.

ACTIVITY 1
DERIVING THE RATIO OF THE SIDES OF A 45-45-90 TRIANGLE

▶ **Materials**
· 1 Blackline 7.3.1 per student
· 1 pencil per student

Have students complete
Blackline 7.3.1.

ACTIVITY 2
WORKING WITH 45-45-90 TRIANGLES

▶ **Structure**
· RallyTable

▶ **Materials**
· 1 Blackline 7.3.2 per pair of students
· 1 sheet of paper and pencil per pair of students.

1. Student A does problem 1, writing in his/her column of the paper.

2. Student B coaches and/or praises Student A for a job well done and does the next problem, writing in his/her column of the paper.

3. Student A coaches and/or praises Student B for a job well done.

4. Repeat steps 1-3 alternating students for the remainder of the questions.

Cooperative Learning and High School Geometry: Becky Bride
Kagan Publishing • 1 (800) WEE CO-OP • www.KaganOnline.com

MATCH MY LEGS AND HYPOTENUSE

1. Each student is given a card.

2. Students mix around the room trading cards while music plays.

3. When the music stops, the students stop.

4. Teacher gives the next set of directions for finding matches.

5. Students search and find their match.

Tips:
To work on curriculum, during the mix stage students can pair.
If a student has a card with a

hypotenuse given on it he/she will ask his/her partner what the length of a leg of the triangle is. If a student has a card with the length of a leg on it then he/she will ask his/her partner what the length of the hypotenuse of the triangle is. Then the students trade cards.

Have students use gambits as they meet to exchange cards and as they leave to find someone else with whom to exchange.

During the match stage, students can talk or it can be done silently.

To help students find matches, have students that have found their match move to the outside perimeter of the room so there are fewer students to search through for those still needing to find their match.

▶ **Structure**
· Mix-N-Match

▶ **Materials**
· 1 set of Mix-N-Match cards (Blackline 7.3.3)

If students have difficulty, repeat the structure.

To collect the cards ask that both cards be given to one member of each pair. Then as the students return to their seats they will hand the pairs of cards to the teacher. By doing this, the matches are together so when the next class comes in with a different number of students, the teacher will be able to ensure that matches be made when the cards are redistributed.

DERIVING THE RATIO OF THE SIDES OF A 30-60-90 TRIANGLE

Have students complete Blackline 7.3.4.

▶ **Materials**
· 1 Blackline 7.3.4 per student
· 1 pencil per student

WORKING WITH 30-60-90 TRIANGLES

1. Student A supplies one sheet paper, folded in half lengthwise with his/her name in one column and a partner's name in the other column.

2. Student B is the first boss and Student A is the first secretary.

3. As the boss, Student B tells Student A how to do the problem. Student A, the secre-

tary, records what Student B says in Student B's column of the paper.

4. If the boss makes a mistake, then the secretary coaches and praises once the boss does it correctly. Otherwise, the secretary praises the boss.

5. Reverse roles for each problem and repeat steps 3 and 4.

▶ **Structure**
· Boss/Secretary

▶ **Materials**
· 1 Blackline 7.3.5 per pair of students
· 1 sheet of paper and pencil per pair of students

Cooperative Learning and High School Geometry: Becky Bride
Kagan Publishing • 1 (800) WEE CO-OP • www.KaganOnline.com

287

Chapter 7: Pythagorean Theorem
and Special Right Triangles

L e s s o n   T h r e e

MATCH MY PARTS

▶ Structure
• Variation of Mix-N-Match

▶ Materials
• 1 set of Mix-N-Match cards (Blackline 7.3.6)

1. Each student is given a card.

2. Students mix around the room, trading cards while music plays.

3. When the music stops, the students stop.

4. Teacher gives the next set of directions for finding matches.

5. Students search and find their match. A match consists of three students—each with one side of a given 30-60-90 triangle.

Tips:
To work on curriculum during the mix stage, students can pair. If a student has a card with a leg measurement on it, he/she will ask his/her partner what the length of the hypotenuse is. If a student has a card with the hypotenuse length on it, then he/she will ask his/her partner what the length of the leg opposite the 30 degree angle is. Then the students trade cards.

Have students use gambits as they meet to exchange cards and as they leave to find someone else with whom to exchange.

During the match stage, students can talk or it can be done silently.

To help students find matches, have students that have found their match move to the outside perimeter of the room so there are fewer students to search through for those still needing to find their match.

If students have difficulty, repeat the structure.

To collect the cards, ask that both cards be given to one member of each pair. Then as the students return to their seats, they will hand the pairs of cards to the teacher. By doing this, the matches are together so when the next class comes in with a different number of students, the teacher will be able to ensure that matches be made when the cards are redistributed.

Note:
The triangles are arranged by their matches on Blackline 7.3.6. That can serve as your key.

APPLICATIONS OF SPECIAL RIGHT TRIANGLES

▶ Structure
• Boss/Secretary

▶ Materials
• 1 Blackline 7.3.7 per pair of students
• 1 sheet of paper and pencil per pair of students

1. Student A supplies one sheet paper, folded in half lengthwise with his/her name in one column and a partner's name in the other column.

2. Student B is the first boss and Student A is the first secretary.

3. As the boss, Student B tells Student A how to do the problem. Student A, the secretary, records what Student B says in Student B's column of the paper.

4. If the boss makes a mistake, then the secretary coaches and praises once the boss does it correctly. Otherwise, the secretary praises the boss.

5. Reverse roles for each problem and repeat steps 3 and 4.

ACTIVITY
1 DERIVING THE RATIO OF THE SIDES OF A 45-45-90 TRIANGLE

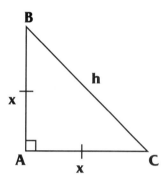

1. What are the measures of ∠B and ∠C? Explain how you arrived at your answer.

2. Write the Pythagorean formula. Write an equation in terms of *x* and *h* by substituting the side lengths into the formula.

3. Solve for *h*. Your answer must be in simplest radical form.

4. Redraw the triangle above, substituting your answer from step 3 for *h* on the diagram.

5. Summarize your findings in a complete sentence.

Cooperative Learning and High School Geometry: Becky Bride
Kagan Publishing • 1 (800) WEE CO-OP • www.KaganOnline.com

289

ACTIVITY 2

WORKING WITH
45-45-90 TRIANGLES

Structure: RallyTable

For each problem, find the lengths of the other two sides of the triangle. All answers must be in simplest radical form. Diagrams are not drawn to scale.

1.

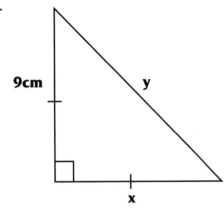

2.

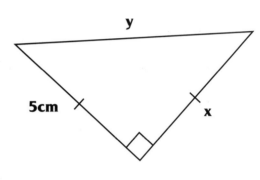

3.

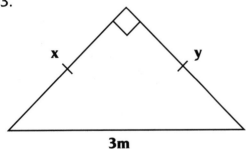

4.

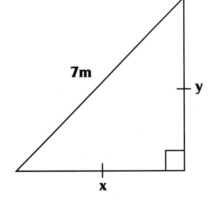

Answers:
1. x=9 y=9√2
2. x=5 y=5√2
3. x=3√2 =y
      2
4. x=y=7√2
        2

Cooperative Learning and High School Geometry: Becky Bride
Kagan Publishing • 1 (800) WEE CO-OP • www.KaganOnline.com

ACTIVITY
3 MATCH MY LEGS AND HYPOTENUSE

Structure: Mix-N-Match

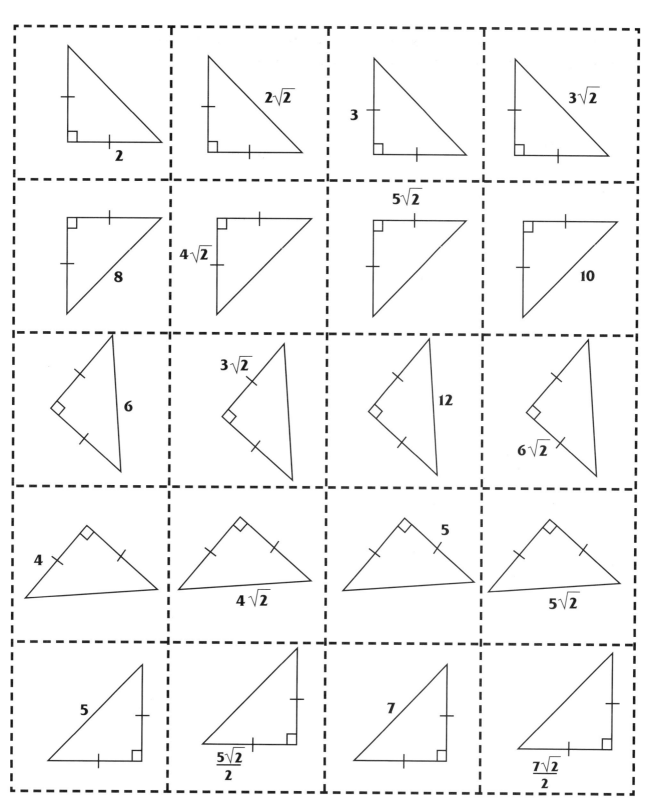

ACTIVITY 3
MATCH MY LEGS AND HYPOTENUSE

Structure: Mix-N-Match

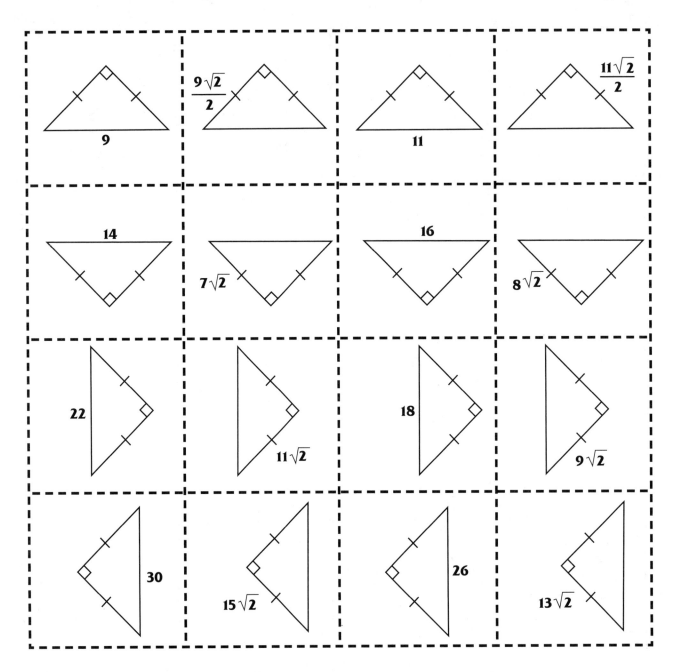

Cooperative Learning and High School Geometry: Becky Bride
Kagan Publishing • 1 (800) WEE CO-OP • www.KaganOnline.com

4 DERIVING THE RATIO OF THE SIDES OF A 30-60-90 TRIANGLE

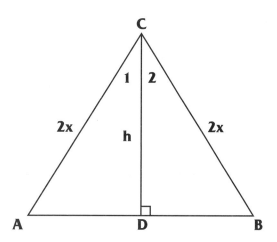

1. △ABC is an equilateral triangle. What is the measure of:

   m∠A =　　　　　m∠B =　　　　　m∠ACB =

2. $\overline{CD}$ is an altitude of the equilateral triangle. What does $\overline{CD}$ do to $\overline{AB}$?

3. Based on your answer to problem #2, find the following lengths in terms of x and write them on the diagram.

   AB =　　　　　AD =　　　　　BD =

4. $\overline{CD}$ is an altitude of the equilateral triangle. What does $\overline{CD}$ do to ∠ACB?

5. Find the following angle measures:

   m∠1 =　　　　　m∠2 =

6. Highlight △DBC. It is a 30-60-90 triangle. Write the Pythagorean formula. Write an equation, substituting the side lengths of $\overline{CD}$, $\overline{CB}$, and $\overline{DB}$ into the formula.

7. Solve the equation written in step 4 for *h*. Leave your answer in simplest radical form.

8. Redraw the triangle above, substituting your answer from step 5 for *h* on the diagram.

9. Summarize your findings in a complete sentence.

Cooperative Learning and High School Geometry: Becky Bride
Kagan Publishing • 1 (800) WEE CO-OP • www.KaganOnline.com

293

WORKING WITH
30-60-90 TRIANGLES

Structure: Boss/Secretary

For each problem, find the lengths of the other two sides of the triangle. **All answers must be in simplest radical form.** *Diagrams are not drawn to scale.*

1.

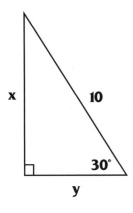

2.

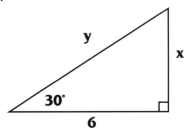

3.

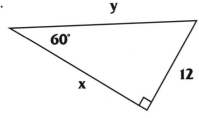

4.

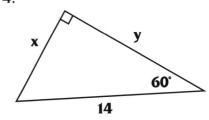

Answers:
1. x=5 y=5$\sqrt{3}$
2. x=2$\sqrt{3}$ y=4$\sqrt{3}$
3. x=4$\sqrt{3}$ y=8$\sqrt{3}$
4. x=7$\sqrt{3}$ y=7

Cooperative Learning and High School Geometry: Becky Bride
Kagan Publishing • 1 (800) WEE CO-OP • www.KaganOnline.com

ACTIVITY

6 MATCH MY PARTS

Structure: Variation of Mix-N-Match

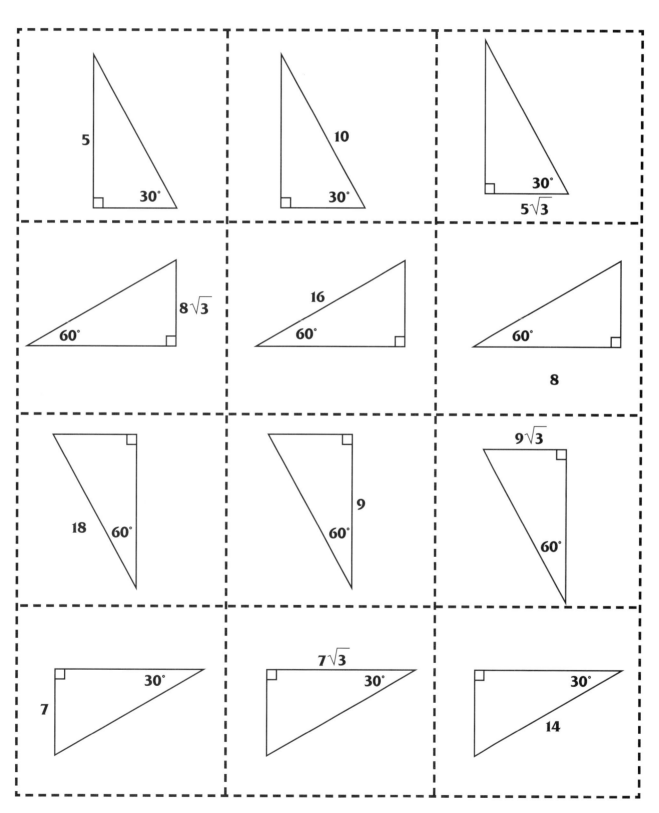

Cooperative Learning and High School Geometry: Becky Bride
Kagan Publishing • 1 (800) WEE CO-OP • www.KaganOnline.com

295

ACTIVITY
6 MATCH MY PARTS

Structure: Variation of Mix-N-Match

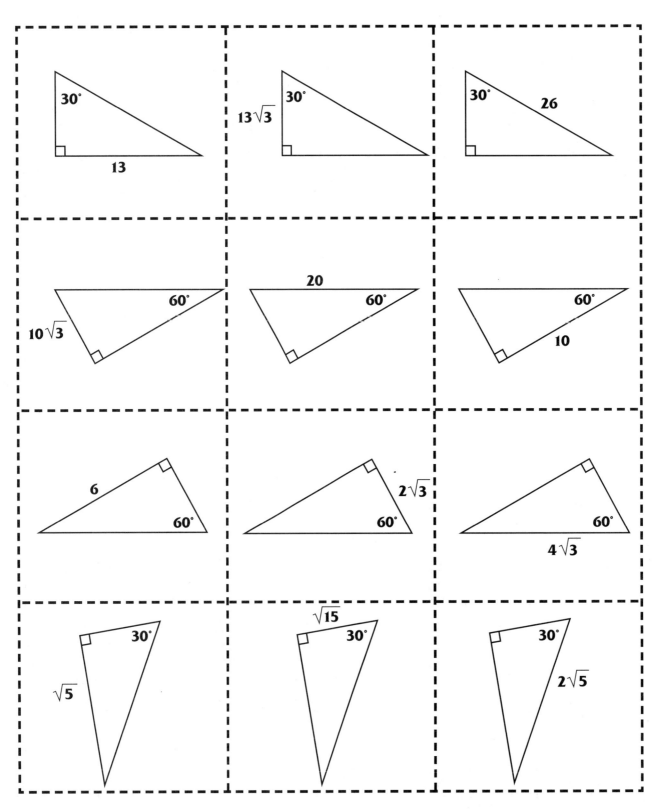

Cooperative Learning and High School Geometry: Becky Bride
Kagan Publishing • 1 (800) WEE CO-OP • www.KaganOnline.com

MATCH MY PARTS

Structure: Variation of Mix-N-Match

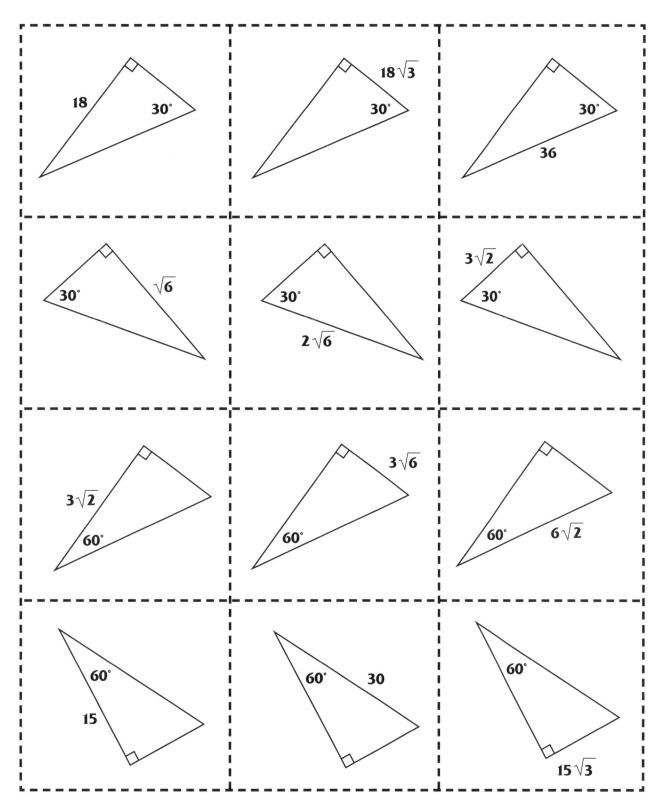

Cooperative Learning and High School Geometry: Becky Bride
Kagan Publishing • 1 (800) WEE CO-OP • www.KaganOnline.com

297

7 APPLICATIONS OF SPECIAL RIGHT TRIANGLES

Structure: Boss/Secretary

For each problem a) draw a diagram, b) write an equation, c) solve the equation, and d) write your answers in complete sentences. Round all answers to the nearest tenth.

1. Sally would like to install crown molding around the ceiling in her living room. The molding forms an isosceles right triangle with the wall and ceiling with the molding being the hypotenuse of the right triangle. What is the distance from the edge of the molding to the corner where the ceiling meets the wall, if the molding is 6 inches wide?

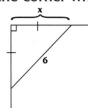

2. A guy wire needs to be attached to a telephone pole that is perpendicular to the ground. The guy wire will make a 60° angle with the ground. It will be anchored to the ground 10 feet from the base of the pole. How high up the pole will the guy wire be anchored?

3. The angle of elevation of a ship to a lighthouse is 60°. If the lighthouse is known to be 90 feet high, how far from the base of the lighthouse is the ship?

4. Ann is building a dog house. She needs to make some trusses to support the roof. The trusses will be isosceles right triangles (right angle at the peak) with the ends of the hypotenuse resting on two walls, which are 4 feet apart. How long will the boards be that are the legs of the right triangle if the boards extend 0.5 feet beyond the hypotenuse?

Answers:
1. 4.2 inches
2. 17.3 feet
3. 52.0 feet
4. 3.3 feet

Cooperative Learning and High School Geometry: Becky Bride
Kagan Publishing • 1 (800) WEE CO-OP • www.KaganOnline.com

AREA

This chapter leads the students through an exploratory exercise for area, concrete development of area formulas, and structures that will reinforce the concepts taught. As a prerequisite to this unit, dimensional analysis is included. The level of student taught will determine if this review is necessary. An honors class may want to go directly to the exploration for area. For a class with average students, the dimensional analysis will be a great review. For a class of struggling students it is a must. The conversions are presented using dimensional analysis because it plays such a key role in science, reinforces ratios, and is easily transferable to conversions with units new to the student.

LESSON 1
DIMENSIONAL ANALYSIS

"Funny Forms of One"

To begin, discuss different ways to write the number one in fraction form. Model with obvious fractions like $\frac{2}{2}$, $\frac{3}{3}$, etc. Then model with more unique ones such as

$$\frac{x}{x} \qquad\qquad \frac{\sqrt{2}}{\sqrt{2}} \qquad\qquad \frac{\frac{2}{3}}{\frac{2}{3}}$$

The challenge now is to make the numerator look different than the denominator yet still be equivalent to one. Model examples like $\frac{3 + 4}{8 - 1}$ and $\frac{1\text{ ft.}}{12\text{ in.}}$

Focus on these kinds of fractions in the RoundTable structure. Following are the steps to get students to generate their own "funny forms of one."

ACTIVITY 1

LISTING FUNNY FORMS OF ONE

▶ **Structure**
  • RoundTable

▶ **Materials**
  • 1 sheet of paper and pencil per team

1. Student 1 gets out a sheet of paper and folds it in fourths. Each teammate puts his/her name in one quadrant of the paper.

2. Student 1 writes one example of a funny form of one in his/her quadrant of the paper.

3. Student 2 writes an example of another funny form of one in his/her quadrant.

4. Student 3 writes one example of another funny form of one in his/her quadrant.

5. Student 4 writes an example of another funny form of one in his/her quadrant.

6. Repeat steps 2-5 for 60 seconds, rotating the paper through all teammates as many times as possible.

Cooperative Learning and High School Geometry: Becky Bride
Kagan Publishing • 1 (800) WEE CO-OP • www.KaganOnline.com

ACTIVITY

2 PROCESSING FUNNY FORMS OF ONE

Note:
Activity 2 processes how an entry in any conversion table or chart can be written as a funny form of one two different ways.

Ex: 1 yd = 3 ft

$$\frac{1\ yd}{3\ ft} \qquad or \qquad \frac{3\ ft}{1\ yd}$$

1. Student A does problem 1, writing in his/her column of the paper.

2. Student B coaches and/or praises Student A for a job well done and does the next problem, writing in his/her column of the paper.

3. Student A coaches and/or praises Student B for a job well done.

4. Repeat steps 1-3 alternating students for the remainder of the questions.

▶ **Structure**
• RallyTable

▶ **Materials**
• Transparency 8.1.2
• 1 sheet of paper and pencil per pair of students

ACTIVITY

3 ONE-STEP CONVERTING WITH FUNNY FORMS OF ONE

1. Student A supplies one sheet of paper, folded in half lengthwise with his/her name in one column and a partner's name in the other column.

2. Student B is the first boss and Student A is the first secretary.

3. As the boss, Student B tells Student A how to do the problem. Student A, the secretary, records what Student B says in Student B's column of the paper.

4. If the boss makes a mistake, then the secretary coaches and praises once the boss does it correctly. Otherwise, the secretary praises the boss.

5. Reverse roles for each problem and repeat steps 3 and 4.

▶ **Structure**
• Boss/Secretary

▶ **Materials**
• Transparency 8.1.3
• 1 sheet of paper and pencil per pair of students

Cooperative Learning and High School Geometry: Becky Bride
Kagan Publishing • 1 (800) WEE CO-OP • www.KaganOnline.com

301

4 MULTI-STEP CONVERTING WITH FUNNY FORMS OF ONE

▶ **Structure**
- Simultaneous RoundTable

▶ **Materials**
- Transparency 8.1.4
- 1 sheet of paper and pencil per pair of students

1. Teammate 1 writes problem 1 on his/her paper, Teammate 2 writes problem 2, Teammate 3 writes problem 3, and Teammate 4 writes problem 4.

2. Each teammate writes the first ratio needed to begin the conversion for their problem. They initial their work and pass the paper to the next person in a clockwise direction.

3. On the paper just received, each teammate checks the previous teammate's work, coaches if wrong, praises once it is right, and then writes the next ratio needed to convert. They pass the paper to the next person in a clockwise direction.

4. Repeat steps 2-3, until no more ratios are needed.

5. Pass the papers to the next person in a clockwise direction. Each student simplifies the problems on the paper they receive.

Tips:
Model this process for students.

Each teammate could write in a different color rather than initial work.

Cooperative Learning and High School Geometry: Becky Bride
Kagan Publishing • 1 (800) WEE CO-OP • www.KaganOnline.com

ACTIVITY
2 **LISTING FUNNY FORMS OF ONE**

Structure: RallyTable

1. 4 qt = 1 gal

2. 5280 ft = 1 mi

3. 1000 m = 1 km

4. 16 oz = 1 lb

Cooperative Learning and High School Geometry: Becky Bride
Kagan Publishing • 1 (800) WEE CO-OP • www.KaganOnline.com

303

ACTIVITY 3 ONE-STEP CONVERTING WITH FUNNY FORMS OF ONE

Structure: Boss/Secretary

Convert each of the following into the units specified. *Round answers to the nearest tenth.*

1. 98 in = ? ft

2. 72 c = ? pt

3. 87 yd = ? ft

4. 23 gal = ? qt

5. 18 g = ? mg

6. 346 mm = ? cm

Answers: 1. 8.2 ft; 2. 36 pt; 3. 261 ft; 4. 92 qt; 5. 18,000 mg; 6. 34.6 cm

Cooperative Learning and High School Geometry: Becky Bride
Kagan Publishing • 1 (800) WEE CO-OP • www.KaganOnline.com

ACTIVITY

4 MULTI-STEP CONVERTING WITH FUNNY FORMS OF ONE

Structure: Simultaneous RoundTable

Round answers to the nearest tenth.

1. 2.3 gal = ? c

2. 0.45 mi = ? in

3. 4,893 mm = ? km

4. 833 tbsp = ? qt

Answers:
1. 36.8 c
2. 28,512 in
3. 0.004893 km
4. 13.0 qt

Cooperative Learning and High School Geometry: Becky Bride
Kagan Publishing • 1 (800) WEE CO-OP • www.KaganOnline.com

305

LESSON 2
EXPLORATION OF AREA

Concrete development is important for understanding the concept of area. This exploratory activity begins with rectangles whose area is easy to count. It then progresses into right triangles whose area is half of the area of the rectangle whose sides are the lengths of the legs of the right triangle. Once students can find the area of right triangles, they can do just about anything because most of the figures can be separated into rectangles and right triangles. The obtuse triangle is a little more difficult. The students begin with a rectangle that surrounds the obtuse triangle. Subtracting the area not in the obtuse triangle from the rectangle is the easiest way to do it. The activity below requires a higher level of thinking, because the student is required to make the figure that has the given the area. For struggling students, a few more problems involving rectangles and right triangles would be beneficial before moving into the other figures.

ACTIVITY

1 EXPLORING AREA

▶ **Structure**
· Numbered Heads Together

▶ **Materials**
· 1 geoboard and rubber bands (or graph paper or dot paper) per team
· Transparency 8.2.1

1. Teacher announces a figure to be formed with a specified area.

2. Allow think time.

3. Students stand and discuss possible ways to form the figure. Students sit when everyone knows at least one way to form the figure. During this stage, there is no writing or use of rubber bands.

4. Teacher spins a student number. Students whose number was spun will make the figure on their geoboards, graph paper, or dot paper.

5. Geoboards are held up and the teacher and teams praise. With graph paper and dot paper, teammates check and praise.

6. Repeat steps 1-5.

Variation: Rather than having one student out of four make the figure have two students at each team make the figure. Using the 1-2 part of the student spinner as an A-B spin, fifty percent of the students will be active.

During think time, if students have dot paper, each student could connect the dots to form the figure, incorporating more individual accountability.

1 EXPLORING AREA

Structure: Numbered Heads Together

Form the following figures with the specified area.

1. Rectangle, with area 12 units²

2. Rectangle, with area 24 units²

3. Right triangle, with area 6 units²

4. Right triangle, with area 1.5 units²

5. Acute triangle, with area 6 units²

6. Acute triangle, with area 4.5 units²

7. Parallelogram, with area 10 units²

8. Parallelogram, with area 12 units²

9. Trapezoid, with area 15 units²

10. Trapezoid, with area 13.5 units²

Cooperative Learning and High School Geometry: Becky Bride
Kagan Publishing • 1 (800) WEE CO-OP • www.KaganOnline.com

LESSON 3
AREA OF RECTANGLES AND SQUARES

The geoboard activity is a wonderful introduction into generating the area of a rectangle. When students are asked how to compute the area of a rectangle without counting squares, they readily reply *length times width*. It is important to move the students to the formula $A = bh$. This makes concrete development of the other area formulas possible. It is essential that students understand that the relationship between any base and height is a perpendicular one, regardless of whether the figure is two-dimensional or three-dimensional. This will be the key for students to accurately choose the base and height of a figure when extraneous information is given.

The area of a square is easily derived from the rectangle because a square is a rectangle. When asked, students will give $A=bh$, $A = b^2$, or $A = h^2$, since the base and height are the same. Lower level students may find $A = bh$ easier because they will have fewer formulas to remember. Since the students know that the sides of a square are equal, they can easily use this formula. To reach many students, the formula can be written to match different intelligences. To reach the verbal/linguistic, write the formula in words: *Area = base x height*. The mathematical/logical student will love the formula in symbols. To reach the visual/spatial students, write the formula in the figure (see below).

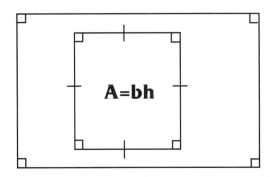

Stress that any time area is computed, the units must be the same. If they are not, then conversions are necessary. Having students include the units within their computations will reinforce algebra skills and will help prepare students for the mathematics required in science.

Examples:
   $A = bh$
   $A = 5m \cdot 7m$
   $A = 35m^2$

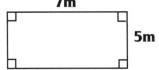

Writing the formula each time students use it helps with long-term memory and gives a framework when the students have to find the base or height, given the area.

308

1 PROCESSING AREA OF RECTANGLES AND SQUARES

1. Student A supplies one sheet paper, folded in half lengthwise with his/her name in one column and a partner's name in the other column.

2. Student B is the first boss and Student A is the first secretary.

3. As the boss, Student B tells Student A how to do the problem. Student A, the secretary, records what Student B says in Student B's column of the paper.

4. If the boss makes a mistake, then the secretary coaches and praises once the boss does it correctly. Otherwise, the secretary praises the boss.

5. Reverse roles for each problem and repeat steps 3 and 4.

▶ **Structure**
• Boss/Secretary

▶ **Materials**
• 1 Blackline 8.3.1 per pair of students
• 1 sheet of paper and pencil per pair of students

Cooperative Learning and High School Geometry: Becky Bride
Kagan Publishing • 1 (800) WEE CO-OP • www.KaganOnline.com

309

Lesson Three   Chapter 8: Area

PROCESSING AREA OF RECTANGLES AND SQUARES

Structure: Boss/Secretary

Compute the area of each figure. Pay attention to units. All figures are rectangles or squares.

1. Answer needs to be in feet.

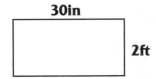

2. Answer needs to be in mm.

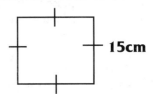

3. Answer needs to be in meters

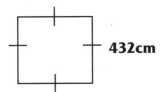

4. Answer needs to be in feet.

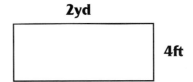

5. Find the area of a rectangular room that measures 24 ft by 21 ft. If carpeting costs $14.00 per square **yard**, how much will it cost to carpet this room?

6. Find the area of a rectangular garden with dimensions 4 yd by 7 yd. If pesticide costs $1.80 per square **foot**, find the total cost to fertilize the garden.

7 A rectangular countertop measures 3 ft by 8 ft. If tile costs $2.15 per square foot, find the cost to cover this countertop with tile.

8. A rectangular wall measures 8 yd by 3.3 yd. If a roll of wallpaper covers 43 square **feet**, how many rolls are needed to cover this wall?

Answers:
1. 5 ft²
2. 22,500 mm²
3. 18.6624 m²
4. 24 ft²
5. $784
6. $453.60
7. $51.60
8. 6 rolls

Cooperative Learning and High School Geometry: Becky Bride
Kagan Publishing • 1 (800) WEE CO-OP • www.KaganOnline.com

LESSON 4
AREA OF PARALLELOGRAMS

In Activity 1 students will see how easily a parallelogram can be transformed into a rectangle and why the formulas for rectangles and parallelograms are the same. The investigation is followed by a journal reflection because students' understanding of concepts deepens when they have to explain them. Since many state assessments and the NCTM standards require students to write about mathematics, this will give them practice.

ACTIVITY

1 EXPLORING AREA OF PARALLELOGRAMS

Have students complete
Blackline 8.4.1.

▶ **Materials**
• 1 Blackline 8.4.1 per student
• 2 pairs of scissors per team
• Tape or glue for the team

ACTIVITY

2 IDENTIFYING BASE AND HEIGHT OF PARALLELOGRAMS

Note:
Since the base and height of a parallelogram no longer both have to be the length of the sides of a parallelogram, a quick structure to identify the base and height is helpful. Activity 2 is designed for this. Then Activity 3 uses the same transparency and requires students to compute the area of the parallelograms.

1. Student A states the base and height of the parallelogram in problem 1 and states why he/she chose those numbers. Stating the reason reinforces that the relationship between a base and height is perpendicular.

2. Student B gives specific praise (i.e.: You did a nice job of remembering that the relationship between any base and height is a perpendicular one). Student B states the base and height for the next problem and states why he/she chose those numbers.

3. Student A gives specific praise.

4. Repeat steps 1-3, alternating Student A and Student B for 60 seconds.

▶ **Structure**
• RallyRobin

▶ **Materials**
• Transparency 8.4.2-3

Cooperative Learning and High School Geometry: Becky Bride
Kagan Publishing • 1 (800) WEE CO-OP • www.KaganOnline.com

311

Chapter 8: Area

Lesson Four

ACTIVITY

3

COMPUTING AREA OF PARALLELOGRAMS

▶ **Structure**
• Pairs Check

▶ **Materials**
• Transparency 8.4.2-3
• 1 sheet of paper and pencil per pair of students

1. Student B supplies one sheet of paper, folded in half lengthwise. Each member of the pair writes his/her name at the top of one column.

2. Student B does problem 1, recording his/her work on his/her side of the paper while Student A watches and coaches if necessary.

3. Student A checks Student B's work, coaches and/or praises. Then Student A does problem 2 on his/her side of the paper.

4. Student B checks Student A's work, coaches and/or praises.

5. After every two problems, the pair checks their answers with the other pair in their team, coaching and/or praising each others' work.

6. Repeat steps 2-5, reversing roles, until all the problems are done.

ACTIVITY

4

REVIEW: AREA OF RECTANGLES, SQUARES, AND PARALLELOGRAMS

▶ **Structure**
• Mix-N-Match

▶ **Materials**
• 1 set of Mix-N-Match cards (Blackline 8.4.4)

Note:
To review area of rectangles, squares, and parallelograms, the structure Mix-N-Match will be used. Make copies of the Mix-N-Match cards 8.4.3 onto card stock and cut on the lines to form cards. Laminating is recommended. For each card with a figure, there is a card that has that figure's area on it.

1. Each student is given a card.

2. Students mix around the room, trading cards while music plays.

3. When the music stops students stop.

4. Teacher announces the next set of directions for finding matches.

5. Students search and find their match.

Tips:
To work on curriculum during the mix stage, students can pair. If a student has a card with a figure on it he/she will ask his/her partner what the area is. Students who have a card with area on it then will ask their partners to give two possible numbers for base and height. Then the students trade cards.

Examples:
12 cm²

Base could be 4 cm and height could be 3 cm.

Have students use gambits as they meet to exchange cards and as they leave to find someone else with whom to exchange.

During the match stage, students can talk or it can be done silently.

To help students find matches, have students that have found their match move to the outside perimeter of the room so there are fewer students to search through for those still needing to find their match.

If students have difficulty, repeat the structure.

To collect the cards, ask that both cards be given to one member of each pair. Then as the students return to their seats they will hand the pairs of cards to the teacher. By doing this, the matches are together so when the next class comes in with a different number of students, the teacher will be able to ensure that matches can be made when the cards are distributed.

Cooperative Learning and High School Geometry: Becky Bride
Kagan Publishing • 1 (800) WEE CO-OP • www.KaganOnline.com

ACTIVITY 1 EXPLORING AREA OF PARALLELOGRAMS

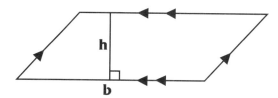

1. Cut the parallelogram out.

2. Cut along the altitude (height) of the parallelogram.

3. Rearrange the two pieces of the parallelogram to form a rectangle and glue or tape the rectangle below.

4. Answer the following questions:

   a. What is the area formula for a rectangle?

   b. With the pieces of the parallelogram rearranged, is the area of the new figure less than, more than, or equal to the area of the original figure? Explain your reasoning.

   c. What is the area formula for a parallelogram?

5. Journal Reflection:
Your teammate is in the hospital and needs to makeup today's work. Write a letter to your ill teammate explaining why the area formula of a parallelogram is the same as the formula for a rectangle.

IDENTIFYING BASE AND HEIGHT AND COMPUTING AREA OF PARALLELOGRAMS

ACTIVITY 2&3

Structures: RallyRobin and Pairs Check

Round 1: Choose the numbers that represent the base and height.

Round 2: Compute the area of the parallelogram.

1.

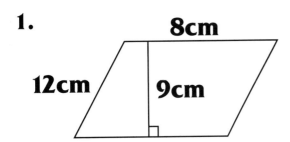

2.

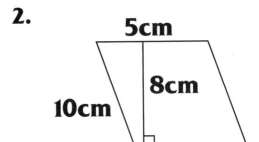

3.

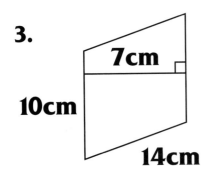

4.

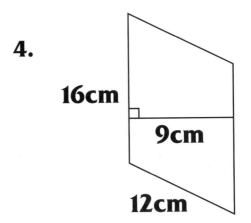

Answers for Activity 2:
1. 72 cm²
2. 40 cm²
3. 70 cm²
4. 144 cm²

Cooperative Learning and High School Geometry: Becky Bride
Kagan Publishing • 1 (800) WEE CO-OP • www.KaganOnline.com

ACTIVITY 4 REVIEW: AREA OF RECTANGLES, SQUARES, AND PARALLELOGRAMS

Structure: Mix-N-Match

4cm / 3cm	5cm / 4cm / 3cm	**12 cm²**	**15 cm²**
2cm	4cm / 2cm	**4 cm²**	**8 cm²**
9cm / 3cm / 2cm	3cm	**18 cm²**	**9 cm²**
4cm	5cm	**16 cm²**	**25 cm²**

Cooperative Learning and High School Geometry: Becky Bride
Kagan Publishing • 1 (800) WEE CO-OP • www.KaganOnline.com

315

REVIEW: AREA OF RECTANGLES, SQUARES, AND PARALLELOGRAMS

Structures: Mix-N-Match

6cm (square)	8cm, 7cm (rectangle)	**56 cm²**	**44 cm²**
7cm, 5cm (rectangle)	16cm, 4cm (rectangle)	**36 cm²**	**60 cm²**
11cm, 4cm, 6cm (parallelogram)	12cm, 4cm (rectangle)	**35 cm²**	**40 cm²**
10cm, 4cm, 6cm (parallelogram)	10cm, 6cm, 8cm (parallelogram)	**64 cm²**	**72 cm²**
12cm, 6cm, 9cm (parallelogram)	11cm, 6cm, 8cm (parallelogram)	**48 cm²**	**66 cm²**

Cooperative Learning and High School Geometry: Becky Bride
Kagan Publishing • 1 (800) WEE CO-OP • www.KaganOnline.com

LESSON 5
AREA OF TRIANGLES

This lesson explores triangular area. The exploratory exercise relates it to the area of a parallelogram, which the students already understand. There is an activity for students to identify the base and height of given triangles. Then two activities follow to process triangular area.

ACTIVITY 1
EXPLORING TRIANGULAR AREA

Have each student perform the investigation using Blackline 8.5.1. The figures the students will form with their two triangles are rectangles if the triangle drawn was a right triangle, otherwise the students will form parallelograms. Either way, the area formula for each is $A = bh$. Since each figure is made of two congruent triangles, it follows that one triangle would be half of the formula for rectangles and parallelograms. Writing the triangle area formula

$$A = \frac{1}{2}\,bh \text{ or } A = \frac{bh}{2}$$

gives students flexibility and reinforces that multiplying by a half is equivalent to dividing by 2. Some students prefer division to using fractions. Again, writing the formula in words, inside a triangle, and in symbols will match different intelligences.

▶ **Materials**
- 1 Blackline 8.5.1 per student
- 1 straightedge per student
- 1 sheet of patty paper per student
- Glue or tape for the team

ACTIVITY 2
IDENTIFYING BASE AND HEIGHT OF TRIANGLES

1. Student A states the base and height of the triangle in problem 1 and states why he/she chose those numbers. Stating why reinforces that the relationship between a base and height is perpendicular.

2. Student B gives specific praise (i.e.: You did a nice job of remembering that the relationship between any base and height is a perpendicular one). Student B states the base and height for the next problem and states why he/she chose those numbers.

3. Student A gives specific praise.

4. Repeat steps 1-3, alternating Student A and Student B, for 60 seconds.

▶ **Structure**
- RallyRobin

▶ **Materials**
- Transparency 8.5.2-3

Cooperative Learning and High School Geometry: Becky Bride
Kagan Publishing • 1 (800) WEE CO-OP • www.KaganOnline.com

317

Chapter 8: Area   Lesson Five

ACTIVITY

3 COMPUTE MY AREA

▶ **Structure**
• Boss/Secretary

▶ **Materials**
• Transparency 8.5.2-3
• 1 sheet of paper and pencil per pair of students

1. Student A supplies one sheet of paper, folded in half lengthwise with his/her name in one column and a partner's name in the other column.

2. Student B is the first boss and Student A is the first secretary.

3. As the boss, Student B tells Student A how to do the problem. Student A, the secretary, records what Student B says in Student B's column of the paper.

4. If the boss makes a mistake, then the secretary coaches and praises once the boss does it correctly. Otherwise, the secretary praises the boss.

5. Reverse roles for each problem and repeat steps 3 and 4.

ACTIVITY

4 PROCESSING AREA OF TRIANGLES PART 1

▶ **Structure**
• Mix-Pair-Discuss

▶ **Materials**
• 1 set of Mix-Pair-Discuss cards (Blackline 8.5.4-5)

1. Teacher distributes one card per student.

2. Students get up and mix. As they mix, they find a classmate who is not a teammate and pair.

3. One student asks his/her partner what the area of the triangle is on the card he/she is holding.

4. Partner responds.

5. Student coaches and/or praises their partner.

6. Roles reverse and steps 3-5 are repeated.

7. The students trade cards.

8. Following a gambit, pairs depart to find someone else to pair with and repeat steps 2-7.

9. Teacher calls time and students stop mixing.

Tips:
Play music to signal the start and stop of the Mix-Pair-Discuss.

Model the Mix-Pair-Discuss and ask a student to repeat your directions to see if they were clearly communicated.

As students look for a partner, they can put their hand up to signal that they are available.

At this point the structure Line Up can be used.

Cooperative Learning and High School Geometry: Becky Bride
Kagan Publishing • 1 (800) WEE CO-OP • www.KaganOnline.com

ACTIVITY

5 PROCESSING AREA OF TRIANGLES PART 2

1. Each student looks at the card he/she is holding and mentally computes the area.

2. Students line up in numerical order, according to the area of the triangle on their cards.

▶ **Structure**
· Line Up

▶ **Materials**
· 1 set of Mix-Pair-Discuss cards 8.5.4-5

Answers to Line Up:
First page

1. 6m²	2. 20m²
3. 27m²	4. 36.45m²
5. 26m²	6. 15m²
7. 40.5m²	8. 72m²
9. 21.7m²	10. 35m²
11. 48m²	12. 30m²
13. 18.45m²	14. 8m²
15. 32m²	16. 24m²
17. 28.7m²	18. 42m²

Second page

19. 49m²	20. 83.7m²
21. 90m²	22. 105m²
23. 25m²	24. 74.2m²
25. 16.4m²	26. 45m²
27. 12m²	28. 120m²
29. 50m²	30. 80m²
31. 54m²	32. 100m²
33. 36m²	34. 56.1m²
35. 60m²	36. 64m²

Cooperative Learning and High School Geometry: Becky Bride
Kagan Publishing • 1 (800) WEE CO-OP • www.KaganOnline.com

319

Chapter 8: Area
L e s s o n   F i v e

EXPLORING TRIANGULAR AREA

ACTIVITY 1

1. Using a straightedge, draw a triangle and its altitude, in the space above.

2. Using a straightedge, trace the triangle, onto a sheet of patty paper.

3. Using both triangles together, form a figure that you already know how to find the area of and tape or glue the patty paper in place above.

4. Share your figure with your teammates.

5. Discuss the questions below with your shoulder-to-shoulder partner.

6. Answer the following questions.
   a. Are the two triangles congruent?

   b. What is the area formula for the figure formed by the two triangles?

   c. What is the area for just one of the triangles, based on your answers to the first two questions?

7. Journal Reflection: You are helping your seventh-grade brother with his math homework. He has to find the area of all sorts of triangles. He refuses to complete his homework until you explain why the triangle area formula is just like the parallelogram's but is divided by two. Write what you tell your brother below.

Cooperative Learning and High School Geometry: Becky Bride
Kagan Publishing • 1 (800) WEE CO-OP • www.KaganOnline.com

IDENTIFYING BASE AND HEIGHT OF TRIANGLES AND COMPUTE MY AREA

Structures: RallyRobin and Boss/Secretary

Round 1: Name the base and height.
Round 2: Compute the area.

1.
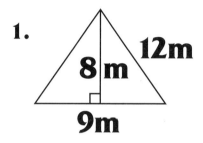

2.
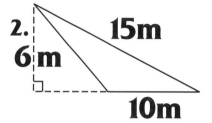

3.
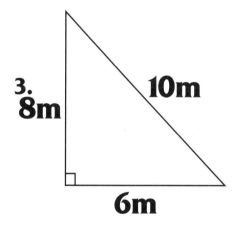

4.
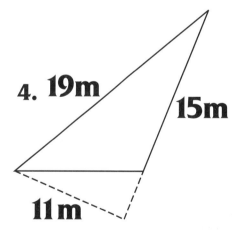

Answers:
1. 36 m²
2. 30 m²
3. 24 m²
4. 82.5 m²

Cooperative Learning and High School Geometry: Becky Bride
Kagan Publishing • 1 (800) WEE CO-OP • www.KaganOnline.com

321

ACTIVITY 4&5 PROCESSING AREA OF TRIANGLES PARTS 1 & 2

Structures: Mix-Pair-Discuss and Line Up

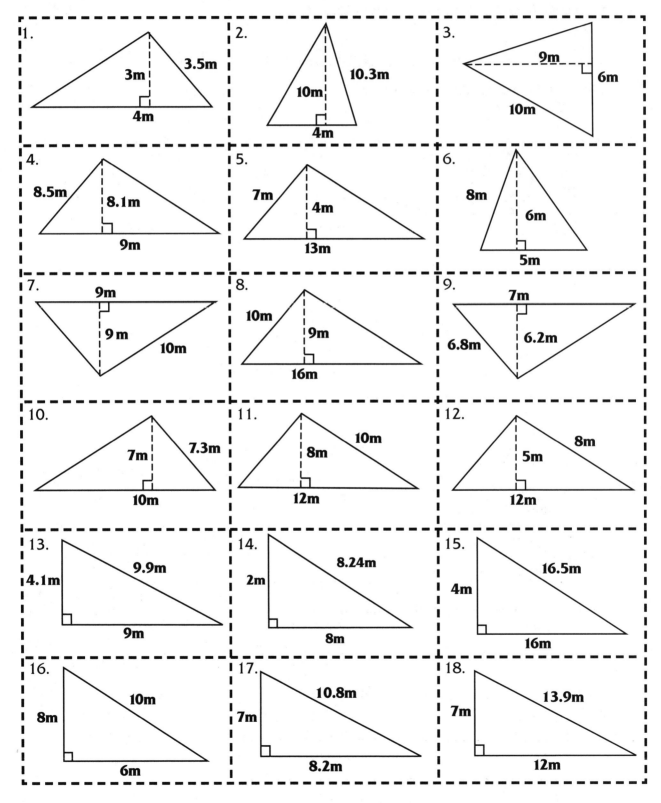

Cooperative Learning and High School Geometry: Becky Bride
Kagan Publishing • 1 (800) WEE CO-OP • www.KaganOnline.com

PROCESSING AREA OF TRIANGLES PARTS 1 & 2

ACTIVITY 4&5

Structures: Mix-Pair-Discuss and Line Up

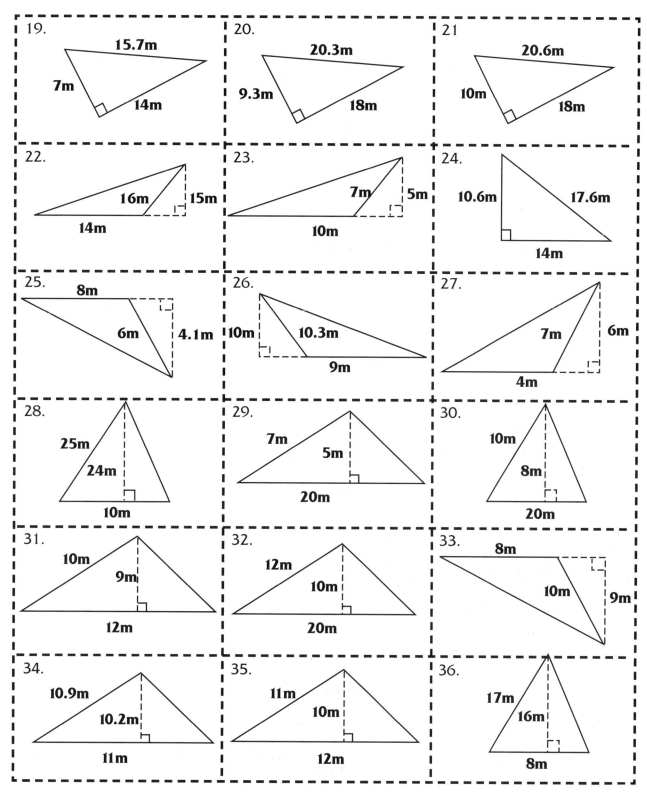

19. 15.7m 7m 14m

20. 20.3m 9.3m 18m

21 20.6m 10m 18m

22. 16m 15m 14m

23. 7m 5m 10m

24. 10.6m 17.6m 14m

25. 8m 6m 4.1m

26. 10m 10.3m 9m

27. 7m 6m 4m

28. 25m 24m 10m

29. 7m 5m 20m

30. 10m 8m 20m

31. 10m 9m 12m

32. 12m 10m 20m

33. 8m 10m 9m

34. 10.9m 10.2m 11m

35. 11m 10m 12m

36. 17m 16m 8m

Cooperative Learning and High School Geometry: Becky Bride
Kagan Publishing • 1 (800) WEE CO-OP • www.KaganOnline.com

323

LESSON 6
AREA OF TRAPEZOIDS

This lesson opens with an investigation that will lead to the area formula for a trapezoid concretely. It will link this formula to the parallelogram formula already developed. Again it is followed by a journal-writing activity to take the students' understanding a level deeper. Then, an activity follows to process this concept.

ACTIVITY 1
EXPLORING TRAPEZOIDAL AREA

▶ **Materials**
- 1 Blackline 8.6.1 per student
- 1 sheet of patty paper per student
- 1 straightedge per student
- Tape or glue for each team

Have students complete Blackline 8.6.1. Remind the students that b_1 and b_2 represents the parallel sides of a trapezoid, which are always the bases.

ACTIVITY 2
JOURNAL REFLECTION

▶ **Materials**
- Transparency 8.6.2
- 1 sheet of paper and pencil per student

Have students respond to the writing prompt on Transparency 8.6.2.

ACTIVITY 3
PROCESSING AREA OF TRAPEZOIDS

▶ **Structure**
- Boss/Secretary

▶ **Materials**
- Transparency 8.6.3
- 1 sheet of paper and pencil per pair of students

1. Student A supplies one sheet of paper, folded in half lengthwise with his/her name in one column and a partner's name in the other column.

2. Student B is the first boss and Student A is the first secretary.

3. As the boss, Student B tells Student A how to do the problem. Student A, the secretary, records what Student B says in Student B's column of the paper.

4. If the boss makes a mistake, then the secretary coaches and praises once the boss does it correctly. Otherwise, the secretary praises the boss.

5. Reverse roles for each problem and repeat steps 3 and 4.

Tip: The Number Heads Together structure could be used for this activity.

324

EXPLORING TRAPEZOIDAL AREA

1. In the space above, using a straightedge, draw two segments, one on each side of the straightedge, and unequal in length. These are the parallel sides. Join the endpoints of these segments to form a trapezoid.

2. Label the parallel sides, one b_1 and the other b_2. Draw the altitude of the trapezoid and label it h.

3. Trace the trapezoid onto a sheet of patty paper. Include the labels b_1, b_2, and h.

4. Using the patty paper trapezoid and the trapezoid at the top of this paper, arrange the patty paper trapezoid so that it, together with the trapezoid at the top, forms a parallelogram. Tape the patty paper in place.

5. Discuss the following questions with your teammates and then answer them in complete sentences below.
   a. Are the two trapezoids congruent?

   b. What variable represents the height of the trapezoid?

   c. The base of the parallelogram is composed of two segments. Write a variable expression for the base.

   d. Write a formula for the area of the parallelogram just formed with the two trapezoids using the information from questions b and c.

   e. Write a formula for just one trapezoid, based on your answers from the questions above.

Cooperative Learning and High School Geometry: Becky Bride
Kagan Publishing • 1 (800) WEE CO-OP • www.KaganOnline.com

325

JOURNAL REFLECTION

You are living in 500 BC along the Nile River. The Nile just flooded again and has left your property in the shape of a trapezoid. The surveyors have come out to survey your land for tax purposes, but they do not know how to find the area of a trapezoid. Since they know how to find the area of a parallelogram and you are the math sage, write to the surveyors your explanation of how to find the area of your land. You must convince them that the formula you propose is correct.

Cooperative Learning and High School Geometry: Becky Bride
Kagan Publishing • 1 (800) WEE CO-OP • www.KaganOnline.com

ACTIVITY 3
PROCESSING AREA OF TRAPEZOIDS

Structure: Boss/Secretary

Find the area of each figure.

1.

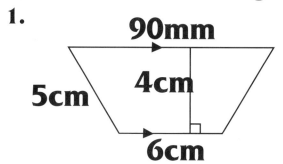

90mm

5cm 4cm

6cm

2.

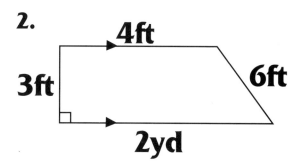

4ft

3ft 6ft

2yd

3.

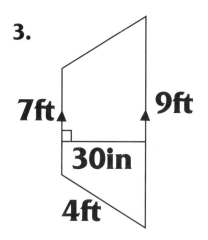

7ft 9ft

30in

4ft

4.

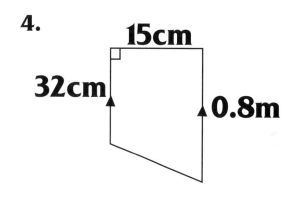

15cm

32cm 0.8m

Answers:
1. 30 cm²
2. 15 ft²
3. 20 ft²
4. 840 cm²

Cooperative Learning and High School Geometry: Becky Bride
Kagan Publishing • 1 (800) WEE CO-OP • www.KaganOnline.com

327

LESSON 7
CIRCUMFERENCE OF A CIRCLE

This lesson begins with an exploratory activity that will lead to the discovery of the irrational number π. It is from here that the circumference formula will be developed with the help of algebra. This exploratory exercise is written to be teacher directed. The last activity processes finding the circumference of a circle.

EXPLORING THE MEANING OF π

▶ Materials
- 1 Blackline 8.7.1 per team
- Transparency 8.7.1
- 1 soft tape measure per team or per pair of students
- 1 sheet of patty paper for each student
- Centimeter rulers
- Circular object that each student brought from home

1. Each student measures the circumference of his/her circular object using the soft tape measure to the nearest millimeter.

2. Each student traces around his/her circular object on a sheet of patty paper, fold the circle on the patty paper in half to form a diameter, then measure the length of the diameter to the nearest millimeter.

3. Student 1 records each teammate's data on the Team Data Chart.

4. Each student divides the circumference of his/her circular object by the length of its diameter.

5. Student 2 records these quotients on the Team Data Chart in the appropriate column.

6. Student 3 computes the average of all the quotients recorded in the data chart.

7. Student 4 records the average in the box labeled "Team Average."

8. The teacher spins the student spinner to choose a student from each team to report their team's average of circumference divided by the diameter. Teacher records each average on the board.

9. The class computes the average of all the teams' averages to give a class average of the circumference divided by the diameter.

10. Have students complete the journal reflection on Transparency 8.7.1.

Note:
The average should be pretty close to the value of π. Students are usually familiar with the value 3.14 for π. This investigation demonstrates the meaning of the number π. From here, with a little bit of algebra, the circumference formula can be derived.

$$\frac{Circumference}{diameter} = \pi$$

Multiplying both sides by the diameter produces the circumference formula.

Circumference = π · diameter

Writing the formula in words, symbols, and around the outside of a circle will match the verbal linguistic, visual spatial, and mathematical logical intelligences.

To finish this exploration, a journal reflection has been included. Once the students respond to the journal reflection, the RoundRobin structure could be used for the students to share what they wrote.

Cooperative Learning and High School Geometry: Becky Bride
Kagan Publishing • 1 (800) WEE CO-OP • www.KaganOnline.com

ACTIVITY

2 COMPUTING CIRCUMFERENCE

1. Student A does problem 1 writing in his/her column of the paper.

2. Student B coaches and/or praises student A for a job well done and does the next problem writing in his/her column of the paper.

3. Student A coaches and/or praises student B for a job well done.

4. Repeat steps 1-3 alternating students for the remainder of the questions.

▶ **Structure**
• RallyTable

▶ **Materials**
• Transparency 8.7.2
• 1 sheet of paper and pencil per pair of students

Cooperative Learning and High School Geometry: Becky Bride
Kagan Publishing • 1 (800) WEE CO-OP • www.KaganOnline.com

329

Chapter 8: Area

Lesson Seven

EXPLORING THE MEANING OF π

π Investigation Chart

	Circumference	Diameter	Circumference Diameter
Teammate 1			
Teammate 2			
Teammate 3			
Teammate 4			

The Average of the team's circumference/diameter column	

Cooperative Learning and High School Geometry: Becky Bride
Kagan Publishing • 1 (800) WEE CO-OP • www.KaganOnline.com

JOURNAL REFLECTION: π

Your pen pal has written you a note explaining how difficult his math has become because he now has to use this strange Greek letter π. He doesn't understand any of it. Write a letter to your pen pal explaining what π is, so he doesn't think it is all Greek.

Cooperative Learning and High School Geometry: Becky Bride
Kagan Publishing • 1 (800) WEE CO-OP • www.KaganOnline.com

331

ACTIVITY
2 COMPUTING CIRCUMFERENCE

Structure: RallyTable

For problems 1-4, find the exact circumference of the circle given the following information.

1. Radius is 10 cm.

2. Diameter is 5 cm.

3. Diameter is 12 cm.

4. Radius is 18 cm.

5. The circumference of a circle is 15π m. Find the length of the radius.

6. The circumference of a circle is 28π m. Find the length of the diameter.

Answers: *1. 20π cm; 2. 5π cm; 3. 12π cm; 4. 36π cm; 5. 7.5 m; 6. 28 m*

Cooperative Learning and High School Geometry: Becky Bride
Kagan Publishing • 1 (800) WEE CO-OP • www.KaganOnline.com

LESSON 8
AREA OF CIRCLES

This lesson begins with an exploratory activity to discover the formula for the area of a circle. It is followed by four activities to process area. Three of the activities link area and circumference.

ACTIVITY

1 EXPLORING CIRCULAR AREA

Have students complete Blackline 8.8.1.

> ▶ **Materials**
> • 1 Blackline 8.8.1 per student
> • 1/2 sheet of colored paper and pencil per student
> • 1 compass per student
> • 1 pair of scissors per student
> • Tape or glue stick per team

ACTIVITY

2 PROCESSING CIRCULAR AREA

1. Student B supplies one sheet of paper, folded in half lengthwise. Each member of the pair writes his/her name at the top of one column.

2. Student B does problem one recording his/her work on his/her side of the paper while Student A watches, checks the work and coaches if necessary.

3. Repeat step 2, reversing roles, until all the problems are done.

> ▶ **Structure**
> • RallyCoach
>
> ▶ **Materials**
> • Transparency 8.8.2
> • 1 sheet of paper and pencil per pair of students

Cooperative Learning and High School Geometry: Becky Bride
Kagan Publishing • 1 (800) WEE CO-OP • www.KaganOnline.com

333

CIRCUMFERENCE TO AREA

▶ **Structure**
- Simultaneous RoundTable

▶ **Materials**
- Transparencies 8.8.3a and 8.8.3b
- 1 sheet of paper and pencil per student

Note:
To have students practice finding the area of a circle given the circumference and vice versa, the Simultaneous RoundTable structure is fun to use. It is important to model the process before the students do the structure so that they understand the directions. This also emphasizes the difference between an exact answer and an approximate answer, since the third step asks for exact and the fourth step asks for approximate.

1. Student 1 writes problem 1, Student 2 writes problem 2, Student 3 writes problem 3, and Student 4 writes problem 4 on his/her paper.

2. Each student finds the length of the diameter for the problem on his or her paper. They initial their work, then pass the papers to the next person in a clockwise direction.

3. On the paper just received, each student checks the previous work, coaches if necessary, and then finds the length of the radius. Students initial their work and pass the papers to the next person in a clockwise direction.

4. On the paper just received,

each student checks the previous work, coaches if necessary, and then computes the exact area of the circle. Students initial their work and pass the papers to the next person in a clockwise direction.

5. On the paper just received, each student checks the previous work, coaches if necessary, and then computes the approximate area of the circle. Students initial their work and pass the papers to the next person in a clockwise direction.

6. On the paper just received, each student checks all the previous work, coaches and/or praises their teammates, then sign the paper, indicating his or her approval of all work done.

AREA TO CIRCUMFERENCE

▶ **Structure**
- Simultaneous RoundTable

▶ **Materials**
- Transparencies 8.8.4a and 8.8.4b
- 1 sheet of paper and pencil per student

1. Student 1 writes problem 1, Student 2 writes problem 2, Student 3 writes problem 3, and Student 4 writes problem 4 on his/her paper.

2. Each student finds the length of the radius for the problem on his or her paper. They initial their work, then pass the papers to the next person in a clockwise direction.

3. On the paper just received, each student will check the previous work, coach if necessary, and then find the length of the diameter. Students will initial their work and pass the papers to the next person in a clockwise direction. (If you use the formula $C = 2\pi r$, then the students could write the formula for this step).

4. On the paper just received, each student checks the previous work, coaches if necessary, and then computes the exact circumference of the circle. Students initial their work and pass the papers to the next person in a clockwise direction.

5. On the paper just received, each student checks the previous work, coaches if necessary, and then computes the approximate circumference of the circle. Students initial their work and pass the papers to the next person in a clockwise direction.

6. On the paper just received, each student checks all the previous work, coaches and/or praise their teammates, then signs the paper indicating his/her approval of all work done.

MATCHING CIRCUMFERENCE TO AREA

▶ Structure
• Mix-N-Match

▶ Materials
• 1 set of Mix-N-Match cards (Blackline 8.8.5)

1. Each student is given a card.

2. Students mix around the room, trading cards while music plays.

3. When the music stops, students stop.

4. Teacher gives the next set of directions for finding matches.

5. Students search and find their match.

Tips:
During the mix stage, students can work on curriculum by pairing and asking their partner what the radius of the circle is for the card they are holding and vice versa. Once they both tell each other what the other's radius is, then they trade cards, depart with an appropriate good bye, and search for a new partner.

Have students use gambits as they meet to exchange cards and as they leave to find someone else with whom to exchange.

During the match stage, students can talk or it can be done silently. For a class of average students, ask the students to take a moment and focus on the radius of the circle for the card they are holding. To match the circumference or area, the students need to find the person whose circle has the same radius. An honors level class would not need this instruction.

To help students find matches, have students that have found their match move to the outside perimeter of the room so there are fewer students to search through for those still needing to find their match.

If students have difficulty, repeat the structure.

To collect the cards, ask that both cards be given to one member of each pair. Then as the students return to their seats, they will hand the pairs of cards to the teacher. By doing, this the matches are together so when the next class comes in with a different number of students, the teacher will be able to ensure that matches can be made when the cards are distributed.

Cooperative Learning and High School Geometry: Becky Bride
Kagan Publishing • 1 (800) WEE CO-OP • www.KaganOnline.com

Lesson Eight Chapter 8: Area

335

1 EXPLORING CIRCULAR AREA

1. Construct a circle on your colored sheet of paper.

2. Cut out the circle.

3. Fold your circle in half, then in half again (fourths), and then in half again so your circle has 8 equal pieces.

4. Cut out all 8 pieces.

5. Take 4 pieces and arrange them onto a sheet of notebook paper as shown below.

6. Take the remaining 4 pieces and fit them between the 4 pieces already arranged, to form a parallelogram and tape or glue these in place.

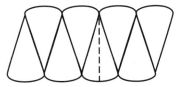

7. What would happen to the curved part of each piece if each piece were subdivided into 4 equal pieces, 10 equal pieces, 100 equal pieces?

8. Would this figure look even more like a parallelogram?

9. What is the area formula for a parallelogram?

10. What figure of the circle is the height of the "parallelogram" above?

11. The base of the "parallelogram" is half of the circumference of the circle. Four of the pieces you cut out would form a semicircle. Write the circumference formula that has r in it.

12. What is an expression for half of the circumference of the circle? Write it below.

13. Substitute the expression for the base of the parallelogram (found in step 12) and the expression for the height of the parallelogram (found in step 10) into the formula for the area of a parallelogram that you wrote in step 9.

14. Summarize your findings in a complete sentence.

Cooperative Learning and High School Geometry: Becky Bride
Kagan Publishing • 1 (800) WEE CO-OP • www.KaganOnline.com

ACTIVITY

2 PROCESSING CIRCULAR AREA

Structure: RallyCoach

Find the exact area of the circle with the given information.

1. Radius is 8 cm

2. Diameter is 14 cm

3. Diameter is 9 cm

4. Radius is 10 cm

5. The area of a circle is 121π m². Find the length of the radius.

6. The area of a circle is 28π m². Find the length of the diameter.

Answers: 1. 64π cm²; 2. 49π cm²; 3. 20.25π cm²; 4. 100π cm²; 5. 11 m; 6. $4\sqrt{7}$ m

Cooperative Learning and High School Geometry: Becky Bride
Kagan Publishing • 1 (800) WEE CO-OP • www.KaganOnline.com

337

ACTIVITY
3

CIRCUMFERENCE TO AREA

Structure: Simultaneous RoundTable

1. C = 16π m

2. C = 18π in

3. C = 9π cm

4. C = 5 π ft

Answers:
1. *64π m²; 200.96 m²*
2. *81π m²; 254.34 in²;*
3. *20.25π m²; 63.59 cm²*
4. *6.25π ft; 19.63 ft²*

Cooperative Learning and High School Geometry: Becky Bride
Kagan Publishing • 1 (800) WEE CO-OP • www.KaganOnline.com

ACTIVITY

3 CIRCUMFERENCE TO AREA

Structure: Simultaneous RoundTable

a) Find the length of the diameter of the circle with the given circumference. Initial your work then pass your paper 1 person in a clockwise direction.

b) Check the previous teammate's work and coach if necessary. Find the length of the radius. Initial your work then pass the paper 1 person in a clockwise direction.

c) Check the previous teammate's work and coach if necessary. Find the exact area of the circle. Initial your work and pass your paper 1 person in a clockwise direction.

d) Check the previous teammate's work and coach if necessary (round answers to the hundreths place). Find the approximate area of the circle. Initial your work and pass your paper 1 person in a clockwise direction.

e) Check all work on the paper you receive and coach and/or praise your teammates for a job well done. Then sign your name, indicating your approval of all work done.

Cooperative Learning and High School Geometry: Becky Bride
Kagan Publishing • 1 (800) WEE CO-OP • www.KaganOnline.com

339

ACTIVITY

4

AREA TO CIRCUMFERENCE

Structure: Simultaneous RoundTable

1. A = 16π in²

2. A = 4π mm²

3. A = 30π km²

4. A = 20π yd²

Answers:
1. 8π in; 25.12 in
2. 4π mm; 12.56 mm
3. 2π√30 km; 34.40 km
4. 4π√5 yd; 28.09 yd

Cooperative Learning and High School Geometry: Becky Bride
Kagan Publishing • 1 (800) WEE CO-OP • www.KaganOnline.com

ACTIVITY

4 AREA TO CIRCUMFERENCE

Structure: Simultaneous RoundTable

a) Find the length of the radius of the circle with the given area. Initial your work then pass your paper to the next person in a clockwise direction.

b) Check the previous teammate's work and coach if necessary. Find the length of the diameter. Initial your work then pass the paper to the next person in a clockwise direction.

c) Check the previous teammate's work and coach if necessary. Find the exact circumference of the circle. Initial your work and pass your paper to the next person in a clockwise direction.

d) Check the previous teammate's work and coach if necessary (round answers to the hundreths place). Find the approximate circumference of the circle. Initial your work and pass your paper to the next person in a clockwise direction.

e) Check all work on the paper you receive and coach and/or praise your teammates for a job well done. Then sign your name, indicating your approval of all work done.

Cooperative Learning and High School Geometry: Becky Bride
Kagan Publishing • 1 (800) WEE CO-OP • www.KaganOnline.com

341

ACTIVITY
5 MATCHING
CIRCUMFERENCE TO AREA

Structure: Mix-N-Match

Circumference 4π	Circumference 22π	Area 4π	Area 121π
Circumference 6π	Circumference 24π	Area 9π	Area 144π
Circumference 8π	Circumference 26π	Area 16π	Area 169π
Circumference 10π	Circumference 28π	Area 25π	Area 196π
Circumference 12π	Circumference $2\sqrt{7}\pi$	Area 36π	Area 7π
Circumference 14π	Circumference $2\sqrt{11}\pi$	Area 49π	Area 11π
Circumference 16π	Circumference 2π	Area 64π	Area 1π
Circumference 18π	Circumference $2\sqrt{13}\pi$	Area 81π	Area 13π
Circumference 20π	Circumference $2\sqrt{15}\pi$	Area 100π	Area 15π

Cooperative Learning and High School Geometry: Becky Bride
Kagan Publishing • 1 (800) WEE CO-OP • www.KaganOnline.com

LESSON 9
SURFACE AREA

Once students know how to find the area of two-dimensional figures, it is natural to work with three-dimensional figures. Finding the surface area of three-dimensional figures is just an application of two-dimensional area. Have students look at a three-dimensional figure and determine what two-dimensional objects form it. Since they know how to find the area of each of these, they can compute the area of the entire figure. This avoids using formulas that really aren't necessary, except for the cone. Ten years from now the students won't remember lateral area or surface area formulas, but if they were taught to compute the area of the two-dimensional figures the shape is comprised of, they will be able to find the surface area.

To demonstrate that the "sides" of a cylinder form a rectangle, a soup can label is a wonderful tool. Cut the label from base to base and take it off. The students will see the rectangle, then a discussion can ensue on the rectangle's length being the circumference of the base. Students know how to find the area of the base of a cone. The "sides" of the cone formula need to be developed. Most geometry books have that development. Having the students draw each different type of polygon the solid is made of gives direction to the problem. Also having the student identify the number of each type of polygon that forms the solid helps the students finish the problem.

PROCESSING SURFACE AREA

1. Student A supplies one sheet of paper, folded in half lengthwise with his/her name in one column and name in the other column.

2. Student B is the first boss and Student A is the first secretary.

3. As the boss, Student B tells Student A how to do the problem. Student A, the secretary, records what Student B says in Student B's column of the paper.

4. If the boss makes a mistake, then the secretary coaches and praises once the boss does it correctly. Otherwise, the secretary praises the boss.

5. Reverse roles for each problem and repeat steps 3 and 4.

▶ **Structure**
• Boss/Secretary

▶ **Materials**
• 1 Blackline 8.9.1 per pair of students
• 1 sheet of paper and pencil per pair of students

Cooperative Learning and High School Geometry: Becky Bride
Kagan Publishing • 1 (800) WEE CO-OP • www.KaganOnline.com

343

Chapter 8: Area

Lesson Nine

PROCESSING SURFACE AREA

Structure: Boss/Secretary

Find the exact surface area of the following figures. They are all right solids.

1.

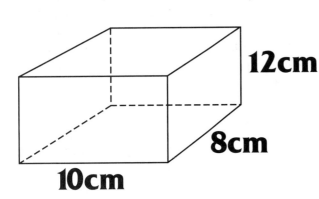

12cm

8cm

10cm

2.

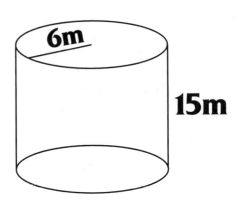

6m

15m

3.

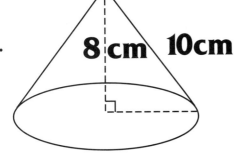

8 cm   10cm

4.

7cm

Square Pyramid

14cm

Answers:
1. 592 cm²
2. 252π m²
3. 96π cm²
4. 392 cm²

Cooperative Learning and High School Geometry: Becky Bride
Kagan Publishing • 1 (800) WEE CO-OP • www.KaganOnline.com

LESSON 10
APPLICATIONS OF PERIMETER AND AREA

This lesson has students determine the change in a figure's area if one or more of the variables changes. Students sometimes have difficulty in real-world application problems determining whether area or perimeter should be used. To help students differentiate between area and perimeter, one activity has students generate applications for perimeter and one activity has students generate applications for area. The last activity has real-world problems, involving area and perimeter, for the students to solve.

1 WHAT IF? EFFECTS OF A CHANGE IN ONE VARIABLE ON AREA

1. Student 1 fans the cards face down.

2. Student 2 picks a card and reads it to Student 3.

3. Student 3 solves the problem.

4. Student 4 augments and praises.

5. Cards are passed to the next person in a clockwise direction and steps 1-4 begin again, rotating roles to the next student in the clockwise direction. This process is repeated for a specific time limit or until cards are exhausted.

Tips:
Instead of four students working with a set of cards, each pair of students could work with a set of cards. This would increase participation to 50 percent.

Use one sheet of paper, which is passed from person to person for recording of the problems.

For individual accountability, have students initial their problems, use different colored pencils, or write on different quadrants of the paper.

Students can do this with replacement of the cards or without replacement of the cards.

▶ **Structure**
· Fan-N-Pick

▶ **Materials**
· 1 set of Fan-N-Pick cards per team (Blackline 8.10.1)
· 1 sheet of paper and pencil per team

Cooperative Learning and High School Geometry: Becky Bride
Kagan Publishing • 1 (800) WEE CO-OP • www.KaganOnline.com

345

Chapter 8: Area   Lesson Ten

ACTIVITY

2 GENERATING APPLICATIONS OF PERIMETER

▶ **Structure**
• Give One, Get One

▶ **Materials**
• 1 sheet of paper and pencil per student or pre-made Give One, Get One form (Blackline 8.10.2)

1. Students receive a pre-made Give One, Get One form, or fold a blank piece of paper lengthwise to create one.

2. With pencils down, in teams, students brainstorm to come up with applications of perimeter.

3. When they agree they have come up with a good application, they take their pencils and in their own words write it in the Give One column on their paper.

4. When their Give One column is full, (six items) they stand.

5. When all students are standing, each student puts a hand up, and pairs with someone who is not a teammate.

6. Students in pairs share an application, and get an application, writing on their own worksheet the application they have received in the Get One column.

7. Pairs part, put a hand up until they find a new partner, then again give one and get one.

8. When their form is full, students stand by the perimeter of the room, offering to give to anyone whose form is not yet full.

9. When all students have finished their forms, they return to their teams and share ideas they have received.

Tips:
When students initially brainstorm, the structure RoundRobin can be used.

When students share ideas at the end of the structure, RoundRobin or Talking Chips can be used to equalize the participation.

ACTIVITY

3 GENERATING APPLICATIONS OF AREA

▶ **Structure**
• Give One, Get One

▶ **Materials**
• 1 sheet of paper and pencil per student or pre-made Give One, Get One form (Blackline 8.10.3)

1. Students receive a pre-made Give One, Get One form, or fold a blank piece of paper lengthwise to create one.

2. With pencils down, in teams, students brainstorm applications of area.

3. When they agree they have come up with a good application, they take their pencils and in their own words write it in the Give One column on their paper.

4. When their Give One column is full, (six items) they stand.

5. When all students are standing, each student puts a hand up, and pairs with someone who is not a teammate.

6. Students in pairs share an application, and get an application, writing on their own

worksheet the application they have received in the Get One column.

7. Pairs part, put a hand up until they find a new partner, then again give one and get one.

8. When their form is full, students stand by the perimeter of the room, offering to give to anyone whose form is not yet full.

9. When all students have finished their forms, they return to their teams and share ideas they have received.

Cooperative Learning and High School Geometry: Becky Bride
Kagan Publishing • 1 (800) WEE CO-OP • www.KaganOnline.com

ACTIVITY 4

APPLICATIONS OF AREA AND PERIMETER

1. Student A supplies one sheet of paper, folded in half lengthwise with his/her name in one column and a partner's name in the other column.

2. Student B is the first boss and Student A is the first secretary.

3. As the boss, Student B tells Student A how to do the problem. Student A, the secretary, records what Student B says in Student B's column of the paper.

4. If the boss makes a mistake, then the secretary coaches and praises once the boss does it correctly. Otherwise, the secretary praises the boss.

5. Reverse roles for each problem and repeat steps 3 and 4.

▶ **Structure**
· Boss/Secretary

▶ **Materials**
· 1 Blackline 8.10.4 per pair of students
· 1 sheet of paper and pencil per pair of students

Cooperative Learning and High School Geometry: Becky Bride
Kagan Publishing • 1 (800) WEE CO-OP • www.KaganOnline.com

ACTIVITY 1 WHAT IF? EFFECTS OF A CHANGE IN ONE VARIABLE ON AREA

Structure: Fan-N-Pick

---

1. What happens to the area of a triangle when the base length is doubled?

Answer: It becomes 2 times bigger

---

5. What happens to the area of a trapezoid when both base lengths are multiplied by 4?

Answer: It becomes 4 times bigger

---

2. What happens to the area of a circle when the radius is tripled?

Answer: It becomes 9 times bigger

---

6. What happens to the area of a parallelogram whose height is multiplied by 6 and base length is doubled?

Answer: It becomes 12 times bigger

---

3. What happens to the circumference of a circle when the radius is doubled?

Answer: It becomes 2 times bigger

---

7. What happens to the area of a trapezoid when the height is multiplied by 10?

Answer: It becomes 10 times bigger

---

4. What happens to the area of a rectangle when the base length is doubled and the height tripled?

Answer: It becomes 6 times bigger

---

8. What happens to the area of a triangle when the base length is multiplied by 4 and the height is doubled?

Answer: It becomes 8 times bigger

Cooperative Learning and High School Geometry: Becky Bride
Kagan Publishing • 1 (800) WEE CO-OP • www.KaganOnline.com

2 GENERATING APPLICATIONS OF PERIMETER

Structure: Give One, Get One

Give One	Get One

Cooperative Learning and High School Geometry: Becky Bride
Kagan Publishing • 1 (800) WEE CO-OP • www.KaganOnline.com

349

ACTIVITY 3 GENERATING APPLICATIONS OF AREA

Structure: Give One, Get One

Give One	Get One

Cooperative Learning and High School Geometry: Becky Bride
Kagan Publishing • 1 (800) WEE CO-OP • www.KaganOnline.com

ACTIVITY
4

APPLICATIONS OF AREA AND PERIMETER

Structure: Boss/Secretary

1. Tiara wants to put fringe on the edge of her tablecloth. Her tablecloth is circular with a diameter of 6 **feet**. If fringe costs $2.49 per **yard**, how much will it cost to purchase the fringe (sales tax not included)?

2. Justin needs to lay sod in his back yard. If his yard measures 60 feet by 70 feet, how many square feet of sod does he need? If sod costs $1.15 a square foot installed, how much will it cost to sod his yard?

3. Sally wants to tile her kitchen countertop. The largest section of countertop is in the form of a rectangle, whose dimensions are 30 **inches** by 7 **feet**. Another section is also a rectangle, whose dimensions are 30 **inches** by 3 **feet**. How many **square feet** of tile does she need?

4. Jonah wants to plant a garden. The garden will be rectangular with dimensions 8 feet by 20 feet. He needs to purchase chicken wire to put around his garden to keep the bunnies out. To save money, he plans to place the garden right next to the back of his house so that the garden extends 8 feet out from his house. How much chicken wire does he need to purchase?

5. Nick wants to carpet his bedroom. His room is L-shaped as shown below. How many square yards of carpeting is needed? If the carpet he wants to purchase is $16.49 per square yard, how much will the carpeting cost?

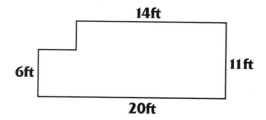

6. Maria wants to fence her back yard. Her yard is U-shaped as shown below. How many feet of fencing will she need to purchase? If each section of fence comes in 8 foot lengths, how many 8 foot lengths will she need to buy?

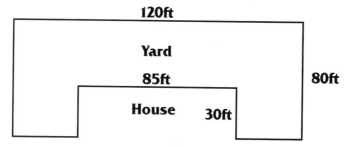

Answers:
1. 6.28 yds rounded to 7 yds; $17.43
2. 4200 ft²; $4830
3. 25 ft²
4. 36 ft
5. 21.1 rounded to 22 yd²; $362.78
6. 315 ft; 39.4 rounded to 40 sections

Cooperative Learning and High School Geometry: Becky Bride
Kagan Publishing • 1 (800) WEE CO-OP • www.KaganOnline.com

351

VOLUME

This chapter includes vocabulary development, exploratory activities to develop volume formulas, activities to process volume, and activities for the ratio of similitude theorem.

LESSON 1

VOCABULARY DEVELOPMENT

ACTIVITY 1: Naming Prisms
ACTIVITY 2: Naming Faces of Prisms
ACTIVITY 3: Naming Edges of Prisms
ACTIVITY 4: Fill My Venn: Prisms vs. Cylinders
ACTIVITY 5: Naming Pyramids
ACTIVITY 6: Naming Faces of Pyramids
ACTIVITY 7: Naming Edges of Pyramids
ACTIVITY 8: Height, Slant Height, and Vertex
ACTIVITY 9: Fill My Venn: Pyramids vs. Cones
ACTIVITY 10: Fill My Venn: Cylinders vs. Cones
ACTIVITY 11: Fill My Venn: Prisms vs. Pyramids

LESSON 2

VOLUME OF PRISMS AND CYLINDERS

ACTIVITY 1: Exploring Volume of Prisms
ACTIVITY 2: Processing Volume of Prisms and Cylinders

LESSON 3

VOLUME OF PYRAMIDS AND CONES

ACTIVITY 1: Exploring Volume of Pyramids and Cones
ACTIVITY 2: Processing Volume of Pyramids and Cones

LESSON 4

SURFACE AREA OF A SPHERE

ACTIVITY 1: Processing Surface Area of a Sphere

LESSON 5

VOLUME OF SPHERES

ACTIVITY 1: Exploring Volume of Spheres
ACTIVITY 2: Processing Volume of a Sphere
ACTIVITY 3: Surface Area to Volume
ACTIVITY 4: Volume to Surface Area
ACTIVITY 5: Applications of Volume

LESSON 6

RATIO OF SIMILITUDE

ACTIVITY 1: Exploring the Ratio of Similitude Theorem
ACTIVITY 2: Processing Ratio of Similitude
ACTIVITY 3: Match the Ratios
ACTIVITY 4: Applying Ratio of Similitude

LESSON 1
VOCABULARY DEVELOPMENT

Teach the vocabulary involving how to name prisms. The first activity takes about 60 seconds to process this.

ACTIVITY

1 NAMING PRISMS

▶ **Structure**
· RallyRobin

▶ **Materials**
· Transparency 9.1.1

1. Student A names the prism in problem 1.

2. Student B coaches and/or praises Student A's answer, then names the prism in the next problem.

3. Repeat step 2, alternating students for 60 seconds.

ACTIVITY

2 NAMING FACES OF PRISMS

▶ **Structure**
· RallyRobin

▶ **Materials**
· Transparency 9.1.2-3

1. Student A states the name of a face of the prism and states whether it is a lateral face or a base.

2. Student B praises Student A or coaches and then praises. Then Student B states the name of a different face of the prism and states whether it is a lateral face or base.

3. Student A praises Student B or coaches and then praises.

4. Repeat steps 1-3 for the remainder of the faces.

ACTIVITY

3 NAMING EDGES OF PRISMS

▶ **Structure**
· RallyRobin

▶ **Materials**
· Transparency 9.1.2-3

1. Student A states the name of an edge of the prism and states whether it is a lateral edge or a base edge.

2. Student B praises Student A or coaches and then praises. Then Student B states the name of a different edge of the prism and states whether it is a lateral edge or base edge.

3. Student A praises Student B or coaches and then praises.

4. Repeat steps 1-3 for the remainder of the edges.

Tip:
If you want a hard copy of activities 1-3, the RallyTable structure can be used instead. The only change would be for students to record their answers on a single sheet of paper that they share.

Cooperative Learning and High School Geometry: Becky Bride
Kagan Publishing • 1 (800) WEE-CO-OP • www.KaganOnline.com

ACTIVITY

4

FILL MY VENN: PRISMS VS. CYLINDERS

1. Student A supplies a sheet of paper and draws the Venn diagram in the center of the paper.

2. Student B writes a property of a prism or cylinder in the appropriate part of the Venn Diagram, using his/her colored pencil.

3. Student A writes a different property in the appropriate part of the Venn diagram using his/her colored pencil.

4. Repeat steps 2 and 3 until time is up or the pairs can't think of anything else. There should be information in each part of the Venn diagram.

5. Have the pairs at each team compare their Venn diagrams. They can add to them or correct them.

▶ **Structure**
• RallyTable

▶ **Materials**
• Transparency 9.1.4
• 1 colored pen/pencil per student
• 1 sheet of paper per pair of student

ACTIVITY

5

NAMING PYRAMIDS

Note:
The next set of activities do for pyramids what the last activities did for prisms. Activities 5, 6 and 7 should only take 30-60 seconds. The teaching of these terms is easier because of the groundwork laid by the prisms.

1. Student A names the pyramid in problem 1.

2. Student B names the pyramid in problem 2.

3. Repeat steps 1-2 alternating Student A and Student B for 60 seconds.

▶ **Structure**
• RallyRobin

▶ **Materials**
• Transparency 9.1.5

ACTIVITY

6

NAMING FACES OF PYRAMIDS

1. Student A states the name of a face of the pyramid and states whether it is a lateral face or a base.

2. Student B praises Student A or coaches and then praises. Then Student B states the name of a different face of the pyramid and states whether it is a lateral face or base.

3. Student A praises Student B or coaches and then praises.

4. Repeat steps 1-3 for the remainder of the faces.

▶ **Structure**
• RallyRobin

▶ **Materials**
• Transparency 9.1.6-8

Cooperative Learning and High School Geometry: Becky Bride
Kagan Publishing • 1 (800) WEE-CO-OP • www.KaganOnline.com

355

ACTIVITY

7

NAMING EDGES OF PYRAMIDS

▶ **Structure**
• RallyRobin

▶ **Materials**
• Transparency 9.1.6-8

1. Student A states the name of an edge of the pyramid and states whether it is a lateral edge or a base edge.

2. Student B praises Student A or coaches and then praises. Then Student B states the name of a different edge of the pyramid and states whether it is a lateral edge or base edge.

3. Student A praises Student B or coaches and then praises.

4. Repeat steps 1-3 for the remainder of the edges.

Tip:
If you want a hard copy of activities 6 and 7, the RallyTable structure can be used instead. The only change would be for students to record their answers on a single sheet of paper that they share.

ACTIVITY

8

HEIGHT, SLANT HEIGHT, AND VERTEX

▶ **Structure**
• Numbered Heads Together

▶ **Materials**
• Transparency 9.1.6-8
• Small white boards (optional)

1. Teacher asks the students, "What is the vertex of the pyramid?"

2. Students lift from their chairs to put their heads together, discuss, and teach if necessary.

3. Students sit down when everyone knows the answer or has something to share.

4. Teacher calls a number. The student with that number from each team answers simultaneously, using
   Slate Share
   Choral Practice
   Chalkboard Responses

5. Teammates praise students who responded.

6. Steps 2-5 are repeated for the question, "Name a slant height of the pyramid."

7. Steps 2-5 are repeated for the question, "Name the height of the pyramid."

Tip:
An easy way to get small white boards to use in the classroom is to go to a lumber store and buy a 4 ft. by 8 ft. white shower board and have them cut it up into white boards the size of your choice.

Cooperative Learning and High School Geometry: Becky Bride
Kagan Publishing • 1 (800) WEE-CO-OP • www.KaganOnline.com

9

FILL MY VENN: PYRAMIDS VS. CONES

1. Student A supplies a sheet of paper and draws the Venn diagram in the center of the paper.

2. Student B writes a property of a pyramid or cone in the appropriate part of the Venn Diagram, using his/her colored pencil.

3. Student A writes a different property in the appropriate part of the Venn diagram, using his/her colored pencil.

4. Repeat steps 2 and 3 until time is up or the pairs can't think of anything else. There should be information in each part of the Venn diagram.

▶ **Structure**
- RallyTable

▶ **Materials**
- Transparency 9.1.9
- 1 colored pen/pencil per student
- 1 sheet of paper per pair of students

10

FILL MY VENN: CYLINDERS VS. CONES

1. Student A supplies a sheet of paper and draws the Venn diagram in the center of the paper.

2. Student B writes a property of a cylinder or cone in the appropriate part of the Venn Diagram, using his/her colored pencil.

3. Student A writes a different property in the appropriate part of the Venn diagram, using his/her colored pencil.

4. Repeat steps 2 and 3 until time is up or the pairs can't think of anything else. There should be information in each part of the Venn diagram.

▶ **Structure**
- RallyTable

▶ **Materials**
- Transparency 9.1.10
- 1 colored pen/pencil per student
- 1 sheet of paper per pair of students

11

FILL MY VENN: PRISMS VS. PYRAMIDS

1. Student A supplies a sheet of paper and draws the Venn diagram in the center of the paper.

2. Student B writes a property of a prism or pyramid in the appropriate part of the Venn Diagram, using his/her colored pencil.

3. Student A writes a different property in the appropriate part of the Venn diagram, using his/her colored pencil.

4. Repeat steps 2 and 3 until time is up or the pairs can't think of anything else. There should be information in each part of the Venn diagram.

▶ **Structure**
- RallyTable

▶ **Materials**
- Transparency 9.1.11
- 1 colored pen/pencil per student
- 1 sheet of paper per pair of students

Cooperative Learning and High School Geometry: Becky Bride
Kagan Publishing • 1 (800) WEE-CO-OP • www.KaganOnline.com

Chapter 9: Volume
Lesson One

357

NAMING PRISMS

Structure: RallyRobin

Name the type of prism.

1.

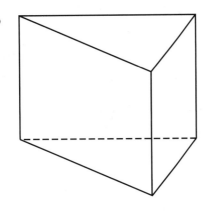

2.

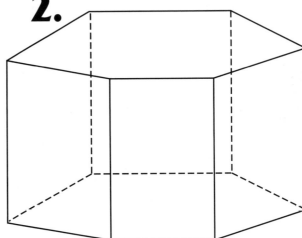

3.

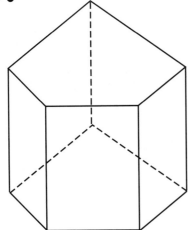

4.

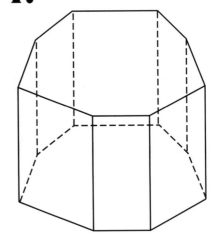

Cooperative Learning and High School Geometry: Becky Bride
Kagan Publishing • 1 (800) WEE-CO-OP • www.KaganOnline.com

NAMING FACES AND EDGES OF PRISMS

Structure: RallyRobin

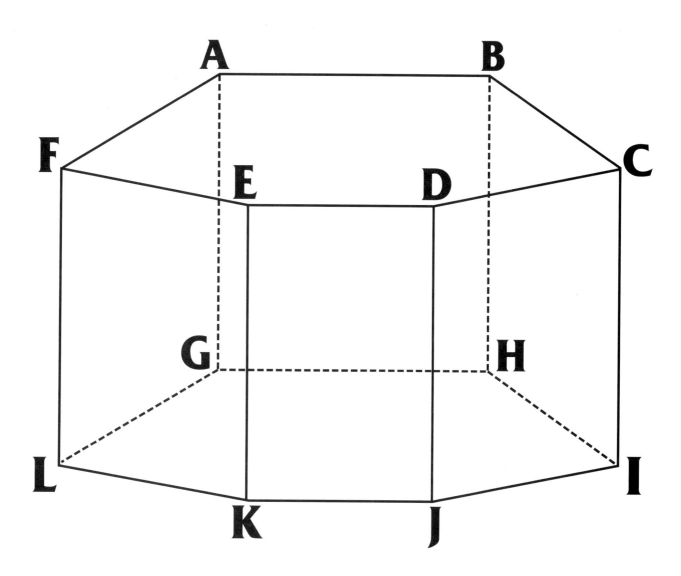

Cooperative Learning and High School Geometry: Becky Bride
Kagan Publishing • 1 (800) WEE-CO-OP • www.KaganOnline.com

359

ACTIVITY 4 FILL MY VENN: PRISMS VS. CYLINDERS

Structure: RallyTable

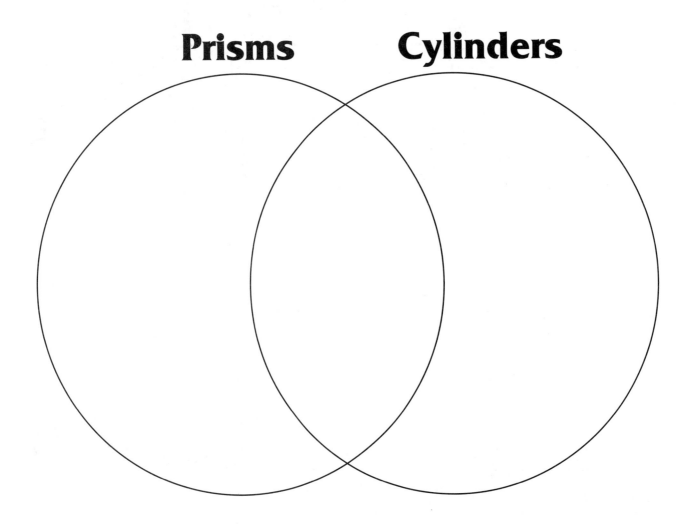

Prisms   Cylinders

Cooperative Learning and High School Geometry: Becky Bride
Kagan Publishing • 1 (800) WEE-CO-OP • www.KaganOnline.com

ACTIVITY

5 **NAMING PYRAMIDS**

Structure: Rally Robin

1.

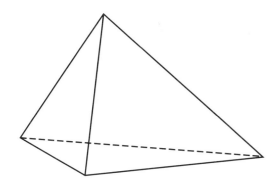

2.

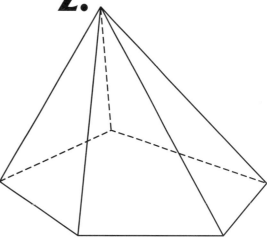

3.

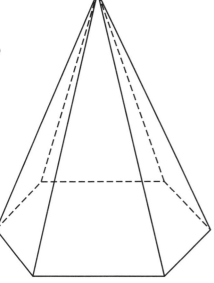

4.

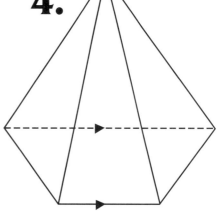

Cooperative Learning and High School Geometry: Becky Bride
Kagan Publishing • 1 (800) WEE-CO-OP • www.KaganOnline.com

361

NAMING FACES, EDGES, HEIGHT, SLANT HEIGHT, AND VERTEX OF PYRAMIDS

Structure: RallyRobin and Numbered Heads Together

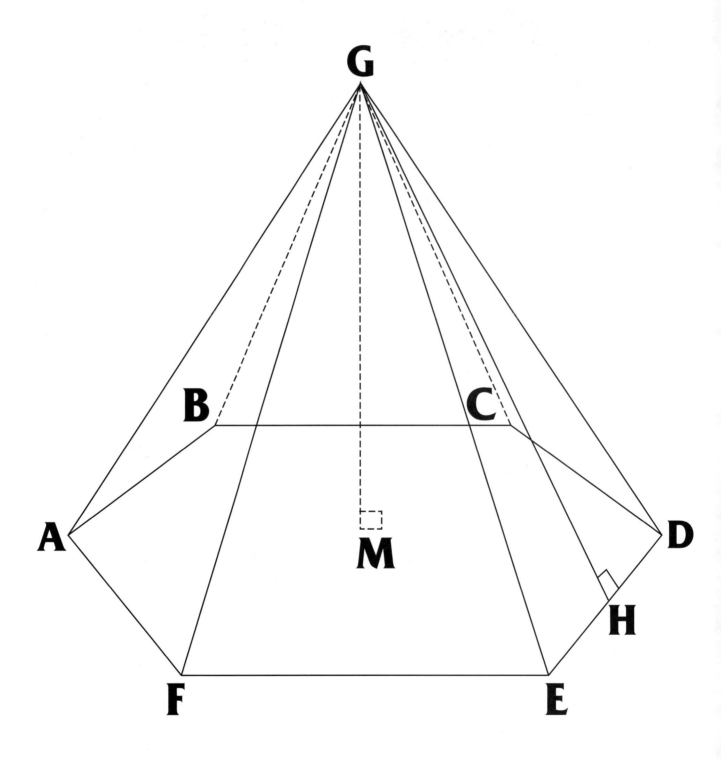

Cooperative Learning and High School Geometry: Becky Bride
Kagan Publishing • 1 (800) WEE-CO-OP • www.KaganOnline.com

ACTIVITY
9
FILL MY VENN:
PYRAMIDS VS. CONES

Structure: RallyTable

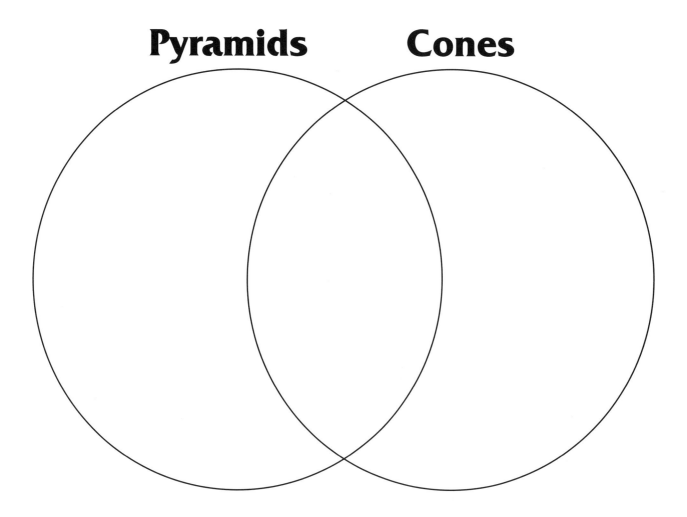

Pyramids   Cones

Cooperative Learning and High School Geometry: Becky Bride
Kagan Publishing • 1 (800) WEE-CO-OP • www.KaganOnline.com

363

ACTIVITY 10
FILL MY VENN: CYLINDERS VS. CONES

Structure: RallyTable

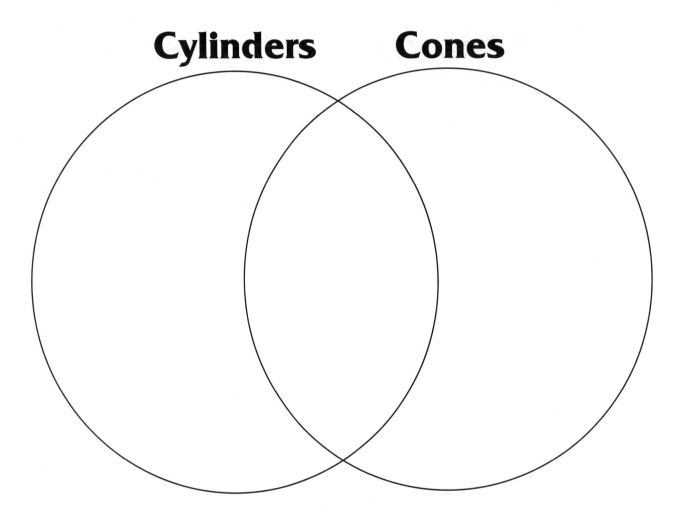

Cylinders   ## Cones

Cooperative Learning and High School Geometry: Becky Bride
Kagan Publishing • 1 (800) WEE-CO-OP • www.KaganOnline.com

ACTIVITY
11
FILL MY VENN: PRISMS VS. PYRAMIDS

Structure: RallyTable

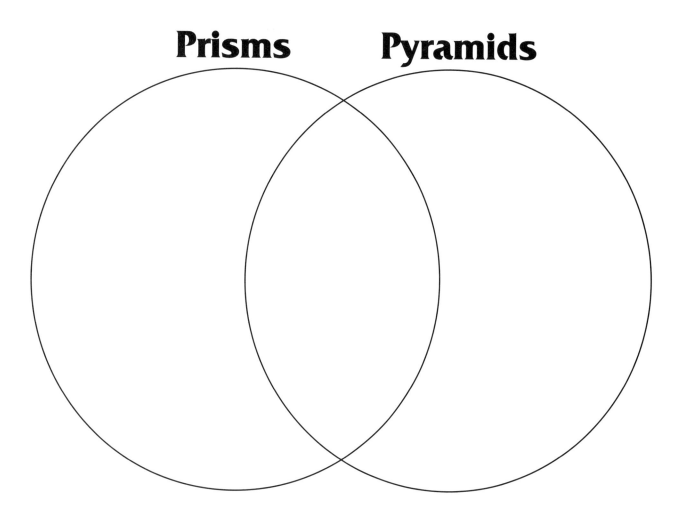

Prisms   Pyramids

Cooperative Learning and High School Geometry: Becky Bride
Kagan Publishing • 1 (800) WEE-CO-OP • www.KaganOnline.com

365

LESSON 2
VOLUMES OF PRISMS AND CYLINDERS

This lesson begins with an exploratory activity for the volume of prisms and finishes with an activity to process this concept.

1 EXPLORING VOLUME OF PRISMS

▶ **Structure**
· Solo and RoundRobin

▶ **Materials**
· 36 centimeter cubes per pair of students
· 1 Blackline 9.2.1 per student
· 1 pencil per student

1. Ask Student 1 to make a prism with six cubes that Is 2 cm wide, 3 cm long, and 1 cm high.

Ask Student 2 to make a prism with eight cubes that is 2 cm wide, 4 cm long, and 1 cm high. Ask Student 3 to make a prism with ten cubes that is 2 cm wide, 5 cm long, and 1 cm high. Ask Student 4 to make a

prism with twelve cubes that is 3 cm wide, 4 cm long and 1 cm high.

2. Individually, each student answers questions 1-3 on the Blackline 9.2.1.

3. Using the RoundRobin structure, have the students share with their teammates the results of their investigation so far.

4. Have students answer questions 4 and 5 on Blackline 9.2.1.

5. Have students work in pairs to do problems 6-8, recording their answers on their Blackline 9.2.1.

Tip:
To demonstrate that an oblique prism has the same volume as a right prism whose length, width, and height are the same, take a ream of paper and skew it to form an oblique prism. Ask the students if any paper was removed from the ream to do so. If not, is the volume of the right prism and oblique prism the same?

To demonstrate that the cylinder formula is the same as the prism formula (base area x height), poker chips or pogs are helpful. Students can see that the layers of a cylinder are just disks with the same base area. So, base area x height still works. The disks can be slanted to show that the volume of the oblique cylinder is the same as when the chips are stacked one on top of the other.

2 PROCESSING VOLUME OF PRISMS AND CYLINDERS

▶ **Structure**
· Boss/Secretary

▶ **Materials**
· 1 Blackline 9.2.2 per pair of students
· 1 sheet of paper and pencil per pair of students

1. Student A supplies one sheet of paper, folded in half lengthwise with his/her name in one column and a partner's name in the other column.

2. Student B is the first boss and Student A is the first secretary.

3. As the boss, Student B tells Student A how to do the problem. Student A, the secre-

tary, records what Student B says in Student B's column of the paper.

4. If the boss makes a mistake, then the secretary coaches and praises once the boss does it correctly. Otherwise, the secretary praises the boss.

5. Reverse roles for each problem and repeat steps 3 and 4.

Cooperative Learning and High School Geometry: Becky Bride
Kagan Publishing • 1 (800) WEE-CO-OP • www.KaganOnline.com

1 EXPLORING VOLUME OF PRISMS

Structure: Solo and RoundRobin

1. For your prism, compute the volume by counting the number of cubes it takes to form the prism and record your answer.

2. What is the area of the base of your prism? Explain how you arrived at your answer.

3. How does the area of the base compare to the volume of the prism?

4. Are the results of your teammates' prisms similar to your results? Explain.

5. How many layers tall is your prism? What can the area of the base of a prism tell you about the number of cubes in one layer?

6. With your partner, form a prism that is 2 cubes wide, 3 cubes long, and 2 cubes high.
    a. What is the area of the base?

    b. How many cubes are in 1 layer?

    c. How many cubes are in 2 layers?

    d. What is the volume of your prism?

7. Add a third layer of cubes.
    a. What is the area of the base?

    b. How many cubes are in 1 layer?

    c. How many cubes are in 3 layers?

    d. What is the volume of your prism?

8. Explain how you can use the area of the base of a prism and its height to compute volume. Write a formula in words to summarize your explanation.

Cooperative Learning and High School Geometry: Becky Bride
Kagan Publishing • 1 (800) WEE-CO-OP • www.KaganOnline.com

367

ACTIVITY 2 PROCESSING VOLUME OF PRISMS AND CYLINDERS

Structure: Boss/Secretary

Find the volume of each solid.

1.
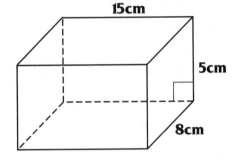
15cm
5cm
8cm

2.
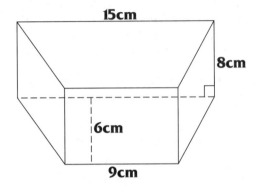
15cm
8cm
6cm
9cm

3.
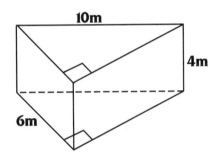
10m
4m
6m

4.
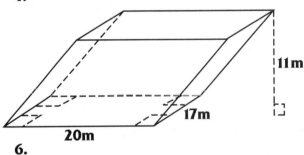
11m
17m
20m

5.
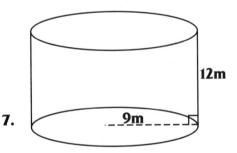
12m
9m

6.
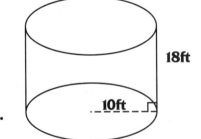
18ft
10ft

7.
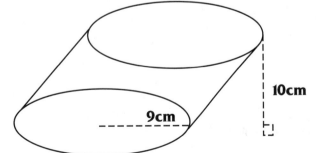
10cm
9cm

8.
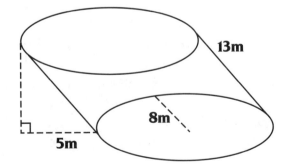
13m
8m
5m

Answers: *1. 600 cm³ 2. 576 cm³ 3. 96 m³ 4. 3,740 m³ 5. 972π m³ 6. 1800π ft³ 7. 810π cm³ 8. 768π m³*

Cooperative Learning and High School Geometry: Becky Bride
Kagan Publishing • 1 (800) WEE-CO-OP • www.KaganOnline.com

LESSON 3
VOLUME OF PYRAMIDS AND CONES

This lesson begins with an exploratory activity. For this activity, a set of pyramids, cones, cylinders, and prisms is necessary along with rice or water. The pyramid and prism need to have congruent bases and the same height. The cone and cylinder also need congruent bases and congruent heights. These will be called relational solids. This activity can be demonstrated by the teacher. However, it is far more powerful if there are enough solids so each pair of students can do the activity. ETA is a math catalog company that sells these relational solids in sets of 15.

1 EXPLORING VOLUME OF PYRAMIDS AND CONES

1. Student 1 takes the cylinder and Student 2 takes the relational cone. They will work together. Student 3 takes the prism and Student 4 takes the relational pyramid. They will work together.

2. Each pair predicts how many cones or pyramids of rice it will take to fill the cylinder or prism. They record their guesses.

3. While one student in each pair holds the cylinder or prism, the other fills the cone or pyramid with rice (being careful not to over fill) and pours the rice into the cylinder/prism as many times as needed to fill them.

4. The students record their results.

▶ **Materials**
• Relational prism and pyramid or relational cone and cylinder per pair of students
• Rice or water
• 1 Blackline 9.3.1 per student
• 1 pencil per student

5. The students answer the last question on their Blackline 9.3.1, which should lead them to the volume formula of a pyramid and cone.

Cooperative Learning and High School Geometry: Becky Bride
Kagan Publishing • 1 (800) WEE-CO-OP • www.KaganOnline.com

369

Chapter 9: Volume

Lesson Three

ACTIVITY

2 PROCESSING VOLUME OF PYRAMIDS AND CONES

▶ **Structure**
· Simultaneous RoundTable

▶ **Materials**
· Transparencies 9.3.2a and 9.3.2b
· 1 sheet of paper and pencil per student

1. Student 1 draws a diagram of the base of the pyramid in problem 1, Student 2 draws a diagram of the base of the pyramid in problem 2, Student 3 draws a diagram of the base of the cone in problem 3, and Student 4 draws a diagram of the base of the cone in problem 4 on his/her paper.

2. Each student records the length of the height on his/her paper. They initial their work then pass the papers to the next person in a clockwise direction.

3. On the paper just received, each student checks to see if the diagrams were drawn correctly and the height was written correctly, and then writes the formula for the area of the base drawn. Students initial their work and pass the papers to the next person in a clockwise direction.

4. On the paper just received, each student checks the previous work, coaches if necessary, and then computes the area of the base. Students initial their work and pass the papers to the next person in a clockwise direction.

5. On the paper just received, each student checks the previous work, coaches if necessary, and then computes the volume for the problem on the paper they just received. Students initial their work and pass the papers to the next person in a clockwise direction.

6. On the paper just received, each student checks the previous work, coach if necessary, and then initials showing his/her approval.

Cooperative Learning and High School Geometry: Becky Bride
Kagan Publishing • 1 (800) WEE-CO-OP • www.KaganOnline.com

ACTIVITY 1 EXPLORING VOLUME OF PYRAMIDS AND CONES

1. Predict how many cones or pyramids it will take to fill the respective cylinder or prism. Record your prediction.

2. While 1 partner holds the cylinder or prism, the other fills the cone or pyramid with rice, being careful not to overfill, and pours it into the cylinder or prism. Continue this process until the cylinder or prism is full.

    How many cones/pyramids did it take to fill the cylinder/prism?

3. If the volume formula for the prisms and cylinders is $V = BH$, what can be done to this formula to generate a new formula for the volume of a cone or pyramid, based on your investigation from above?

4. Your friend, who is in a different class, missed school the day that the volume formula for pyramids and cones was taught. Write a description of how you would teach this to your friend.

Cooperative Learning and High School Geometry: Becky Bride
Kagan Publishing • 1 (800) WEE-CO-OP • www.KaganOnline.com

371

ACTIVITY 2 PROCESSING VOLUME OF PYRAMIDS AND CONES

Structure: Simultaneous RoundTable

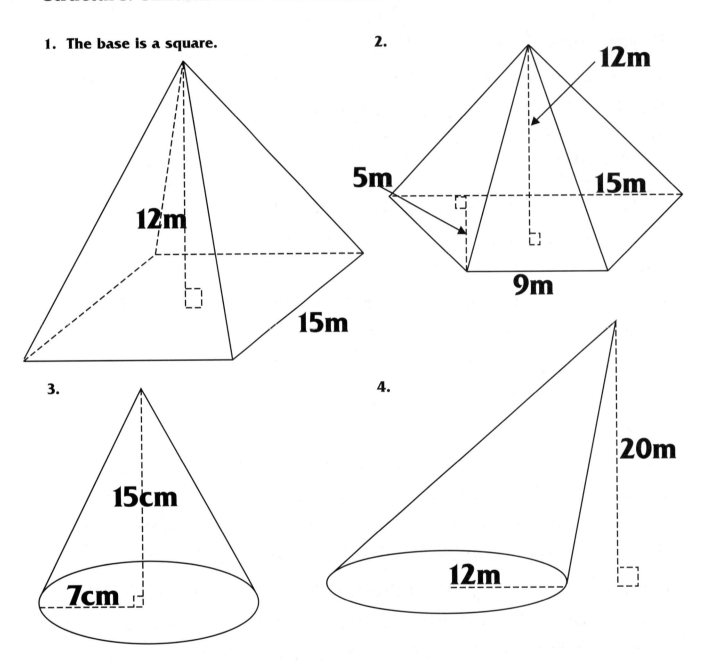

1. The base is a square.

    12m
    15m

2.

    12m
    5m
    15m
    9m

3.

    15cm
    7cm

4.

    20m
    12m

Answers:
1. 900 m³
2. 240 m³
3. 245π cm³
4. 960π m³

Cooperative Learning and High School Geometry: Becky Bride
Kagan Publishing • 1 (800) WEE-CO-OP • www.KaganOnline.com

ACTIVITY 2
PROCESSING VOLUME OF PYRAMIDS AND CONES

Structure: Simultaneous RoundTable

Directions:

1. Draw a diagram of the base of your figure, record the height, initial it, and pass your paper to the next person in the clockwise direction.

2. On the new paper, check the previous work and coach if necessary. Write the formula necessary to compute the base area of the figure on your paper, initial it, and pass your paper to the next person in the clockwise direction.

3. On the new paper, check the previous work and coach if necessary. Compute the area of the base for the problem on your paper, initial it, and pass your paper to the next person in the clockwise direction.

4. On the new paper, check the previous work and coach if necessary. Compute the volume of the figure for the problem on your paper, initial it, and pass your paper to the next person in the clockwise direction.

5. On the new paper, check the previous work and coach if necessary. Initial it showing your approval of all the work done.

Cooperative Learning and High School Geometry: Becky Bride
Kagan Publishing • 1 (800) WEE-CO-OP • www.KaganOnline.com

373

LESSON 4
SURFACE AREA OF A SPHERE

There is no exploratory exercise for this lesson. Videos on surface area of a sphere can be very helpful in demonstrating why the surface area formula for a sphere is $4\pi r^2$. One particular video in the Math Vantage series called, "Containers: Surface Area and Volume," shows the students that it takes four great circles of a sphere to completely cover it. Sunburst Communications sells the video. When the graphic is finished, the four great circles cover the sphere with the pattern that is found on a basketball. Taking the area formula of a circle, then multiplying it by four generates the sphere surface-area formula.

ACTIVITY
1 PROCESSING SURFACE AREA OF A SPHERE

▶ **Structure**
· Boss/Secretary

▶ **Materials**
· Transparency 9.4.1
· 1 sheet of paper and pencil per pair of students

1. Student A supplies one sheet of paper, folded in half lengthwise with his/her name in one column and a partner's name in the other column.

2. Student B is the first boss and Student A is the first secretary.

3. As the boss, Student B tells Student A how to do the problem. Student A, the secretary, records what Student B says in Student B's column of the paper.

4. If the boss makes a mistake, then the secretary coaches and praises once the boss does it correctly. Otherwise, the secretary praises the boss.

5. Reverse roles for each problem and repeat steps 3 and 4.

Cooperative Learning and High School Geometry: Becky Bride
Kagan Publishing • 1 (800) WEE-CO-OP • www.KaganOnline.com

PROCESSING SURFACE AREA OF A SPHERE

Structure: Boss/Secretary

1. Find the surface area of a sphere whose radius is 19 mm.

2. Find the surface area of a sphere whose diameter is 14 ft.

3. The surface area of a sphere is 900π m². Find the length of the diameter of the sphere.

4. The surface area of a sphere is 2500π m². Find the length of the radius of the sphere.

Answers:
1. 1444π m²
2. 196π ft²
3. 30 m
4. 25 m

Cooperative Learning and High School Geometry: Becky Bride
Kagan Publishing • 1 (800) WEE-CO-OP • www.KaganOnline.com

375

LESSON 5
VOLUME OF SPHERES

This lesson begins with an exploratory exercise to develop the volume formula for a sphere. This requires the type of relational solids also needed for the pyramid/cone exercise. Students will need a cylinder, sphere, and hemisphere whose radii are congruent so that the base of the cylinder is equal to the great circle of the sphere. The students can verify this by placing the base of the cylinder against the base of the hemisphere.

Another special relationship between the cylinder and sphere is that the height of the cylinder is equivalent to the diameter of the sphere. The students can verify this by placing the base of the hemisphere against the side of the cylinder. Since the diameter of the sphere is 2r, the height of the cylinder is 2r. Three activities to process volume follow the exploratory activity. The final activity is one that involves application of volume for any of the solids studied.

EXPLORING VOLUME OF SPHERES

▶ **Materials**
- Relational cylinder, hemisphere, and sphere with congruent radii.
- Rice or water
- 1 Blackline 9.5.1 per student
- 1 pencil per student

1. Each pair of students needs a cylinder, sphere, and hemisphere whose radii are congruent.

2. Working in pairs, one student picks up the cylinder while the other picks up the hemisphere. The students predict how many hemispheres it will take to fill the cylinder.

3. The student with the hemisphere fills it with rice or water (making sure not to over fill) and pours the rice or water into the cylinder his/her partner is holding. The student will continue this process until the cylinder is full.

4. The students answers problems 3-5.

5. From this point, as a class the volume formula for the sphere can be developed. Space is provided in problem 6 for students to take notes.

$\frac{2}{3}$ (volume of the cylinder) = volume of the sphere

$\frac{2}{3}(BH)$ = volume of the sphere

$\frac{2}{3}(\pi r^2)(2r)$ = volume of the sphere

$\frac{4\pi r^3}{3}$ = volume of the sphere

Chapter 9: Volume
Lesson Five

376

Cooperative Learning and High School Geometry: Becky Bride
Kagan Publishing • 1 (800) WEE-CO-OP • www.KaganOnline.com

PROCESSING VOLUME OF A SPHERE

1. Student B supplies one sheet of paper, folded in half lengthwise. Each member of the pair writes his/her name at the top of one column.

2. Student B does problem 1, recording his/her work on his/her side of the paper while Student A watches and coaches if necessary.

3. Student A checks Student B's work, coaches and/or praises. Then Student A does problem 2 on his/her side of the paper.

4. Student B checks Student A's work, coaches and/or praises.

5. After every two problems the pair checks their answers with the other pair in their team, coaching and/or praising each others' work.

6. Repeat steps 2-5, reversing roles, until all the problems are done.

▶ **Structure**
• Pairs Check

▶ **Materials**
• Transparency 9.5.2
• 1 sheet of paper and pencil per pair of students

SURFACE AREA TO VOLUME

1. Student 1 copies problem 1 on his/her paper, Student 2 copies problem 2 on his/her paper, Student 3 copies problem 3 on his/her paper, Student 4 copies problem 4 on his/her paper.

2. Each student finds the length of the radius for his/her problem, initials his/her work, and passes his/her paper to the next person in the clockwise direction.

3. Each student checks the work already done on the paper received and coaches if necessary. Then each student calculates the exact volume of the sphere, initials his/her work, and passes his/her paper to the next person in the clockwise direction.

4. Each student checks the work already done on the paper received and coaches if necessary. Then each student calculates the approximate volume of the sphere, initials his/her work, and passes his/her paper to the next person in the clockwise direction.

5. Each student checks the work already done on the paper he/she receives and initials the paper showing his/her approval.

▶ **Structure**
• Simultaneous RoundTable

▶ **Materials**
• Transparencies 9.5.3a and 9.5.3b
• 1 piece of paper and pencil per student

Cooperative Learning and High School Geometry: Becky Bride
Kagan Publishing • 1 (800) WEE-CO-OP • www.KaganOnline.com

377

Chapter 9: Volume   Lesson Five

ACTIVITY

4 VOLUME TO SURFACE AREA

▶ **Structure**
· Simultaneous RoundTable

▶ **Materials**
· Transparencies 9.5.4a and 9.5.4b
· 1 sheet of paper and pencil per student

1. Student 1 copies problem 1 on his/her paper, Student 2 copies problem 2 on his/her paper, Student 3 copies problem 3 on his/her paper, Student 4 copies problem 4 on his/her paper.

2. Each student finds the length of the radius for his/her problem, initials his/her work, and passes his/her paper to the next person in the clockwise direction.

3. Each student checks the work already done on the paper received and coaches if necessary. Then each student calculates the exact surface area of the sphere, initials

his/her work, and passes his/her paper to the next person in the clockwise direction.

4. Each student checks the work already done on the paper received and coaches if necessary. Then each student calculates the approximate surface area of the sphere, initials his/her work, and passes his/her paper to the next person in the clockwise direction.

5. Each student checks the work already done on the paper he/she receives and initials the paper showing his/her approval.

ACTIVITY

5 APPLICATIONS OF VOLUME

▶ **Structure**
· Boss/Secretary

▶ **Materials**
· 1 Blackline 9.5.5 per pair of students
· 1 sheet of paper and pencil per pair of students

1. Student A supplies one sheet paper, folded in half lengthwise with his/her name in one column and a partner's name in the other column.

2. Student B is the first boss and Student A is the first secretary.

3. As the boss, Student B tells Student A how to do the problem. Student A, the secretary, records what Student B says in Student B's column of the paper.

4. If the boss makes a mistake, then the secretary coaches and praises once the boss does it correctly. Otherwise, the secretary praises the boss.

5. Reverse roles for each problem and repeat steps 3 and 4.

378

1 EXPLORING VOLUME OF SPHERES

1. Predict and record below how many hemispheres it will take to fill the cylinder.

2. Working in pairs, one student holds the cylinder while his/her partner fills the hemisphere with rice or water (being careful not to over fill) and pours the contents of the hemisphere into the cylinder. Continue doing this until the cylinder is full, counting how many times you have to do it.

    How many hemispheres did it take to fill the cylinder?

3. How many hemispheres does it take to form a sphere?

4. What fraction of the cylinder is filled by one hemisphere?

5. What fraction of the cylinder is filled by one sphere (two hemispheres)?

6. Based on the above observations and your knowledge of the volume of the cylinder, generate the volume formula for a sphere showing all work.

Cooperative Learning and High School Geometry: Becky Bride
Kagan Publishing • 1 (800) WEE-CO-OP • www.KaganOnline.com

379

ACTIVITY 2 PROCESSING VOLUME OF A SPHERE

Structure: Pairs Check

1. Find the exact volume of a sphere whose radius is 12 cm.

2. Find the approximate volume of a sphere whose diameter is 15 m.

3. If the volume of a sphere is 36,000π mm³, find the length of its diameter.

4. If the volume of a sphere is 26,244π cm³, find the length of its radius.

Answers:
1. 2,304π cm³
2. 1,766.25 m³
3. 60 mm
4. 27 cm

Cooperative Learning and High School Geometry: Becky Bride
Kagan Publishing • 1 (800) WEE-CO-OP • www.KaganOnline.com

ACTIVITY

3

SURFACE AREA TO VOLUME

Structure: Simultaneous RoundTable

Round approximate answers to the nearest tenth. Use π=3.14.

1. If the surface area of a sphere is 1,156π m², find the volume of the sphere.

2. If the surface area of a sphere is 1,600π m², find the volume of the sphere.

3. If the surface area of a sphere is 2,704π m², find the volume of the sphere.

4. If the surface area of a sphere is 1,296π m², find the volume of the sphere.

Answers:
1. 19,652π m³; 20,569.1 m³
 3
2. 32,000π m³; 33,493.3 m³
 3
3. 70,304π m³; 73,584.9 m³
 3
4. 7,776π m³; 24,416.6 m³

ACTIVITY 3 SURFACE AREA TO VOLUME

Structure: Simultaneous RoundTable

Directions

1. Student 1 copies problem 1 on his/her paper, Student 2 copies problem 2 on his/her paper, Student 3 copies problem 3 on his/her paper, and Student 4 copies problem 4 on his/her paper.

2. Calculate the length of the radius of the sphere for the problem on your paper, initial your work, and pass your paper to the next person in the clockwise direction.

3. Check the previous work and coach if necessary. Calculate the exact volume of the sphere for the problem on the paper you just received, initial your work, and pass your paper to the next person in the clockwise direction.

4. Check the previous work and coach if necessary. Calculate the approximate volume of the sphere for the problem on the paper you just received, initial your work, and pass your paper to the next person in the clockwise direction.

5. Check the previous work and coach if necessary. Initial the work showing your approval.

Cooperative Learning and High School Geometry: Becky Bride
Kagan Publishing • 1 (800) WEE-CO-OP • www.KaganOnline.com

ACTIVITY 4 VOLUME TO SURFACE AREA

Structure: Simultaneous RoundTable

1. If the volume of a sphere is 18,432π cm³, find the surface area of the sphere.

2. If the volume of a sphere is 12,348π cm³, find the surface area of the sphere.

3. If the volume of a sphere is 4,500π cm³, find the surface area of the sphere.

4. If the volume of a sphere is 36π cm³, find the surface area of the sphere.

Answers:
1. 2,304π cm²; 7,234.56 cm²
2. 1,764π cm²; 5,583.96 cm²
3. 900π cm²; 2,826 cm²
4. 36π cm²; 113.04 cm²

4 VOLUME TO SURFACE AREA

Structure: Simultaneous RoundTable

Directions

1. Student 1 copies problem 1 on his/her paper, Student 2 copies problem 2 on his/her paper, Student 3 copies problem 3 on his/her paper, and Student 4 copies problem 4 on his/her paper.

2. Calculate the length of the radius of the sphere for the problem on your paper, initial your work, and pass your paper to the next person in the clockwise direction.

3. Check the previous work and coach if necessary. Calculate the exact surface area of the sphere for the problem on the paper you just received, initial your work, and pass your paper to the next person in the clockwise direction.

4. Check the previous work and coach if necessary. Calculate the approximate surface area of the sphere for the problem on the paper you just received, initial your work, and pass your paper to the next person in the clockwise direction.

5. Check the previous work and coach if necessary. Initial the work showing your approval.

Cooperative Learning and High School Geometry: Becky Bride
Kagan Publishing • 1 (800) WEE-CO-OP • www.KaganOnline.com

ACTIVITY 5 APPLICATIONS OF VOLUME

Structure: Boss/Secretary

1. How many cubic centimeters of air is required to fill a basketball whose diameter is 10 cm? Round your answer to the nearest tenth.

2. A silo is formed by a cylinder with a hemisphere on top. Farmers store grain in them. How many cubic feet are in a silo whose diameter is 20 ft and whose height is 30 ft? Round your answer to the nearest tenth.

3. How many cubic centimeters of gun powder are needed to fill a cone shaped firecracker whose diameter is 4 cm and whose slant height is 10 cm? Round your answer to the nearest tenth.

4. How many cubic centimeters can a soup can hold if its radius is 6.2 cm and its height is 12 centimeters? Round your answer to the nearest tenth.

5. How many cubic feet are in a box whose dimensions are 1 ft by 1.8 ft by 2 ft?

6. An ice cream cone has a diameter of 2.5 inches and a height of 6 inches. If there is a sphere of ice cream on top of the cone whose radius is 3 inches, will the cone be able to hold all of the ice cream if the ice cream melts? Explain. Round your answer to the nearest tenth.

Answers:
1. 523.3 cm³
2. 11,513.3 ft³
3. 41.0 cm³
4. 1,448.4 cm³
5. 3.6 ft³
6. volume of cone: 117.75 in³;
volume of sphere: 113.04 in³

Cooperative Learning and High School Geometry: Becky Bride
Kagan Publishing • 1 (800) WEE-CO-OP • www.KaganOnline.com

385

LESSON 6
RATIO OF SIMILITUDE

This lesson begins with an exploratory activity and then processes the concept and ends with applications.

1 EXPLORING THE RATIO OF SIMILITUDE THEOREM

▶ **Materials**
• 1 Blackline 9.6.1 per student
• 1 pencil per student

Have each student complete the exploratory activity found on Blackline 9.6.1.

2 PROCESSING RATIO OF SIMILITUDE

▶ **Structure**
• Fan-N-Pick
Materials
▶ • 1 set of Fan-N-Pick cards per team (Blackline 9.6.2)
• 1 sheet of paper and pencil to record answers per team

Note:
Both activities 2 and 3 process ratio of similitude. One activity may be enough for your students. You may find some classes could benefit from both. Both are included to give you choices.

1. Student 1 fans the cards face down.

2. Student 2 picks a card and reads it to Student 3.

3. Student 3 answers the questions on the card.

4. Student 4 records the answers, augments and/or praises.

5. Students pass cards to the next person in a clockwise direction and steps 1-4 begin again, rotating roles to the next student in a clockwise direction. This process is repeated for a specific time limit or until cards are exhausted.

ACTIVITY

3

MATCH THE RATIOS

1. Each student is given a card.

2. Students mix around the room, trading cards while music plays.

3. When the music stops, students stop.

4. The teacher gives the next set of directions for finding matches. A match consists of three students, one with scale factor, one with area ratio, and one with volume ratio.

5. Students search to find their match.

Tips:
To work on curriculum during the mix stage, students can pair. If a student has a card with a scale factor on it he/she asks his/her partner what the ratio of surface area and ratio of volume would be. If a student has a card with ratio of surface area on it then he/she gives the scale factor and ratio of volume. If a student has a card with a ratio of volume then he/she gives the scale factor and ratio of surface area. Then the students trade cards.

Have students use gambits as they meet to exchange cards and as they leave to find someone else with which to exchange.

During the match stage, students can talk or it can be done silently.

▶ **Structure**
 • Mix-N-Match
▶ **Materials**
 • 1 set of Mix-N-Match cards (Blackline 9.6.3)

To help students find matches, have students that have found their match move to the outside perimeter of the room so there are fewer students to search through for those still needing to find their match.

If students have difficulty, repeat the structure.

To collect the cards, ask that both cards be given to one member of each trio. Then as the students return to their seats, they will hand the set of three of cards to the teacher. By doing this, the matches are together so when the next class comes in with a different number of students the teacher will be able to ensure that matches can be made when the cards are redistributed.

ACTIVITY

4

APPLYING RATIO OF SIMILITUDE

1. Student A supplies one sheet paper, folded in half lengthwise with his/her name in one column and a partner's name in the other column.

2. Student B is the first boss and Student A is the first secretary.

3. As the boss, Student B tells Student A how to do the problem. Student A, the secretary, records what Student B says in Student B's column of the paper.

4. If the boss makes a mistake, then the secretary coaches and praises once the boss does it correctly. Otherwise, the secretary praises the boss.

5. Reverse roles for each problem and repeat steps 3 and 4.

▶ **Structure**
 • Boss/Secretary

▶ **Materials**
 • 1 Blackline 9.6.4 per pair of students
 • 1 sheet of paper and 1 pencil per pair of students

Cooperative Learning and High School Geometry: Becky Bride
Kagan Publishing • 1 (800) WEE-CO-OP • www.KaganOnline.com

387

The prisms are similar

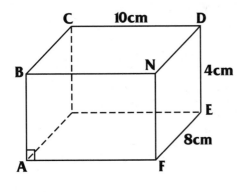

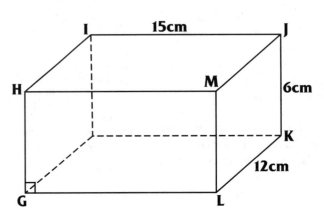

1. Write the following ratios in simplest form: $\dfrac{AF}{GL}$ = ?; $\dfrac{FE}{LK}$ = ?; $\dfrac{DE}{JK}$ = ?;
   $\dfrac{\text{Perimeter of rectangle BCDN}}{\text{Perimeter of rectangle HIJM}}$ = ?

2. What is the scale factor for the two solids above?

3. Compute the area of rectangle BCDN and rectangle HIJM.

4. Write the ratio in simplest form: $\dfrac{\text{Area of rectangle BCDN}}{\text{Area of rectangle HIJM}}$ = ?

5. Compute the surface area of the small prism and the large prism.

6. Write the ratio in simplest form: $\dfrac{\text{Surface area of small prism}}{\text{Surface area of large prism}}$ =

7. Compare the scale factor found in step 2 with the ratios in steps 4 and 6. What mathematical operation can be performed on the scale factor ratio to produce a ratio equivalent to the ratios in steps 4 and 6?

8. Compute the volumes of each prism.

Cooperative Learning and High School Geometry: Becky Bride
Kagan Publishing • 1 (800) WEE-CO-OP • www.KaganOnline.com

ACTIVITY 1
EXPLORING THE RATIO OF SIMILITUDE THEOREM

9. Write the ratio in simplest form: $\dfrac{\text{Volume of small prism}}{\text{Volume of large prism}}$ = ?

10. What operation could be performed on the scale factor to produce a ratio equivalent to the ratio of the volumes?

The cylinders are similar

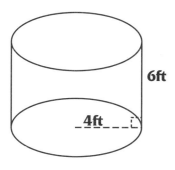 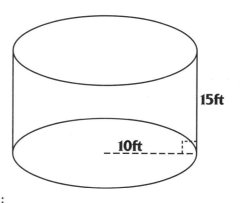

11. Write the following ratios in simplest form:
$\dfrac{\text{Radius of small cylinder}}{\text{Radius of large cylinder}}$ = ? $\dfrac{\text{Height of small cylinder}}{\text{Height of large cylinder}}$ = ?

12. What is the scale factor of the two cylinders?

13. Compute the circumference of the base of each cylinder.

14. Write the ratio in simplest form: $\dfrac{\text{Ratio of the circumference of the base of small cylinder}}{\text{Ratio of the circumference of the base of large cylinder}}$=?

15. How does the ratio of the circumferences compare to scale factor?

16. Compute the area of the base of each cylinder.

Cooperative Learning and High School Geometry: Becky Bride
Kagan Publishing • 1 (800) WEE-CO-OP • www.KaganOnline.com

389

17. Write the ratio in simplest form: $\dfrac{\text{Area of the base of small cylinder}}{\text{Area of the base of large cylinder}}$ = ?

18. Compute the surface area of each cylinder.

19. Write the ratio in simplest form: $\dfrac{\text{Surface area of small cylinder}}{\text{Surface area of large cylinder}}$ = ?

20. Compare the area ratios in steps 17 and 19 to the scale factor. What operation can be performed on the scale factor to get a ratio equivalent to the area ratios? How does this compare to the prisms?

21. Compute the volume of each cylinder.

22. Write the ratio in simplest form: $\dfrac{\text{Volume of small cylinder}}{\text{Volume of large cylinder}}$ = ?

23. Compare the ratio of the volumes to the scale factor. What operation can be performed on the scale factor to form a ratio equal to the volume ratio?

24. How does the answer to problem 23 compare to the answer in problem 10?

25. If the scale factor of two similar pyramids is 4:3, based on this investigation what would be the
    a) Ratio of base areas?
    b) Ratio of surface areas?
    c) Ratio of volumes?

Cooperative Learning and High School Geometry: Becky Bride
Kagan Publishing • 1 (800) WEE-CO-OP • www.KaganOnline.com

ACTIVITY 2 PROCESSING RATIO OF SIMILITUDE

Structure: Fan-N-Pick

If the ratio of the surface
area of two solids is 100:49,
a) What is the scale factor?
b) What is the ratio of their volumes?

Answers: a) 10:7 b) 1000:343

If the ratio of the
volumes of two solids is 64:27,
a) What is the scale factor?
b) What is the ratio of their base area?

Answers: a) 4:3 b) 16:9

If the ratio of the
heights of two solids is 3:4,
a) What is the ratio of their surface area?
b) What is the ratio of their volumes?

Answers: a) 9:16 b) 27:64

If the ratio of the
volumes of two solids is 125:8,
a) What is the scale factor?
b) What is the ratio of their base area?

Answers: a) 5:2 b) 25:4

If the ratio of the
volumes of two cones is 27:1,
a) What is the ratio of their radii?
b) What is the ratio of
their surface areas?

Answers: a) 3:7 b) 9:1

If the ratio of the base
areas of two solids is 64:25,
a) What is the ratio of the
perimeters of their bases?
b) What is the ratio of their volumes?

Answers: a) 8:5 b) 512:125

If the ratio of the surface
area of two prisms is 81:49,
a) What is the ratio of their heights?
b) What is the ratio of their volumes?

Answers: a) 9:7 b) 729:343

If the ratio of the circumference
of the bases of two cylinders is 5:9,
a) What is the ratio of their heights?
b) What is the ratio of their volumes?

Answers: a) 5:9 b) 125:729

Cooperative Learning and High School Geometry: Becky Bride
Kagan Publishing • 1 (800) WEE-CO-OP • www.KaganOnline.com

391

ACTIVITY
3

MATCH THE RATIOS

Structure: Mix-N-Match

Scale Factor $\dfrac{3}{1}$	Ratio of Surface Area $\dfrac{9}{1}$	Ratio of Volume $\dfrac{27}{1}$
Scale Factor $\dfrac{2}{3}$	Ratio of Surface Area $\dfrac{4}{9}$	Ratio of Volume $\dfrac{8}{27}$
Scale Factor $\dfrac{4}{3}$	Ratio of Surface Area $\dfrac{16}{9}$	Ratio of Volume $\dfrac{64}{27}$
Scale Factor $\dfrac{2}{5}$	Ratio of Surface Area $\dfrac{4}{25}$	Ratio of Volume $\dfrac{8}{125}$
Scale Factor $\dfrac{3}{5}$	Ratio of Surface Area $\dfrac{9}{25}$	Ratio of Volume $\dfrac{27}{125}$
Scale Factor $\dfrac{1}{2}$	Ratio of Surface Area $\dfrac{1}{4}$	Ratio of Volume $\dfrac{1}{8}$

Cooperative Learning and High School Geometry: Becky Bride
Kagan Publishing • 1 (800) WEE-CO-OP • www.KaganOnline.com

ACTIVITY
3 MATCH THE RATIOS

Structure: Mix-N-Match

Scale Factor	Ratio of Surface Area	Ratio of Volume
$\dfrac{4}{1}$	$\dfrac{16}{1}$	$\dfrac{64}{1}$
$\dfrac{5}{1}$	$\dfrac{25}{1}$	$\dfrac{125}{1}$
$\dfrac{5}{4}$	$\dfrac{25}{16}$	$\dfrac{125}{64}$
$\dfrac{3}{4}$	$\dfrac{9}{16}$	$\dfrac{27}{64}$
$\dfrac{5}{6}$	$\dfrac{25}{36}$	$\dfrac{125}{216}$
$\dfrac{7}{2}$	$\dfrac{49}{4}$	$\dfrac{343}{8}$

ACTIVITY
4 **APPLYING RATIO OF SIMILITUDE**

Structure: Boss/Secretary

1. If the ratio of the slant heights of 2 pyramids is 2:5 and the volume of the large pyramid is 500π m³, find the volume of the small pyramid.

2. If the ratio of the heights of 2 cylinders is 3:2 and the surface area of the small cylinder is 48π cm², find the surface area of the large cylinder.

3. If the ratio of the surface areas of 2 spheres is 4:9 and the volume of the large sphere is 243π m³, find the volume of the small sphere.

4. The ratio of the volumes of 2 prisms is 125:1. If the base area of the small prism is 12m², find the base area of the large prism.

5. The ratio of the volumes of 2 pentagonal prisms is 343:8. If the surface area of the large prism is 147 cm², find the surface area of the small prism.

6. The ratio of the base areas of 2 square pyramids is 16:25. If the volume of the small pyramid is 192π m³, find the volume of the large pyramid.

Answers:
1. 32 m³
2. 108π cm²
3. 72π m³
4. 300 m²
5. 12 cm²
6. 375 m³

Cooperative Learning and High School Geometry: Becky Bride
Kagan Publishing • 1 (800) WEE-CO-OP • www.KaganOnline.com

CIRCLES

This chapter deals with arcs, chords, special angles of circles, and tangents. Lesson One begins with vocabulary development and identification. Activities to process measure of minor arcs and central angles have been included. A good foundation in these topics is critical for success later in this chapter. Lesson Two explores properties of chords including: equal chords have equal arcs and equal central angles; a radius perpendicular to a chord bisects the chord and its arc; and if radii are perpendicular to congruent chords, then the chords are equally distant from the center. Activities follow each exploratory investigation to process the properties discovered. Some activities involve only algebra and arithmetic and others pull in properties of special right triangles and the Pythagorean Theorem. The students' level will determine how many of these activities they need to do. Lesson Three explores the perpendicular relationship between a tangent and a radius drawn to the point of tangency. It also explores and processes the property of tangent segments to a circle from a point outside the circle. Lesson Four explores and processes inscribed angles. Finally, Lesson Five combines the properties learned in this chapter with area and circumference.

LESSON 1
VOCABULARY DEVELOPMENT

This lesson has the students develop some of the vocabulary. The first vocabulary processed in this lesson has been left up to the teacher to develop. That includes minor arc, major arc, semicircle, radius, diameter (which should have already been developed in the area chapter), and circle. The first activity gives students the opportunity to practice naming arcs. The second activity processes the definitions of arcs by having students compute measures of arcs given an arc measure. The third activity has students generate definitions and Activity 4 processes those definitions. Measure of a minor arc has been left to the teacher to define. Activity 5 processes that definition. Circles will be named by the center. So if the center of a circle is point P, then the circle will be referred to as circle P.

ACTIVITY 1
NAME AN ARC

▶ **Structure**
· Inside-Outside Circle

▶ **Materials**
· Transparency 10.1.1

1. Ask the As to stand and form a large circle with everyone facing toward the inside of the circle.

2. Ask the Bs to get up and go stand in front of their partner (students should now be face to face with the Bs facing out and As facing in).

3. Ask the inside circle students to name either a minor arc, major arc, or semicircle; outside circle students then have to name the same arc their partner just named in a different way. If the inside student disagrees, the pair discusses until they reach a consensus.

4. Students thank each other for working together.

5. Inside circle students rotate clockwise to a new partner. (Outside students could do the rotating or both inside and outside students can rotate in opposite directions).

6. Repeat steps 3-6, reversing roles, until students feel comfortable with the terminology.

ACTIVITY 2
FIND MY MEASURE

▶ **Structure**
· RallyTable

▶ **Materials**
· 1 Blackline 10.1.2 per pair of students
· 1 sheet of paper and pencil per pair of students

1. Student A does problem 1, writing in his/her column of the paper.

2. Student B coaches and/or praises Student A for a job well done and does the next problem, writing in his/her column of the paper.

3. Student A coaches and/or praises Student B for a job well done.

4. Repeat steps 1-3 alternating students for the remainder of the questions.

Cooperative Learning and High School Geometry: Becky Bride
Kagan Publishing • 1 (800) WEE-CO-OP • www.KaganOnline.com

ACTIVITY

3 DEVELOPING VOCABULARY

1. Have students generate their own definitions first or give adequate think time for each student to formulate a definition in his/her mind.

2. As a team, the students will discuss how to define the term.

3. Once the team reaches a consensus, then Student 1 will record the team definition on a sheet of paper.

4. Repeat steps 1-3 with a different student recording each time on the team paper.

Note:
To develop a class definition, spin the team spinner to choose a team and the student spinner to choose a student of the chosen team to read the team's definition. Record the team's definition on the board. Ask the class if they agree with parts 1 and 2 of the definition, reworking what they want to change. Then begin working with part three, drawing a picture of what was communicated to help students see where refinement is needed. Sometimes asking students if part of the definition could be reworded using fewer words will get the students thinking again. Once everyone has agreed, including the teacher, then it is recorded as the definition the class will use.

▶ **Structure**
• Team Discuss with RoundTable Recording

▶ **Materials**
• 1 Blackline 10.1.3 per student
• 1 sheet of paper and pencil per team

Tip:
In step 2, RoundRobin or Talking Chips can be used to equalize participation.

ACTIVITY

4 GIVE AN EXAMPLE

1. When the music begins, the students stand and mix around the room.

2. When the music stops, the students freeze, and partner with the person closest to them.

3. The teachers gives a statement so the pairs can determine who is Student A and who is Student B. An example would be "The person with the most jewelry on is Student A."

4. The teachers asks Student A to tell his/her partner to name a certain figure.

5. Student B coaches and/or praises Student A.

6. Repeat steps 4-5, reversing roles.

7. The music starts again and the entire process begins again.

▶ **Structure**
• Mix-Music-Meet

▶ **Materials**
• Transparency 10.1.4

Cooperative Learning and High School Geometry: Becky Bride
Kagan Publishing • 1 (800) WEE-CO-OP • www.KaganOnline.com

Volume: 10 Circles
Lesson One

397

CIRCLES

ARITHMETIC, ALGEBRA, CENTRAL ANGLES, AND ARCS

▶ **Structure**
  • RallyCoach

▶ **Materials**
  • 1 Blackline 10.1.5 per pair of students
  • 1 sheet of paper and pencil per pair of students

1. Student B supplies one sheet of paper, folded in half lengthwise. Each member of the pair writes his/her name at the top of one column.

2. Student B does problem one, recording his/her work on his/her side of the paper while Student A watches, checks the work, and coaches if necessary.

3. Repeat step 2, reversing roles until all the problems are done.

Cooperative Learning and High School Geometry: Becky Bride
Kagan Publishing • 1 (800) WEE-CO-OP • www.KaganOnline.com

Chapter 10: Circles
Lesson One

1 NAME AN ARC

Structure: Inside-Outside Circle

O is the center of the circle.

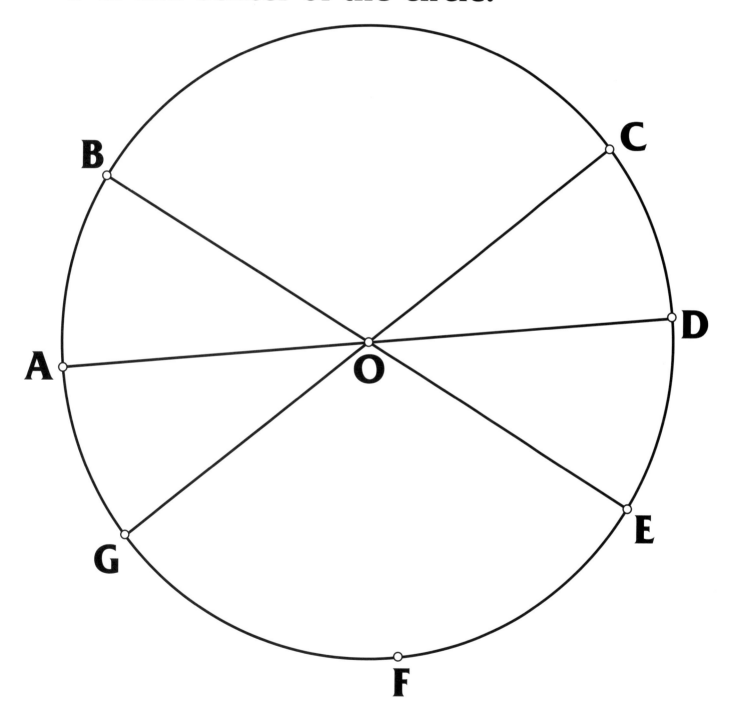

Cooperative Learning and High School Geometry: Becky Bride
Kagan Publishing • 1 (800) WEE-CO-OP • www.KaganOnline.com

399

ACTIVITY

2 **FIND MY MEASURE**

Structure: RallyTable

The center of the circle below is point E. *The circle is not necessarily drawn to scale.*

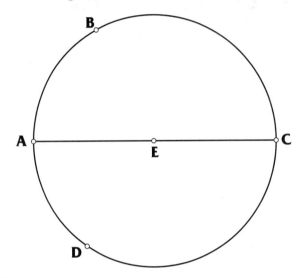

1. If m$\overset{\frown}{AB}$ = 70°, find m$\overset{\frown}{BC}$.

2. If m$\overset{\frown}{AB}$ = 50°, find m$\overset{\frown}{ACB}$.

3. If m $\overset{\frown}{AB}$ = 80°, find m$\overset{\frown}{BC}$.

4. If m$\overset{\frown}{DC}$ = 120°, find m$\overset{\frown}{AD}$.

5. If m$\overset{\frown}{AB}$ = 40° and m$\overset{\frown}{DC}$ = 80°, find m$\overset{\frown}{BCD}$.

6. If m$\overset{\frown}{AB}$ = 60°, and m$\overset{\frown}{AD}$ = 50°, find m$\overset{\frown}{BCD}$.

Answers:
1. 110°
2. 310°
3. 100°
4. 60°
5. 220°
6. 250°

Cooperative Learning and High School Geometry: Becky Bride
Kagan Publishing • 1 (800) WEE-CO-OP • www.KaganOnline.com

ACTIVITY 3

DEVELOPING VOCABULARY

Structure: Team Discuss with RoundTable Recording

1. Chord $\overline{AB}$ is a chord

Examples

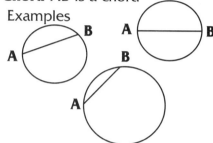

Counterexamples

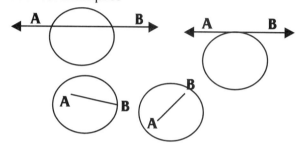

2. Tangent $\overleftrightarrow{CD}$ is a tangent

Examples

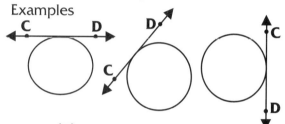

Counterexamples

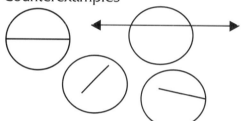

3. Secant $\overleftrightarrow{EF}$ is a secant

Examples

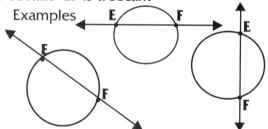

Counterexamples

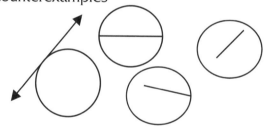

4. Central Angle O is the center of each circle
$\angle AOB$ is a central angle

Examples

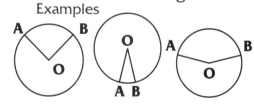

Counterexamples
O is the center of each circle

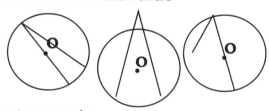

5. Inscribed Angle
$\angle COD$ is and inscribed angle
Examples

Counterexamples

Cooperative Learning and High School Geometry: Becky Bride
Kagan Publishing • 1 (800) WEE-CO-OP • www.KaganOnline.com

401

4 GIVE AN EXAMPLE

Structure: Mix-Music-Meet

O is the center of the circle.

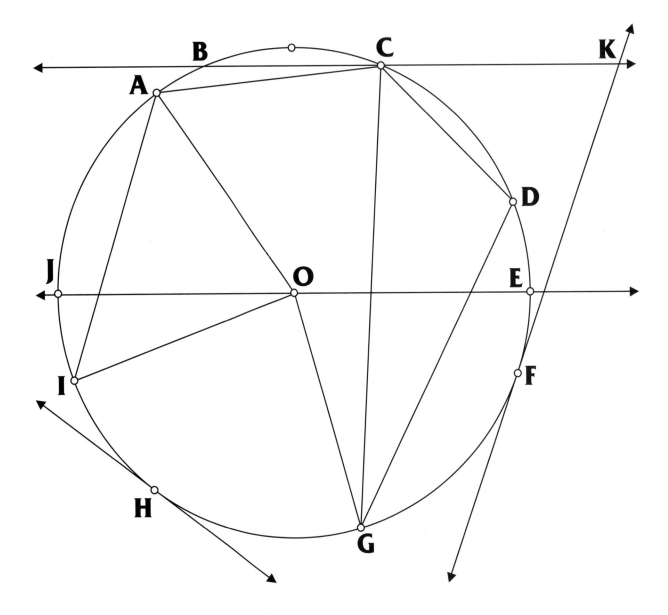

Cooperative Learning and High School Geometry: Becky Bride
Kagan Publishing • 1 (800) WEE-CO-OP • www.KaganOnline.com

ACTIVITY 5 ARITHMETIC, ALGEBRA, CENTRAL ANGLES, AND ARCS

Structure: RallyCoach

E is the center of the circle. The diagram is not drawn to scale.

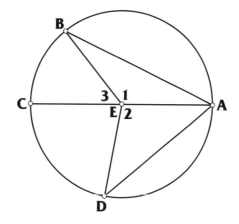

1. If m∠2 = 64°, find mABD.

2. If mAB = 108°, find m∠3.

3. If m BDA = 290°, find m∠1.

4. If m∠2 = 137°, find mACD.

5. If m∠3 = 50°, find mAB.

6. If mBAD = 298°, and m∠1 = 137°, find mAD.

Answers:
1. 296°
2. 72°
3. 70°
4. 223°
5. 130°
6. 161°

LESSON 2
PROPERTIES OF CHORDS

This lesson explores congruent chords, radii perpendicular to chords, and radii perpendicular to congruent chords. Activities follow each exploration to process the concepts learned. Activities 5 and 7 require students to use 30-60-90 triangles, 45-45-90 triangles, and the Pythagorean Theorem. This may be too advanced for lower level students. For average students, it will be rigorous. For honors level students, it will be fine.

1 EXPLORING PROPERTIES OF CONGRUENT CHORDS

▶ **Materials**
 · 1 sheet of patty paper per student
 · 1 straightedge per student
 · 1 compass per student
 · 1 Blackline 10.2.1 per student

Have students complete Blackline 10.2.1.

2 ARITHMETIC, ALGEBRA, AND CHORDS

▶ **Structure**
 · Find Someone Who

▶ **Materials**
 · 1 Blackline10.2.2 per student
 · 1 pencil per student

1. Students mix in the class, keeping a hand raised until they find a new partner who is not a teammate.

2. In pairs, Partner A asks a question from the worksheet; Partner B explains how to do the problem as Partner A records what B has said on his/her own worksheet.

3. Partner B checks and initials the problem.

4. Partner B asks a question from the worksheet; Partner B records what partner A says on his/her worksheet.

5. Partner A checks and initials the problem.

6. Partners shake hands, part, and raise a hand again as they search for a new partner.

7. Students repeat steps 1-6 until their worksheets are complete.

8. When their worksheets are completed, students sit down; seated students can be approached by others as a resource. Students cannot pair with the same student twice.

9. In teams, students compare answers; coach and/or praise each other. If there is disagreement or uncertainty, they raise four hands to ask a team question.

Chapter 10: Circles
Lesson Two

404

Cooperative Learning and High School Geometry: Becky Bride
Kagan Publishing • 1 (800) WEE-CO-OP • www.KaganOnline.com

3 EXPLORING RADII PERPENDICULAR TO CHORDS

Have students complete
Blackline 10.2.3.

> ## ▶ Materials
> • 1 Blackline 10.2.3 per student
> • 1 compass per student
> • 1 straightedge per student
> • 1 sheet of patty paper per student
> • 1 protractor per student

4 ARITHMETIC, ALGEBRA, AND RADII PERPENDICULAR TO CHORDS

1. Student A supplies one sheet paper, folded in half lengthwise with his/her name in one column and a partner's name in the other column.

2. Student B is the first boss and Student A is the first secretary.

3. As the boss, Student B tells Student A how to do the problem. Student A, the secretary, records what Student B says in Student B's column of the paper.

4. If the boss makes a mistake, then the secretary coaches and praises once the boss does it correctly. Otherwise, the secretary praises the boss.

5. Reverse roles for each problem and repeat steps 3 and 4.

> ## ▶ Structure
> • Boss/Secretary
>
> ## ▶ Materials
> • 1 Blackline 10.2.4 per pair of students
> • 1 sheet of paper/pencil per pair of students

5 SPECIAL RIGHT TRIANGLES, PYTHAGORAS, AND RADII PERPENDICULAR TO CHORDS

1. Student A supplies one sheet of paper, folded in half lengthwise with his/her name in one column and a partner's name in the other column.

2. Student B is the first boss and Student A is the first secretary.

3. As the boss, Student B tells Student A how to do the problem. Student A, the secretary, records what Student B says in Student B's column of the paper.

4. If the boss makes a mistake, then the secretary coaches and praises once the boss does it correctly. Otherwise, the secretary praises the boss.

5. Reverse roles for each problem and repeat steps 3 and 4.

> ## ▶ Structure
> • Boss/Secretary
>
> ## ▶ Materials
> • 1 Blackline 10.2.5 per pair of students
> • 1 sheet of paper/pencil per pair of students
>
> *Variation: Pairs Check or Numbered Heads Together are other structures that would work here.*

Cooperative Learning and High School Geometry: Becky Bride
Kagan Publishing • 1 (800) WEE-CO-OP • www.KaganOnline.com

405

Volume: 10 Circles   Lesson Two

CIRCLES

6 EXPLORING RADII PERPENDICULAR TO CONGRUENT CHORDS

▶ **Materials**
• 1 Blackline 10.2.6 per student
• 1 compass per student
• 1 straightedge per student
• 1 sheet of patty paper per student
• 1 protractor per student

Have students complete
Blackline 10.2.6

ACTIVITY

7 ARITHMETIC, SPECIAL RIGHT TRIANGLES, RADII, AND CONGRUENT CHORDS

▶ **Structure**
•Pairs Check

▶ **Materials**
• 1 Blackline 10.2.7 per pair of students
• 1 sheet of paper and a pencil per pair of students

1. Student B supplies one sheet of paper, folded in half lengthwise. Each member of the pair writes his/her name at the top of one column.

2. Student B does problem 1, recording his/her work on his/her side of the paper while Student A watches and coaches if necessary.

3. Student A checks Student B's work coaches and/or praises. Then Student A does problem 2 on his/her side of the paper.

4. After every 2 problems, the pair checks their answers with the other pair in their team, coaching and/or praising each others' work.

5. Repeat steps 2-4 reversing roles until all the problems are done.

Chapter 10: Circles
Lesson Two

1. In the space above, construct a circle and label the center *O*.

2. The properties this exploration investigates are easier to see if the chords do not intersect. On circle *O*, locate 2 points, labeling one point *A* and the other point *B*. Placing points *A* and *B* close to each other will help keep the diagram from getting complicated. The properties are still true if the chords intersect, but your diagram will be complicated to see.

3. You will construct 2 congruent chords. Placing the compass point on point *A* and using any radius you wish, draw an arc that intersects the circle, labeling the point of intersection *C*. Draw segment $\overline{AC}$.

4. Placing the compass point on point *B* and using the same radius (compass opening) as before, draw an arc that intersects the circle, labeling the point of intersection *D*. Draw segment $\overline{BD}$. Your diagram should look something like the diagram below.

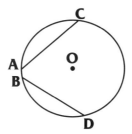

5. Join points *A* and *O*, *C* and *O* with a segment to form central angle ∠AOC. Join points *B* and *O*, *D* and *O* with a segment to form central angle ∠BOD.

6. Trace ∠AOC onto a sheet of patty paper and compare to it ∠BOD (or measure both ∠AOC and ∠BOD with a protractor). What appears to be their relationship?

7. Trace $\overset{\frown}{AC}$ onto a sheet of patty paper. Compare this arc to $\overset{\frown}{BD}$. What appears to be their relationship?

8. Summarize your findings in a complete sentence.

Cooperative Learning and High School Geometry: Becky Bride
Kagan Publishing • 1 (800) WEE-CO-OP • www.KaganOnline.com

407

ACTIVITY 2 ARITHMETIC, ALGEBRA, AND CHORDS

Structure: Find Someone Who

E is the center of the circle. $\overline{AB} \cong \overline{CD}$. *The diagram is not necessarily drawn to scale.*

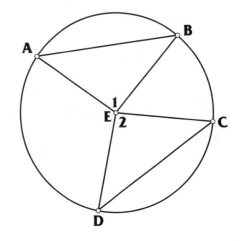

1. If $m\overset{\frown}{AB} = 40°$, then find $m\overset{\frown}{CD}$.

2. If $m\angle 1 = 88°$, then find $m\overset{\frown}{AB}$.

3. If $m\overset{\frown}{BAD} = 215°$ and $m\angle 2 = 120°$, then find $m\overset{\frown}{AD}$.

4. If $m\overset{\frown}{BD} = 140°$ and $m\overset{\frown}{AB} = 110°$, then find the $m\overset{\frown}{BC}$.

5. If $m\overset{\frown}{AB} = 6x\text{-}1$ and $m\overset{\frown}{CD} = 3x+20$, find x.

6. If $m\angle 1 = 4x\text{-}3$ and $m\overset{\frown}{CD} = 2x+71$, find x.

7. If $m\angle 2 = 9x\text{-}7$ and $m\overset{\frown}{AB} = 2x+21$, find x.

8. If $m\angle 1 = 7x\text{-}8$ and $m\angle 2 = 3x+36$, find x.

Answers:
1. 40°
2. 88°
3. 95°
4. 30°
5. 7
6. 37
7. 4
8. 11

Cooperative Learning and High School Geometry: Becky Bride
Kagan Publishing • 1 (800) WEE-CO-OP • www.KaganOnline.com

EXPLORING RADII PERPENDICULAR TO CHORDS

1. In the space above, construct a circle and label the center O.

2. Draw a radius in circle O, labeling the end point of the radius on the circle A.

3. Using a protractor, draw a chord (that is not a diameter) that is perpendicular to radius OA. Label the endpoints of the chord B and C.

4. Label the point of intersection of the radius and the chord, point D.

5. Trace onto a sheet of patty paper segment $\overline{BD}$. Compare this segment to $\overline{DC}$. What appears to be their relationship?

6. Trace $\overset{\frown}{BA}$ onto a sheet of patty paper. Compare this arc with $\overset{\frown}{AC}$. What appears to be their relationship?

7. Based on your answers to steps 5 and 6, what did radius $\overline{OA}$ do to $\overset{\frown}{BC}$ and chord $\overline{BC}$?

8. Summarize your findings in a complete sentence.

Cooperative Learning and High School Geometry: Becky Bride
Kagan Publishing • 1 (800) WEE-CO-OP • www.KaganOnline.com

409

ARITHMETIC, ALGEBRA, AND RADII PERPENDICULAR TO CHORDS

Structure: Boss/Secretary

D is the center of the circle. $\overline{BD}$ is perpendicular to $\overline{AC}$. *The diagram is not drawn to scale.*

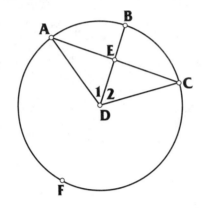

1. If m$\overarc{BC}$ = 70°, then find m$\overarc{AB}$.

2. If m$\overarc{AFC}$ = 300°, then find m∠2.

3. If m∠1 = 44°, then find m$\overarc{CFA}$.

4. If m∠2 = 67°, then find the m$\overarc{AC}$.

5. If m$\overarc{BC}$ = 75°, then find m∠1.

6. If m$\overarc{AB}$ = 6x-1 and m$\overarc{BC}$ = 4x+19, then find x.

7. If AE = 2x+1 and AC = 2x+20, then find x.

8. If m$\overarc{AB}$ = 3x+1 and m$\overarc{AC}$ = 2x+38, then find x.

9. If m∠1 = 5x+3 and m$\overarc{BC}$ = 2x+33, find x, then find m$\overarc{AC}$.

10. If m∠2 = x+1 and m$\overarc{AC}$ = 4x-22, find x, then find m$\overarc{BC}$.

Answers:
1. 70°
2. 30°
3. 272°
4. 134°
5. 75°
6. 10
7. 9
8. 9
9. 10=x; 106°
10. 12=x; 13°

Cooperative Learning and High School Geometry: Becky Bride
Kagan Publishing • 1 (800) WEE-CO-OP • www.KaganOnline.com

ACTIVITY 5 — SPECIAL RIGHT TRIANGLES, PYTHAGORAS, AND RADII PERPENDICULAR TO CHORDS

Structure: Boss/Secretary

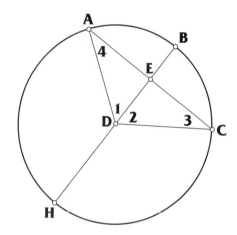

D is the center of the circle. $\overline{BD}$ is perpendicular to $\overline{AC}$. Put all answers in simplest radical form when appropriate. *The diagram is not drawn to scale.*

1. If $m\overarc{AC} = 120°$ and DE = 4, then find AC.

2. If $m\overarc{AC} = 90°$ and DH = 6, then find EC.

3. If BH = 16 and AC = 4, then find DE.

4. If $m\angle ADC = 60°$ and BH = 20, then find the AC.

5. If $m\overarc{AHC} = 270°$ and AC = 12, then find BH.

6. If ED = 6 and DH = 14, then find AC.

Answers:
1. $8\sqrt{3}$
2. $3\sqrt{2}$
3. $2\sqrt{15}$
4. 10
5. $12\sqrt{2}$
6. $8\sqrt{10}$

EXPLORING RADII PERPENDICULAR TO CONGRUENT CHORDS

ACTIVITY 6

1. In the space above, construct a circle and label the center *O*.

2. The properties this exploration investigates are easier to see if the chords do not intersect. Placing points *A* and *B* close to each other will help keep the diagram from getting complicated. The properties are still true if the chords intersect, but your diagram will be complicated to see. On circle *O*, locate 2 points, labeling one point *A* and the other point *B*.

3. You will construct 2 congruent chords. Placing the compass point on point *A* and using any radius you wish, draw an arc that intersects the circle, labeling the point of intersection *C*. Draw segment $\overline{AC}$.

4. Placing the compass point on point B and using the same radius (compass opening) as before, draw an arc that intersects the circle, labeling the point of intersection *D*. Draw segment $\overline{BD}$. Your diagram should look something like the diagram below.

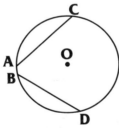

5. Using a protractor, draw a radius that is perpendicular to chord $\overline{AC}$. Label the point of intersection of the chord and radius point *E*.

6. Using a protractor, draw a radius that is perpendicular to chord $\overline{BD}$. Label the point of intersection of the chord and radius point *F*.

7. Trace segment $\overline{OE}$ onto a sheet of patty paper and compare it to segment $\overline{OF}$. What appears to be the relationship?

8. Summarize your findings in a complete sentence.

Cooperative Learning and High School Geometry: Becky Bride
Kagan Publishing • 1 (800) WEE-CO-OP • www.KaganOnline.com

7 ARITHMETIC, SPECIAL RIGHT TRIANGLES, RADII, AND CONGRUENT CHORDS

Structure: Pairs Check

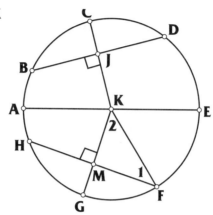

K is the center of the circle. $\overline{BD} \cong \overline{HF}$. All radical answers must be in simplest form. *The diagram is not drawn to scale.*

1. If m∠2 = 60° and AK = 12, then find MF.

2. If BD = 12 and AE = 20, then find KJ.

3. If m∠2 = 45° and KG = 8, then find HF.

4. If m∠1 = 60° and BD = 16, then find the AE.

5. If m∠1 = 30° and KJ = 9, then find BD.

6. If KE = 12 and BD = 10, then find KM.

Answers:
1. $6\sqrt{3}$
2. 8
3. $8\sqrt{2}$
4. 32
5. $18\sqrt{3}$
6. $\sqrt{119}$

Cooperative Learning and High School Geometry: Becky Bride
Kagan Publishing • 1 (800) WEE-CO-OP • www.KaganOnline.com

413

LESSON 3
PROPERTIES OF TANGENTS

This lesson explores the relationship between a tangent and the radius drawn to the point of tangency and the relationship between tangent segments who share a common endpoint outside of the circle. An activity follows to process each concept.

1 EXPLORING THE RELATIONSHIP BETWEEN TANGENTS AND RADII

▶ **Materials**
- 1 Blackline 10.3.1 per student
- 1 protractor per student
- 1 pencil per student

Have students complete Blackline 10.3.1.

2 EXPLORING TANGENT SEGMENTS

▶ **Materials**
- 1 Blackline 10.3.2 per student
- 1 compass per student
- 1 straightedge per student
- 1 protractor per student
- 1 sheet of patty paper per student
- 1 pencil per student

Have students complete Blackline 10.3.2.

3 PROCESSING TANGENT PROPERTIES

▶ **Structure**
- RallyTable

▶ **Materials**
- 1 Blackline 10.3.3 per pair of students
- 1 sheet of paper/pencil per pair of students

1. Student A does problem 1, writing in his/her column of the paper.

2. Student B coaches and/or praises Student A for a job well done and does the next problem, writing in his/her column of the paper.

3. Student A coaches and/or praises Student B for a job well done.

4. Repeat steps 1-3, alternating students for the remainder of the questions.

Chapter 10: Circles
Lesson Three

414

Cooperative Learning and High School Geometry: Becky Bride
Kagan Publishing • 1 (800) WEE-CO-OP • www.KaganOnline.com

1 EXPLORING THE RELATIONSHIP BETWEEN TANGENT AND RADII

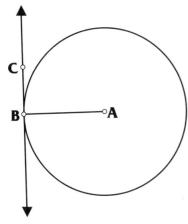

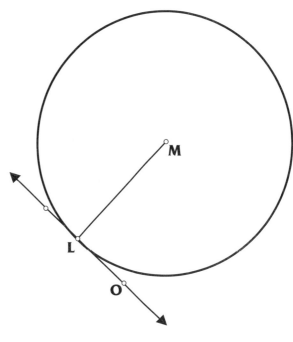

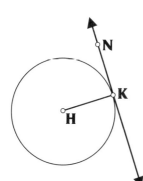

1. Line $\overleftrightarrow{BC}$ is tangent to circle A at point B. Measure ∠ABC and record your measurement below.

m ∠ABC = _____

2. Line $\overleftrightarrow{LO}$ is tangent to circle M at point L. Measure ∠MLO and record your measurement below.

m ∠MLO = _____

3. Line $\overleftrightarrow{NK}$ is tangent to circle H at point K. Measure ∠HKN and record your measurement below.

m∠HKN = _____

4. What appears to be the relationship between a tangent and the radius drawn to the point of tangency?

5. Summarize your findings in a complete sentence.

Cooperative Learning and High School Geometry: Becky Bride
Kagan Publishing • 1 (800) WEE-CO-OP • www.KaganOnline.com

415

EXPLORING TANGENT SEGMENTS

1. In the space above, construct a circle and label the center *O*.

2. Mark 2 points on your circle and label one point A and the other point B. Place the points so they are <u>NOT</u> endpoints of a diameter. Draw radii $\overline{OA}$ and $\overline{OB}$.

3. Using a protractor, draw a line perpendicular to radius $\overline{OA}$ that passes through *A*.

4. Using a protractor, draw a line perpendicular to radius $\overline{OB}$ that passes through *B*.

5. If the two tangents do not intersect, extend them until they do and label the point of intersection C. If your tangents are parallel, relocate point *B* so the tangents will intersect.
$\overline{CA}$ and $\overline{CB}$ are tangent segments.

6. Trace $\overline{CA}$ onto a sheet of patty paper and compare its length with the length of $\overline{CB}$. What appears to be true about the tangent segments?

7. Check with your teammates. Did they get similar findings?

8. Summarize your findings in a complete sentence.

9. Draw $\overline{OC}$.

10. Either measure $\angle AOC$ and $\angle BOC$ with a protractor or compare them using patty paper. What appears to be true?

11. Compare your finding with your teammates.

12. Summarize your finding in a complete sentence.

Cooperative Learning and High School Geometry: Becky Bride
Kagan Publishing • 1 (800) WEE-CO-OP • www.KaganOnline.com

ACTIVITY

3 PROCESSING TANGENT PROPERTIES

Structure: RallyTable

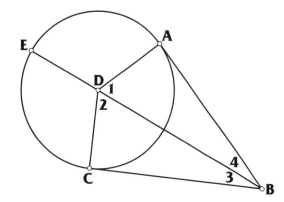

D is the center of the circle. $\overline{AB}$ and $\overline{BC}$ are tangent to circle D at points A and C respectively. **Round answers to the nearest tenth.** *The diagram is not necessarily drawn to scale.*

1. m∠A = ?

2. m∠C = ?

3. If m∠1 = 57°, find m∠4.

4. If m∠3 = 63°, find m∠2.

5. If m∠4 = x + 3 and m∠1 = x - 1, find x.

6. If m∠2 = $2x$ + 6 and m∠3 = $3x$ - 1, find x.

7. If AD = 6 cm and BD = 12 cm, find BC.

8. If BC = 12 mm and AD = 9 mm, find BD.

9. If AB = $4x$ - 9 and BC = $2x$ + 17, find x.

10. If BC = $3x$ + 21 and AB = $6x$ - 42, find x.

Answers:
1. 90°
2. 90°
3. 33°
4. 27°
5. 44
6. 17
7. 10.4
8. 15
9. 13
10. 21

LESSON 4
INSCRIBED ANGLES

This lesson explores the measure of inscribed angles and the relationship between inscribed angles that intercept the same arc. Each investigation has activities that follow to process the concepts discovered.

1 EXPLORING INSCRIBED ANGLES

▶ **Materials**
- 1 Blackline 10.4.1 per student
- 1 compass per student
- 1 straightedge per student
- 1 sheet of patty paper per student
- 1 pencil per student

Have students complete Blackline 10.4.1.

2 ARITHMETIC, ALGEBRA, AND INSCRIBED ANGLES

▶ **Structure**
- RallyCoach

▶ **Materials**
- 1 Blackline 10.4.2 per pair of students
- 1 sheet of paper and pencil per pair of students

1. Student B supplies one sheet of paper, folded in half lengthwise. Each member of the pair writes his/her their name at the top of one column.

2. Student B does problem 1, recording his/her work on his/her side of the paper while Student A watches, checks the work and coaches if necessary.

3. Repeat step 2, reversing roles until all the problems are done.

Chapter 10: Circles
Lesson Four

418

Cooperative Learning and High School Geometry: Becky Bride
Kagan Publishing • 1 (800) WEE-CO-OP • www.KaganOnline.com

3 ANGLES, ANGLES, AND MORE ANGLES

1. Student A supplies one sheet of paper, folded in half lengthwise with his/her name in one column and a partner's name in the other column.

2. Student B is the first boss and Student A is the first secretary.

3. As the boss, Student B tells Student A how to do the problem. Student A, the secretary, records what Student B says in Student B's column of the paper.

4. If the boss makes a mistake, then the secretary coaches and praises once the boss does it correctly. Otherwise, the secretary praises the boss.

5. Reverse roles for each problem and repeat steps 3 and 4.

▶ **Structure**
- Boss/Secretary

▶ **Materials**
- 1 Blackline master 10.4.3 per pair of students
- 1 sheet of paper and pencil per pair of students

Answers:

1. 42	8. 78	15. 74
2. 67	9. 46	16. 39
3. 51	10. 87	17. 39
4. 56	11. 93	18. 99
5. 32	12. 55	19. 99
6. 51	13. 55	20. 35
7. 42	14. 74	

4 EXPLORING INSCRIBED ANGLES INTERCEPTING THE SAME ARC

Have students complete Blackline 10.4.4.

▶ **Materials**
- 1 Blackline 10.4.4 per student
- 1 compass per student
- 1 straightedge per student
- 1 sheet of patty paper per student
- 1 pencil per student

5 ARITHMETIC, ALGEBRA, AND ANGLES INTERCEPTING THE SAME ARC

1. Student A does problem 1, writing in his/her column of the paper.

2. Student B coaches and/or praises Student A for a job well done and does the next problem, writing in his/her column of the paper.

3. Student A coaches and/or praises Student B for a job well done.

4. Repeat steps 1-3, alternating students for the remainder of the questions.

▶ **Structure**
- RallyTable

▶ **Materials**
- 1 Blackline 10.4.5 per pair of students
- 1 sheet of paper and pencil per pair of students

Cooperative Learning and High School Geometry: Becky Bride
Kagan Publishing • 1 (800) WEE-CO-OP • www.KaganOnline.com

419

1 EXPLORING INSCRIBED ANGLES

1. In the space above, construct a circle and label the center *O*.

2. Locate 3 points on circle *O*, labeling one point *A*, another point *B,* and the last one point *C,* making sure that $\overset{\frown}{AC}$ is a minor arc and B is not on $\overset{\frown}{AC}$.

3. Draw in ∠ABC. Angle ABC is an inscribed angle.

4. Draw segments $\overline{AO}$ and $\overline{CO}$, using a straightedge. What special type of angle is ∠AOC?

5. Trace ∠AOC onto a sheet of patty paper using a straightedge.

6. Using ∠AOC on the patty paper and ∠ABC at the top of this page, how many angles of ∠ABC does it take to equal ∠AOC?

7. Measure ∠AOC and record the measurement below.
    m∠AOC = _____

8. What is the m$\overset{\frown}{AC}$? Explain your answer.

9. Describe the relationship between ∠ABC and $\overset{\frown}{AC}$.

10. Summarize you findings in a complete sentence.

Cooperative Learning and High School Geometry: Becky Bride
Kagan Publishing • 1 (800) WEE-CO-OP • www.KaganOnline.com

ARITHMETIC, ALGEBRA, AND INSCRIBED ANGLES

Structure: RallyCoach

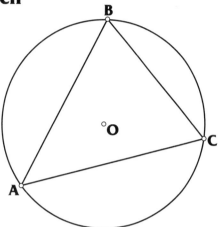

The diagram is not necessarily drawn to scale. Point O is the center of a circle.

1. If m$\widehat{BC}$ = 110°, then find m∠A.

2. If m∠B = 62°, then find m$\widehat{ABC}$.

3. If m∠C = x+3 and m$\widehat{AB}$ = 6x-18, find x.

4. If m$\widehat{BC}$ = 84°, then find the m∠A.

5. If m∠C = 41°, then find m$\widehat{ACB}$.

6. If m∠B = 2x-1 and m$\widehat{AC}$ = 6x-18, then find x.

7. If m$\widehat{BA}$ = 83° and m$\widehat{AC}$ = 140°, then find m∠A.

8. If m$\widehat{ACB}$ = 200°, then find m∠C.

Answers:
1. 55°
2. 236°
3. 6
4. 42°
5. 278°
6. 8
7. 68.5°
8. 80°

Cooperative Learning and High School Geometry: Becky Bride
Kagan Publishing • 1 (800) WEE-CO-OP • www.KaganOnline.com

ANGLES, ANGLES, AND MORE ANGLES

ACTIVITY 3

Structure: Boss/Secretary

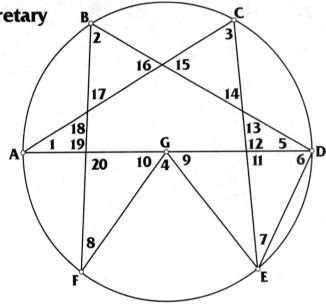

G is the center of the circle. $\overline{AD}$ is a diameter.

$m\overset{\frown}{AB} = 64°$; $m\overset{\frown}{ED} = 78°$; $m\overset{\frown}{CD} = 84°$; and $m\overset{\frown}{FE} = 56°$

The diagram is not drawn to scale.

Find the measures of the following angles.

1. ∠1

2. ∠2

3. ∠3

4. ∠4

5. ∠5

6. ∠6

7. ∠7

8. ∠9

9. ∠10

10. ∠11

11. ∠12

12. ∠13

13. ∠14

14. ∠15

15. ∠16

16. ∠17

17. ∠18

18. ∠19

19. ∠20

20. ∠8

Cooperative Learning and High School Geometry: Becky Bride
Kagan Publishing • 1 (800) WEE-CO-OP • www.KaganOnline.com

4 EXPLORING INSCRIBED ANGLES INTERCEPTING THE SAME ARC

1. In the space above, construct a circle and label the center O.

2. Locate 4 points on circle O, labeling in a clockwise direction one point A, another point B, the third point C, and the last point D. Spread the points out around the circle.

3. Using a straightedge, draw segments $\overline{AD}$, $\overline{AC}$, $\overline{BD}$, and $\overline{BC}$.

4. Trace ∠A onto a sheet of patty paper and compare its measure with ∠B. What appears to be true about ∠A and ∠B?

5. What arc does ∠A intercept?

6. What arc does ∠B intercept?

7. Explain why the relationship you observed in step 4 is true, using your responses from steps 5 and 6 in your explanation.

8. Repeat steps 4-7, except use ∠D and ∠C.

9. Summarize your findings in a complete sentence.

Cooperative Learning and High School Geometry: Becky Bride
Kagan Publishing • 1 (800) WEE-CO-OP • www.KaganOnline.com

423

ACTIVITY 5 ARITHMETIC, ALGEBRA, AND ANGLES INTERCEPTING THE SAME ARC

Structure: RallyTable

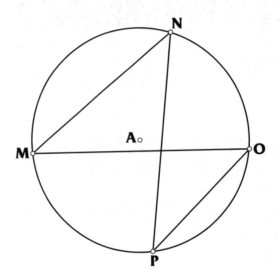

A is the center of the circle. *The diagram is not drawn to scale.*

1. If m∠N = 2x + 3 and m∠O = 5x - 21, find x.

2. If m∠M = 7x - 20 and m∠P = 3x + 12, find x.

3. If m$\overarc{MOP}$ = 250°, find m∠O.

4. If m$\overarc{NMO}$ = 236°, find m∠M.

Answers:
1. 8
2. 8
3. 55°
4. 62°

Cooperative Learning and High School Geometry: Becky Bride
Kagan Publishing • 1 (800) WEE-CO-OP • www.KaganOnline.com

LESSON 5
ANGLES, CHORDS, CIRCUMFERENCE, AND AREA

This lesson is a culmination of chapters 7, 8, and 10. It works with angles and chords and asks students to compute area, circumference, arc length, and area of sectors.

1 AREA, CIRCUMFERENCE, ANGLES, AND CHORDS

1. Student B supplies one sheet of paper, folded in half lengthwise. Each member of the pair writes his/her name at the top of one column.

2. Student B does problem 1, recording his/her work on his/her side of the paper while Student A watches and coaches if necessary.

3. Student A checks Student B's work, coaches and/or praises. Then Student A does problem 2 on his/her side of the paper.

4. Student B checks Student A's work, coaches and/or praises.

5. After every 2 problems, the pair checks their answers with the other pair in their team, coaching and/or praising each others' work.

6. Repeat steps 2-5, reversing roles until all the problems are done.

▶ **Structure**
• Pairs Check

▶ **Materials**
• 1 blackline 10.5.1 per pair of students
• 1 sheet of paper and pencil per pair of students

2 ARC LENGTH

1. Student A supplies one sheet paper, folded in half lengthwise with his/her name in one column and a partner's name in the other column.

2. Student B is the first boss and Student A is the first secretary.

3. As the boss, Student B tells Student A how to do the problem. Student A, the secretary, records what Student B says in Student B's column of the paper.

4. If the boss makes a mistake, then the secretary coaches and praises once the boss does it correctly. Otherwise, the secretary praises the boss.

5. Reverse roles for each problem and repeat steps 3 and 4.

▶ **Structure**
• Boss/Secretary

▶ **Materials**
• 1 Blackline 10.5.2 per pair of students
• 1 sheet of paper and pencil per pair of students

Cooperative Learning and High School Geometry: Becky Bride
Kagan Publishing • 1 (800) WEE-CO-OP • www.KaganOnline.com

ACTIVITY

3 AREA OF SECTORS

▶ **Structure**
  • RallyTable

▶ **Materials**
  • 1 Blackline 10.5.3 per pair of students
  • 1 sheet of paper and pencil per pair of students

1. Student A does problem 1, writing in his/her column of the paper.

2. Student B coaches and/or praises Student A for a job well done and does the next problem, writing in his/her column of the paper.

3. Student A coaches and/or praises Student B for a job well done.

4. Repeat steps 1-3, alternating students for the remainder of the questions.

Note:
This activity is very challenging.

Cooperative Learning and High School Geometry: Becky Bride
Kagan Publishing • 1 (800) WEE-CO-OP • www.KaganOnline.com

1 AREA, CIRCUMFERENCE, ANGLES, AND CHORDS

Structure: Pairs Check

M is the center of the circle. $\overline{AC} \cong \overline{GE}$. The diagram is not drawn to scale. Round all answers to the tenths place. Use 3.14 for π.

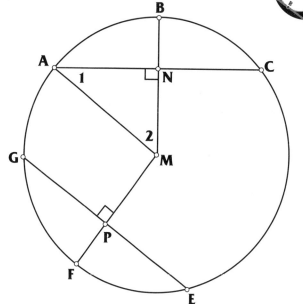

1. If m∠1 = 60° and MN = 9, find the circumference of circle M.

2. If m∠2 = 45° and AN = 6, find the circumference of circle M.

3. If the circumference of circle M is 12π and m∠2 = 45°, find GE.

4. If the circumference of circle M is 18π and m∠2 = 30°, find MP.

5. If GE = 18 and MN = 5, find the area of circle M.

6. If m∠2 = 45° and GE = 12, find the area of circle M.

7. If the area of circle M is 81π and MN = 4, find GE.

8. If the area of circle M is 65π and m∠1 = 30°, find MP.

Answers:
1. 65.3
2. 53.3
3. 8.5
4. 7.8
5. 332.8
6. 226.1
7. 16.1
8. 4.1

Cooperative Learning and High School Geometry: Becky Bride
Kagan Publishing • 1 (800) WEE-CO-OP • www.KaganOnline.com

427

Blackline 10.5.2

ACTIVITY

2 ARC LENGTH

Structure: Boss/Secretary

K is the center of the circle. $\overline{BD} \cong \overline{HF}$. Round answers to the hundreths place. Use 3.14 for π. The diagram is not drawn to scale.

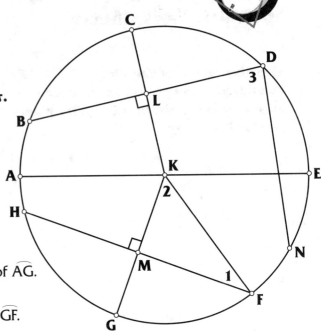

1. If m∠AKG = 40°, and KC = 9, find the length of $\overarc{AG}$.

2. If m∠2 = 60°, and AK = 12, find the length of $\overarc{GF}$.

3. If m$\overarc{AC}$ = 75° and AE = 20, find the length of $\overarc{CE}$.

4. If m$\overarc{AG}$ = 80°, and KG = 8, find the length $\overarc{GE}$.

5. If m∠3 = 80°, and AE = 14, find the length of $\overarc{BGN}$.

6. If m∠3 = 98° and AE = 18, find the length of $\overarc{BDN}$.

7. If m∠2 = 45° and KM = 5, find the length of $\overarc{HF}$.

8. If m∠1 = 30°, and KM = 8, find the length of $\overarc{BD}$.

Answers:
1. 6.28
2. 12.56
3. 18.32
4. 13.96
5. 19.54
6. 25.75
7. 11.10
8. 33.49

428

Cooperative Learning and High School Geometry: Becky Bride
Kagan Publishing • 1 (800) WEE-CO-OP • www.KaganOnline.com

ACTIVITY 3 — AREA OF SECTORS

Structure: RallyTable

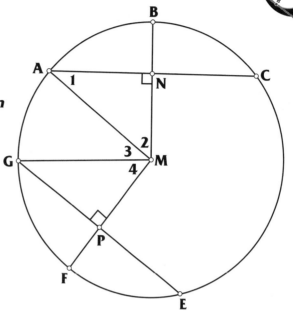

M is the center of the circle. $\overline{AC} \cong \overline{GE}$. Round all answers to the tenths place. Use 3.14 for π. The diagram is not drawn to scale.

1. If m∠2 = 45° and MP = 6 cm, find the area of sector AMB.

2. If m∠3 = 36°, AC = 18, and NM = 6 cm, find the area of sector AMG.

3. If m∠2 = 60°, m∠3 = 25°, and GE = 12 mm, find the area of sector FMB.

4. If m∠3 = 100°, m∠2 = 45°, and GE = 14 m, find the area of sector AMF.

5. If GE = 24 cm, MN = 8 cm, m ∠GMB = 80°, find the area of sector AMF.

6. If ∠FMB = 135°, m∠2 = 41°, and the circumference of circle M is 54 cm, find the area of sector GMA.

Answers:
1. 28.3 cm²
2. 36.6 cm²
3. 60.7 mm²
4. 123.9 m²
5. 144.7 cm²
6. 34.2 cm²

Cooperative Learning &
GEOMETRY

Cooperative Learning and High School Geometery: Becky Bride
Kagan Publishing • 1 (800) WEE-CO-OP • www.KaganOnline.com